METHUEN LIBRARY REPRINTS

SBN/416 32510 6/33

THE COMPLETE WORKS

OF

WALTER SAVAGE LANDOR

———

VOLUME IX

Rose Aylmer's Tomb at Calcutta.

THE
COMPLETE WORKS

OF

WALTER SAVAGE
LANDOR

EDITED BY

T. EARLE WELBY

VOLUME IX

BARNES & NOBLE, Inc.
New York
METHUEN & CO. Ltd
London

This edition, published in 1969

by Barnes & Noble, Inc., New York
and Methuen & Co., Ltd. London

is reproduced from the edition
published by Chapman & Hall, Ltd.
between 1927 and 1936

CONTENTS

IMAGINARY CONVERSATIONS

ORIENTAL (*continued*)

PAGE

VIII. Emperor of China and Tsing-Ti 1

VARIOUS

I. King of the Sandwich Isles, Mr. Peel, Mr. Croker, and
   Interpreter 81
II. Queen Pomare, Pritchard, Captains Polverel and des
    Mitrailles, Lieutenant Poignaunez, Mariners . . 88
III. John Dryden and Henry Purcell 100
IV. Lord Mountjoy and Lord Edward Fitzgerald . . 108

APPENDIX TO IMAGINARY CONVERSATIONS . . 117
SUPPRESSED DEDICATIONS 134

THE PENTAMERON

The Editor's Introduction 145
First Day's Interview 149
Second Day's Interview 177
Third Day's Interview 204
Fourth Day's Interview 231
Fifth Day's Interview 255
Pievano Grigi to the Reader 278
Heads of Confession ; A Monthful 282
The Translator's Remarks 283

IMAGINARY CONVERSATIONS

ORIENTAL—(continued)

VIII. EMPEROR OF CHINA AND TSING-TI *

(*Wks.*, ii., 1846 ; *Wks.*, vi., 1876.)

A SUSPICION was entertained by the Emperor of China, that England was devising schemes, commercial and political, to the detriment of the Celestial Empire. His majesty, we know, was ill-informed on the subject. Never were ministers so innocent of devices to take any advantages in trade or policy ; and whatever may bubble up of turbid and deleterious, is brewed entirely for home consumption.

It requires no remark, it being universally known, that the Emperor deems it beneath his dignity to appoint ambassadors to reside in foreign courts. On the present occasion he employed a humbler observer, known in our northern latitudes by the more ordinary appellation of *Spy*, although the titular is never gazetted. Personages of this subordinate dignity are often the real ambassadors ; and in zeal, information, and integrity, are rarely inferior to the ostensible representatives of majesty.

Whatever might have been the Emperor's uneasiness, whether at the near expiration of the East India Company's charter, as liable to produce new and less favourable relations between his empire and England, or from any other cause, the real motive of Tsing-Ti's mission hath been totally misunderstood by the most intelligent of our journalists. Politically much mistaken and traduced, personally Tsing-Ti is become as well known almost in England as in his native country. At Canton it is reported that he was educated by the late Emperor, as the companion of his son ; nor are there wanting those who would trace his origin to the very highest source, celestiality itself. Certain it is, that he long enjoyed the confidence and friendship of his imperial master. Whispers are

* This was written several years before our invasion of China.—W. S. L.

I

afloat in the British factory, that his mission was hastened by the dissemination of certain religious *tracts*, imported from England into the maritime towns of China. Several of these were laid before his majesty the Emperor, in all which it was declared by the pious writers that Christianity is utterly extinct. His majesty did not greatly care at first whether the assertion were true or false, otherwise than as a matter of history; but protested that he would not allow a fact, even of such trivial importance (such was his expression), to be incorrectly stated in the annals of his reign. By degrees however, the more he reflected on the matter, the more he was convinced that it was by no means trivial. He entertained some hopes, although faint indeed, that the case in reality was not quite so desperate as the later religionists had represented it. From the manuscript reports he had perused, relating to the Jesuits on their expulsion, and from many old Chinese authors, he was induced to believe that the Christians were more quarrelsome and irreconcilable than any other men; and he wished to introduce a few of the first-rate zealots among the Tartars, to sow divisions and animosities, and to divert them hereafter from uniting their tribes against him. No time, he thought, was to be lost; and Tsing-Ti received his majesty's command to go aboard the *Ganges* East Indiaman, and communicate with the captain. He had studied the English language from his earliest youth, and soon spoke it fluently and correctly. His good-nature made him a favourite with the officers and crew, and they were greatly pleased and edified by his devotion. It was remarked of him by one of the sailors, that " he must have a cross of the Englishman in him, he takes so kindly to his grog and his Bible."

He seems to have been much attached to the Christian religion before his voyage. No doubt, he had access to the imperial library early in life, and then probably he laid the foundations of his faith. Few can be unaware that the spoils of the Jesuits still enrich it, and that the gospel in the Chinese tongue is among the treasures it contains.

On his arrival in England, Tsing-ti bought a good number of books, but they were little to his taste, so that when he left us he took with him only *Hoyle on the Game of Whist*, and a *Treatise on Husbandry*, beside a manuscript which he purchased as a specimen of caligraphy. He discoursed with admiration on the merits of the two printed authors, declaring that throughout the whole dissertation neither of them had ruffled his temper, or spoken contumeliously of his predecessors. He regretted that he could not in his conscience pay a similar compliment to any other, seeing that *Spiritual Guides* went booted and spurred, that *Pastoral Poets* were bitten by mad sheep, and that *Sonnetteers* sprang up from their mistresses, or down from the moon, to grunt and butt at one another. Such were the literal expressions of Tsing-Ti, who protested he would not chew such bitter betel nor such hot areeka.

TSING-TI'S NARRATIVE

FIRST AUDIENCE

Entering the chamber of audience through the *azure dragon* and the *two leopards*, the green and the yellow (such being the apartments, as all men know, which are open from time immemorial to the passage of him who bringeth glad tidings), the eyes of his majesty met me with all their light ; and, on my last prostration, he thus bespake me with condescension and hilarity :

" Tsing-Ti ! Tsing-Ti ! health, prosperity, long life and long nails to thee ! and a tail at thy girdle which might lay siege to the *great wall.*"

Overcome by such ineffable goodness, I lessened in all my limbs ; nevertheless my skin seemed too small for them, it tightened so. His celestiality then waved his hand, that whatever was living in his presence, excepting me only, might disappear. He ordered me to rise and stand before him, desirous to pour fresh gladness into me. He then said, what, although it may surpass credibility, and subject me also to the accusation of pride or the suspicion of deafness, I think it not only my glory, but my duty, to record.

" O companion of my youth ! " said his majesty, " O dragon-claw of my throne ! " said Chan-ting,* " O thou who hast hazarded thy existence and hast wetted thy slippers in a sea-boat for me ! Verily they shall be yellow † all thy days, shining forth like the sun, after this self-devotion. So then thou hast returned to my court from the shores of England ! How couldst thou keep thy footing on deck, where the ocean bends under it like a cat's back in a rage, as our philosophers say it does between us and the White Island ? "

* Chan-ting, *Supreme Court :* the Emperor is often so called.—W. S. L.
† The colour of the highest distinction in China.—W. S. L.

3

Whereunto I did expand both palms horizontally, and abase my half-closed eyes, answering with such gravity as became the occasion and the presence : " Fables ! O my Emperor and protector ! mere fables ! I looked out constantly from the vessel, and found it rise no higher the second day than the first, nor the third day than the second, nor more subsequently. The sea, if not always quite level, had only little curvatures upon it, which the Englishmen, in their language, call *waves* and *billows* and *porpoises*. There are many of the sailors who believe these porpoises to be living creatures ; for mariners are superstitious. Indeed they have greatly the resemblance of animals ; but so likewise have the others. For sometimes they lie seemingly asleep ; then are they froward and skittish, and resolute to make the vessel play with them ; then querulous and petulant, if not attended to ; then sluggish and immovable and malicious ; then rising up and flapping the sides, growing more and more gloomy ; then glaring and fierce ; then rolling and dashing, and calling to comrades at a distance ; then hissing and whistling and mutinously roaring ; white, black, purple, green ; then lifting and shaking us, and casting us abroad, to fall upon anything but our legs."

EMPEROR. I never met before with such a tremendous description of the sea.

TSING-TI. I could give a more tremendous one, if imperial ears might entertain it.

EMPEROR. Our ears are open.

TSING-TI. Without any apparent exertion of its potency, without the ministry of billow or porpoise, it made me, a mandarin of the Celestial Empire, surrender, from the interior provinces of my person, the stores and munitions there deposited by the bounty of my Emperor.

EMPEROR. Whereas the time hath elapsed for demanding their restitution, it shall be compensated unto thee tenfold. And now, Tsing-Ti, to business. In this audience I have shown less anxiety than thou mightest have expected about the success of thy mission. The reason is, I have subdued my enemies, and do not care a rush any longer whether they are converted to Christianity or not. Such is my clemency. However, if thou hast brought back any popes or preachers for the purpose, feed them well at my expense ; and let them, if popes, swear and swagger and blaspheme, without

4

scourge or other hindrance ; if ordinary preachers, let them take one another by the throat, get drunk, and perform all the other ceremonies of their religion, as freely as at home, according to their oaths and consciences.

TSING-TI. I have brought none with me, O celestiality !

EMPEROR. So much the better, as things have turned out. But, not knowing of my victories and the submission of the rebels, how happens it that none attend thee ? Were none in the market ?

TSING-TI. Plenty, of all creeds and conditions, bating the genuine old Christians. On my first landing indeed they were scarcer, being all busied in running from house to house, *canvassing* (as it is called) for votes.

EMPEROR. Explain thy meaning ; for verily, Tsing-ti, thou hast brought with thee some fogginess from the West.

TSING-TI. In England the *hereditarily wise* constitute and appoint a somewhat more numerous assembly, without which they can not lawfully seize any portion of what belongs to the citizens, nor prohibit them from raising plants to embitter their beverage, nor even from heating their barley to brew it with. Harder still ; they can not make wars to make their children's fortunes, nor execute many other little things without which they might just as well never have been *hereditarily wise*. But having in their own hands the formation and management of those whose consent is necessary, they lead happy lives. These however, once in seven years, are liable to disturbance. For in England there are some wealthy and some reflecting men, and peradventure some refractory, who oppose these appointments. On which occasion it seems better to call out the clergy than the military ; for the clergy are all appointed by the *hereditarily wise*, and the people are obliged both to listen to them and to pay them, whether they like it or not ; nor can they be removed from their places for any act of criminality. They direct the votes by which are elected those who, under the *hereditarily wise*, manage the affairs of England.

EMPEROR. I am bewildered. I should have liked very well a couple of popes for curiosities.

TSING-TI. They have none.

EMPEROR. What dost thou mean, Tsing-Ti ? Hereditarily wise, and no popes !

5

TSING-TI. None ; beside, in the country where they are bred, there are seldom two found together. When this happens, they are apt to fight in their couples, like a pair of cockerels across a staff on a market-man's shoulder.

EMPEROR. But some other of the many preachers are less pugnacious.

TSING-TI. I have heard of none, except one scanty sect. These never work in the fields or manufactories, but buy up corn when it is cheap, sell it again when it is dear, and are more thankful to God for a famine than others are for plenteousness. Painting and sculpture they condemn ; they never dance, they never sing ; music is as hateful to them as discord. They always look cool in hot weather, and warm in cold. Few of them are ugly, fewer handsome, none graceful. I do not remember to have seen a person of dark complexion or hair quite black, or very curly, in this confraternity. None of them are singularly pale, none red, none of diminutive stature, none remarkably tall. They have no priests among them, and constantly refuse to make oblations to the priests royal.

EMPEROR. Naturally ; not believing them.

TSING-TI. Naturally, yes ; but oppositely to the customs of the country.

EMPEROR. The service of the Christians, you have told me heretofore, is the service of free will.

TSING-TI. In England, the best Christianity, like the best apple, bears no longer. The fruit of the new plants is either sour or insipid. No genuine ones of the old stock are left anywhere. I heard this from many opposite pulpits ; and it was the only thing they agreed in. Yet if one preacher had asserted it in the presence of another, they would forthwith have bandied foul names. An Englishman has more of abusive ones for his neighbour than a Portuguese has of baptismal for his god-child. The first personal proof I received of this copious nomenclature, was upon the identical day I ascertained the suppression of the exercise of Christianity in public.

EMPEROR. These *tracts*, they are not so lying in the main point ? Give me thy exemplification.

TSING-TI. Among the authors held in high repute for piety, and whose hymns are still sung in many of the temples, is one King David, a Jew. Whether those who continue to sing them, sang in

6

earnest or in joke, I can not say. Probably in ridicule ; for, on the first Sunday after my arrival, I followed his example, where he says,

I will sing unto the Lord a new song.

Resolved to do the same to the best of my poor ability, I too composed a new one, and began to sing it in the streets. Suddenly I was seized and thrown into prison.

EMPEROR. Thrown into prison ! my mandarin !

TSING-TI. On the morrow I was brought before the magistrate, who told me I had broken the peace and the sabbath. I protested to him the contrary : that nobody had fought or quarrelled in my presence or hearing, and that the only smiling faces I had seen the whole day were around me while I was singing. " Smiling faces ! " said he, " upon a Sunday ! during service ! in the teeth of an Act of Parliament." I soon had reason to think the Act of Parliament had rather long and active ones, when twenty or thirty more such offenders as myself came under their pressure, for dancing on the night preceding, and several minutes (it was asserted) after the hour of its close had struck in some parts of the city. Dancing is forbidden, not only to the poor, but also to the middle ranks ; and this was an aggravation of the offence.

EMPEROR. Tsing-ti ! thou art a good jurist in the institutions of my empire, and I did not depute thee to enrich it with the enactments of another : but this can not be among the statutes of a nation which pretends to as much civility and freedom as most in Asia. That such an order was given from court, on some unlucky day when the King was much afflicted with lumbago, is credible enough.

TSING-TI. Nothing more probable : and the magistrate told us, to our cost, it was an Act of Parliament.

EMPEROR. I can not but smile at thy simplicity. It was of course an Act of Parliament if the King willed it. Doubtless when his loins came into order again, his people might dance. There are occasions when it would be unseasonable and undutiful to exercise such agility near the palace of an elderly prince, grown somewhat unwieldy : otherwise might not music and dancing keep a people like the English out of political discontent and civil commotions ? Might not these amusements relieve the weight of their taxes and dispell the melancholy of their tempers ? No idler can get drunk while he is dancing or while he is singing ; and against debauchery

7

there is no surer preservative than opening as many sluices as possible to joy and happiness. Where innocent pleasures are easily obtained, the guiltier shun the competition. But how long is it since the race of Christians, I mean the pure breed, has quite disappeared from the land ?

TSING-TI. Nobody could inform me : it can not be long. I saw several thousand men who were dressed exactly like them ; having cases for their heads, cases for their bodies, cases for their thighs. These the Christians, during many ages, wore from pure humility ; it being the very dress in which monkeys are carried about to play their tricks before the populace, and which was invented by a king of France ; whence he and his successors are styled, unto this day, the *most Christian*. Never was there anything upon earth so ugly and inconvenient. They devised it for mortification, which they carried by this invention to such an extremity, as should prevent the possibility of a sculptor or painter giving them the appearance of humanity. Several of the wickeder went still farther in self-abasement; not only covering their heads with dust, which they contrived to procure as white as possible, to give them the appearance of extreme old age and imbecility, but mingled with it (abominable to record) the fat of swine !

EMPEROR. I have some miniatures which attest the fact. Adultresses, and some other women of ill repute, were marked with a black riband round the neck, and their hair was drawn up tight, exposing the roots, and fastened to a footstool, which they were obliged to carry on their heads. No rank exempted an offender. I possess several favourites of the Most Christian King, the late Loo-Hi, labouring under the infliction of this disgrace.

TSING-TI. Self-imposed tortures survive Christianity. I have seen a portrait of the reigning King of England,* in which he appears so pious and devout, so resolved to please God at any price, that he is represented with his legs confined in narrow japanned cabinets, which the English, when applied to these purposes, call *boots*. They are stiff and black, without gold or other ornament, or even an inscription to inform us on what occasion he made the vow of endurance.

EMPEROR. Humble soul ! may God pardon him his sins ! I pity the people too. When will the feeble blind whelps see the light and

* George the Fourth.—W. S. L.

8

stand upon their legs ? No wonder there are eternal changes in those countries. Such filthy litter wants often a fresh tossing on the fork. The axe grapples the neck of some among their rulers : others take a neighbourly pinch out of the same box as the rats : others have subjects who play the nightmare with them ; as lately in Muscovy. I find such accidents occurring the most frequently where the religion is most flourishing. My father, who was curious in learning the customs and worships of the West, related to me that the people of one sect refuse to bury those of another, leaving them exposed to the dogs.

TSING-TI. This, O my Emperor ! was never the custom in England all the time I resided there. But indeed it can not be said that in England there are any customs at all. The very words of their language, I am informed, change their signification and spelling, twice or thrice in a man's lifetime. On my first arrival in London, I was somewhat unwell in consequence of the voyage, yet I could not resist the impulse of curiosity, and the desire of walking about in the spacious and lofty streets. After the second day however I was constrained by illness to keep within my chamber for five ; at the end of those five, so great a change had taken place in the habiliments of the citizens, that I fancied another people had invaded and vanquished them ; and, such were my fears, I kept my bed for seven. At last I ventured to ask whether all was well. My inquiry raised some surprise ; and, fancying that I had spoken less plainly than I might have done, I took courage to ask distinctly whether all in the city was safe and quiet. After many interrogatories for the motive and cause of mine, the first circuitous, the last direct, I was highly gratified at finding that I had succumbed to a false alarm, and that novelty in dress is a religious duty celebrated on the seventh day.

EMPEROR. Tsing-Ti ! thou never shalt command for me against the Tartars, should they in future dare to show their broad faces and distant eyes over the desert.

TSING-TI. God's will and the Emperor's be done ! In this wide empire there is no lack of valour ; I will offend none by aspiring to an undue precedency. Modesty becomes the wise, and more the unwise. Greatness may follow, and ambition urge forward the bold, but the tardy man cometh sooner to contentment. May we never see the outermost corner of the Tartar's eye ! none hath more evil in it.

EMPEROR. It must shoot far if it overtake and harm thee, Tsing-Ti! But prythee go on about the fact of burial, and tell me whether there is any nation so western, as to refuse it in time of peace.

TSING-TI. The nations of Europe are so infinitely more barbarous than anything we in China can conceive, that, however incredible it may appear, the story is not unfounded. The first avowed enemies of Christianity were the associates of a sorcerer, who shaved his head that he might fit a crown upon it. He told people that he could forgive more sins than they could commit. Both parties tried, and it turned out that he was the winner. He pocketed the stakes, and tempted them to try again : and the game has been going on ever since. Ill-tempered men were scandalized at this exhibition, and many disturbances and battles have been the consequence. The sorcerer, now become a priest-king, refuses burial to those who deny his power of remitting sins, and his right to open the gates of paradise on paying toll and tariff. Many of these begin to think they have gone too far, and have slunk back to the old sorcerer, who reproves them sharply, and treats them like conger eels, putting salt into their mouths for purification. If they spit it out again, they frequently are medicated with minerals more corrosive.

EMPEROR. Why, I wonder, do not the neighbouring princes catch and cage him ?

TSING-TI. He frightens them. He has the appointment of their nurses, who tell them marvellous tales about his potency, and how he can turn one thing into another. The English were among the first to expose and abolish his impostures ; but many are coming back to him, now they are tired of Christianity ; and already they begin to stick up again the images of idlers and fanatics, whom the magistrates of old whipt and hung for sedition.

EMPEROR. Better such fellows should be venerated (were it only that they are dead and out of the way) than intolerant and blood-thirsty varlets, who carry hatred in their bosoms as carefully as an amulet, and who will not let the grave open and close upon it.

TSING-TI. They are all of the same quality : they are all either bark or blossom of that tree of which the Jesuits are the nutmegs.

EMPEROR. I thought my ancestors, of blessed memory, had given an intelligible lesson to the potentates of Europe, how to grate those said nutmegs into powder. I thought our wisdom had entered into their councils, and such malefactors were everywhere supprest.

EMPEROR OF CHINA AND TSING-TI

Tsing-Ti. They were so, for a time. But there are many things which were formerly known only as poisons, and which are now employed as salutary drugs. Jesuitism is one of these.

Emperor. After all our inquiries, how very imperfect is our knowledge of Europe ! The books of Europeans serve only to perplex us. Those which have been interpreted to me, on their polity, represent the English as a free people, that is, a people in which several hundred mandarins have a certain weight in the government. Yet it appears that there are provinces in the empire where the inhabitants pay stipends to priests, who abominate and curse them, and with whom they have nothing in common but their corn and cattle. Furthermore it is represented, that those who are making the noisiest appeals to liberality, would leave exposed to the fowls of the air the dead bodies of other sects.

Tsing-Ti. This inhumanity can not be practised in England : it belongs to the old sorcerers : it however is gaining ground in every part of Europe. Where it predominates, all dissentients are denied the rites of burial ; and some entire professions lie under the same interdict. Actors of comedy, who render men ashamed of their follies and vices, are conceived to intrench on the attributes of the priesthood : they must lie unburied. Actors of tragedy, who have awakened all the sympathies of the human heart, must hope for none when they have left the scene.

Emperor. Yet haply the sage himself, when living, hath less deeply impressed the lessons of wisdom than his representative in the theatre ; and even the hero hath excited less enthusiasm. The English, I suspect, are too humane, too generous, too contemplative, to countenance or endure so hideous an imposture.

Tsing-Ti. Gratification is not sterile in their country : gratitude, lovely gratitude, is her daughter. The great actor is received on equal terms among the other great. I have inquired of almost every sect, to the number of forty or fifty, and everyone abhors the imputation of posthumous rancour, excepting the old sorcerers. The arguments of another, with a priest of that persuasion, are fresh in my memory.

Emperor. What an ice-house must thy memory be, Tsing-Ti ! to keep such things fresh in it !

Tsing-Ti. They might have been uttered in the serenity of the Celestial Empire, and in the most holy place.

IMAGINARY CONVERSATIONS: ORIENTAL

EMPEROR. Indeed! I would hear 'em then.

TSING-TI. " Good God ! " said the appellant to the sorcerer's man, " if anyone hath injured us in life, ought we not at least to cast our enmity aside when life is over ? Even supposing we disregard the commandment of our heavenly father, *to forgive as we hope to be forgiven;* even supposing we disbelieve him when he tells us that on this condition, and on this only, we can expect it ; would not humanity lead us through a path so pleasant, to a seat so soft, to so wholesome and invigorating a repose ? The pagan, the heathen, the idolater, the sacrificer of his fellow-men, beholding a corpse on the shore, stopt, bent over it, tarried, cast upon it three handfuls of sand, and bade the spirit that had dwelt in it, and was hovering (as they thought) uneasily about it, go its way in peace. Would you do less than this, for one who had lived in the same city, and bowed to the same God as yourself ? "

EMPEROR. The sorcerer's man must have learnt more than sorcery, if his ingenuity supplied him with an answer in the affirmative.

TSING-TI. " Yes," replied he, " if the holiness of our lord commanded it."

EMPEROR. Moderate the prancing of thy speech, O Tsing-Ti, that I may mount it easily, look down from it complacently, and descend from it again without sore or irksomeness. What holiness ? What lord ? Thou wert talking of the sorcerer. Are these ruffians called lords and holinesses ? Do people at once obey and ridicule them ? How can this be ?

TSING-TI. I know not, O celestiality ! but so it is.

EMPEROR. The other spoke rationally and kindly. Had he a tail ? a top-knot ?

TSING-TI. None whatever.

EMPEROR. He must have travelled into far regions under milder skies ; not peradventure to our beautiful coast, but midway. He may, by God's providence, have enjoyed the conversation of those hermits, now under the protection of England, the Ho-Te-Nto-Ts. This surely is something in advance of such as believe that one chapman can procure eternal life, on commission, for another who corresponds with him ! that mummery can dispense with obligations, and that money can absolve from sin. Call for tea ; my head is dizzy, and my stomach is out of order.

12

EMPEROR OF CHINA AND TSING-TI

SECOND AUDIENCE

On the morrow I was received at the folding doors by Pru-Tsi, and ushered by him into the presence of his majesty the Emperor, who was graciously pleased to inform me that he had rendered thanks to Almighty God for enlightening his mind, and for placing his empire far beyond the influence of the persecutor and fanatic. " But," continued his majesty, " this story of the sorcerer's man quite confounds me. Little as the progress is which the Europeans seem to have made in the path of humanity, yet the English, we know, are less cruel than their neighbours, and more given to reflection and meditation. How then is it possible they should allow any portion of their fellow-citizens to be hoodwinked, gagged, and carried away into darkness, by such conspirators and assassins? Why didst thou not question the man thyself? "

Tsing-Ti. I did, O Emperor! and his reply was, " We can bury such only as were in the household of the faith. It would be a mockery to bid those spirits go in peace which we know are condemned to everlasting fire."

Emperor. Amazing! have they that? Who invented it? Everlasting fire! It surely might be applied to better purposes. And have those rogues authority to throw people into it? In what part of the kingdom is it? If natural, it ought to have been marked more plainly in the maps. The English, no doubt, are ashamed of letting it be known abroad that they have any such places in their country. If artificial, it is no wonder they keep such a secret to themselves. Tsing-Ti, I commend thy prudence in asking no questions about it; for I see we are equally at a loss on this curiosity.

Tsing-Ti. The sorcerer has a secret for diluting it. Oysters and the white of eggs, applied on lucky days, enter into the composition; but certain charms in a strange language must also be employed, and must be repeated a certain number of times. There are stones likewise, and wood cut into particular forms, good against this eternal fire, as they believe. The sorcerer has the power, they pretend, of giving the faculty of hearing and seeing to these stones and pieces of wood; and when he has given them the faculties, they become so sensible and grateful, they do whatever he orders.

13

Some roll their eyes, some sweat, some bleed ; and the people beat their breasts before them, calling themselves miserable sinners.

EMPEROR. *Sinners* is not the name I should have given them, although no doubt they are in the right.

TSING-TI. Sometimes, if they will not bleed freely, nor sweat, nor roll their eyes, the devouter break their heads with clubs, and look out for others who will.

EMPEROR. Take heed, Tsing-Ti ! Take heed ! I do believe thou art talking all the while of idols. Thou must be respectful ; remember I am head of all the religions in the empire. We have something in our own country not very unlike them, only the people do not worship them ; they merely fall down before them as representatives of a higher power. So they say.

TSING-TI. I do not imagine they go much farther in Europe, excepting the introduction of this club-law into their adoration.

EMPEROR. And difference enough, in all conscience. Our people is less ferocious and less childish. If any man break an idol here for not sweating, he himself would justly be condemned to sweat, showing him how inconvenient a thing it is when the sweater is not disposed. As for rolling the eyes, surely they know best whom they should ogle ; as for bleeding, that must be regulated by the season of the year. Let every man choose his idol as freely as he chooses his wife ; let him be constant if he can ; if he can not, let him at least be civil. Whoever dares to scratch the face of any one in my empire, shall be condemned to varnish it afresh, and moreover to keep it in repair all his lifetime.

TSING-TI. In Europe such an offence would be punished with the extremities of torture.

EMPEROR. Perhaps their idols cost more, and are newer. Is there no chance, in all their changes, that we may be called upon to supply them with a few ?

TSING-TI. They have plenty for the present, and they dig up fresh occasionally.

EMPEROR. In regard to the worship of idols, they have not a great deal to learn from us ; and what is deficient will come by degrees as they grow humaner. But how little care can any ruler have for the happiness and improvement of his people, who permits such ferocity in the priesthood. If its members are employed by the government to preside at burials, as according to thy discourse I

14

suppose, a virtuous prince would order a twelvemonth's imprisonment, and spare diet, to whichever of them should refuse to perform
the last office of humanity toward a fellow-creature. What separation of citizen from citizen, and necessarily what diminution of
national strength, must be the consequence of such a system ! A
single act of it ought to be punished more severely than any single
act of sedition, not only as being a greater distractor of civic union,
but, in its cruel sequestration of the best affections, a fouler violator
of domestic peace. I always had fancied, from the books in my
library, that the Christian religion was founded on brotherly love
and pure equality. I may calculate ill ; but, in my hasty estimate,
damnation and dog-burial stand many removes from these.

" Wait a little," the Emperor continued : " I wish to read in
my library the two names that my father said are considered the two
greatest in the West, and may vie nearly with the highest of our own
country."

Whereupon did his majesty walk forth into his library ; and my
eyes followed his glorious figure as he passed through the doorway,
traversing the *gallery of the peacocks*, so called because fifteen of
those beautiful birds unite their tails in the centre of the ceiling,
painted so naturally as to deceive the beholder, each carrying in his
beak a different flower, the most beautiful in China, and bending
his neck in such a manner as to present it to the passer below.
Traversing this gallery, his majesty with his own hand drew aside
the curtain of the library-door. His majesty then entered ; and,
after some delay, he appeared with two long scrolls, and shook them
gently over the fish-pond, in this dormitory of the sages. Suddenly
there were so many splashes and plunges that I was aware of the
gratification the fishes had received from the grubs in them, and the
disappointment in the atoms of dust. His majesty, with his own
right hand, drew the two scrolls trailing on the marble pavement,
and pointing to them with his left, said,

" Here they are ; Nhu-Tong : Pa-Kong.* Suppose they had
died where the sorcerer's men held firm footing, would the priests
have refused them burial ? "

I bowed my head at the question ; for a single tinge of red,
whether arising from such ultra-bestial cruelty in those who have
the impudence to accuse the cannibals of theirs, or whether from

* Newton, Bacon. The Chinese have no B.—W. S. L.

abhorrent shame at the corroding disease of intractable super-
stition, hereditary in the European nations for fifteen centuries, a
tinge of red came over the countenance of the Emperor. When I
raised up again my forehead after such time as I thought would have
removed all traces of it, still fixing my eyes on the ground, I answered,

"O Emperor ! the most zealous would have done worse. They
would have prepared these great men for burial, and then have left
them unburied."

EMPEROR. So ! so ! they would have embalmed them, in their
reverence for meditation and genius, although their religion prohibits
the ceremony of interring them.

TSING-TI. Alas, sire, my meaning is far different. They would
have dislocated their limbs with pulleys, broken them with hammers,
and then have burnt the flesh off the bones. This is called an *act
of faith*.

EMPEROR. *Faith*, didst thou say ? Tsing-Ti, thou speakest bad
Chinese : thy native tongue is strangely occidentalised.

TSING-TI. So they call it.

EMPEROR. God hath not given unto all men the use of speech.
Thou meanest to designate the ancient inhabitants of the country,
not those who have lived there within the last three centuries.

TSING-TI. The Spaniards and Italians (such are the names of
the nations who are most under the influence of the spells) were
never so barbarous and cruel as during the first of the last three
centuries. The milder of them would have refused two cubits of
earth to the two philosophers ; and not only would have rejected
them from the cemetery of the common citizens, but from the side
of the common hangman ; the most ignorant priest thinking himself
much wiser, and the most enlightened prince not daring to act openly
as one who could think otherwise. The Italians had formerly two
illustrious men among them ; the earlier was a poet, the later a
philosopher ; one was exiled, the other was imprisoned, and both
were within a span of being burnt alive.

EMPEROR. We have in Asia some odd religions and some barbarous princes, but neither are like the Europeans. In the name of
God ! do the fools think of their Christianity as our neighbours in
Tartary (with better reason) think of their milk ; that it will keep
the longer for turning sour ? or that it must be wholesome because
it is heady ? Swill it out, swill it out, say I, and char the tub.

THIRD AUDIENCE

The third morning had dawned, and the skies had assumed the colour of a beautiful maiden's nails, when the Emperor my master sent unto me Pru-Tsi, to command me to be of good health and to have a heart in my bosom. Flattered and gratified beyond all measure by the graciousness of such commands, I ordered tea to be brought to Pru-Tsi, who no sooner heard the servant on the other side of the door, than he told me that he saw in my tea-cup the ocean of my bounty, the abysses of my wisdom, the serene and interminable sky of my favour and affection. To which I replied, that in the countenance of Pru-Tsi I beheld the sun which irradiated them all. He was dissatisfied at the shortness and incompleteness of my compliment, as wanting two divisions : and from that instant may be dated his ill offices toward me. Here I must confess my deficiency in politeness, which, not having been neglected in my education, I can attribute to nothing but my long absence from our civilised and courteous people.

Observing by the profusion of Pru-Tsi's gentilities, and by the fluttering of his tamarind-tree vest under which his breast wheezed and laboured, that my rusticity had wounded him, I took from off the table the finest rose in the central vase, and entreated that, by touching it, he would render those of next year more fragrant and more double. " The parent," said I, " will be penetrated by the glory shed upon her daughter." I remarked that he smelt it only on one side, and only once ; and that he bowed but when he received it, and when he smelt it, and the last time less profoundly ; yet he could not but have noticed that, in rising, I laid above half of each hand on the table, with the fingers spread, and that I rested for seven or eight seconds in an inclined position, looking up at his face, as one irresolute and deferential. I record it not in anger, but I hope there are few Chinese who could have seen this unmoved. God forbid that we should degenerate from our fathers, or that even a signification of our desire to please should fail in obtaining pardon, even for a voluntary and a grave offence. No acknowledgment of a fault is so explicit, none can so little wound the delicacy of the offended, none so gracefully show our reliance on his generosity and affability. Let the westernman call *satisfaction* that which humiliates and afflicts another ; but, oh, Chinese ! let us demand much more—the contentment of both parties. I have often mused on these reflections; I must now return to Pru-Tsi, who caused them. He informed me that the Emperor was ready to receive me under *his* " guidance." This word has much meaning. Pru-Tsi drew it with all dexterity and gracefulness, but he showed too plainly its edge and point. I then added, " My heart is a cabinet on which all the figures and all the letters are embossed in high relief by your hands, most munificent lord ! "

" Deign, O Tsing-Ti, to place us within it," said Wi-Hong, who stood behind, " and it shall be our glory to become the camphor, preservative against the moths and insects which would consume its precious stores."

" The cedar wants not the camphor," said Flthat-Wang, bowing at the back of Wi-Hong, three paces off. Whereat the pupils of Pru Tsi's eyes verged toward the bridge of his nose ; for he remembered not in what book the words were written. This made him the readier to depart. He walked at my left-hand, Wi-Hong and Flthat-Wang following us at equal distances. On my entering the chamber of audience, Pru-Tsi was dismissed ; which (I was sorry to observe) made his mouth as low as a lamprey's, and elicited a sound not unlike the drawing off a somewhat wet boot. Scarcely had he passed into the *corridor of the dancers*, so called because there are painted on each side the figures of young maidens, some dancing, but the greater part inviting the passer-by, either with open arms or only with the fingers, and others behind, among the lofty flowers, with various seductive signs : scarcely had Pru-Tsi reached this corridor, when the Emperor's children entered from the opposite one, the *corridor of the parrots*, so called because it represents these birds performing various actions ; one flying with a boy into the air, having caught him by a bunch of prodigiously large cherries, which he will not let go ; one teaching an ancient mandarin his letters, and much resembling him in physiognomy ; two playing at chess for little girls in cages on the table ; and a flight of smaller ones clawing a sceptre and pecking at a globe ; while several apes creep on their bellies close behind, and several more from furnaces in the distance, each with his firebrand ready to singe their plumage. The parrots do not see the mischievous beasts that are so near, nor do those see, coming from under scarlet drapery, a vast serpent's

18

jaw, wide enough to swallow them all. The serpent's jaw is in a
corner, near a sofa, in the shape of a woolsack, off which a comely
man (apparently) has tumbled, extending both feet in the air over
it, and holding the serpent's tail between his teeth, and trying
(apparently) to urge him onward. I am thus particular in my
description of this corridor, because there is no part of the whole
palace which has been described in general so inaccurately, and
because there are few who can pretend to have examined it so
closely or so long as I have : added to which, in all due humility
be it spoken, few in China have a better eye for forms and
colours.

The celestial sons and daughters, I have said already, had passed
through the *corridor of the parrots* and entered the *hall of audience.*
What I am now about to say will subject me to much obloquy, and
render my name suspected in veracity, but the graciousness of my
patron is commensurate with the greatness of my emperor. He
made a sign to the children that they should walk into the smaller
library, and when he had signified the same by words, and they,
after all of them had long fixed their eyes on his majesty, were quite
certain, the elder son, Fo-Kien, advanced toward his elder sister,
Rao-Fa, kissed her little fair hand and then her forehead, and conducted her : after his seventh step, Min-Psi, the second son, acted
in like manner ; but when he rose on tiptoe (being, as the world
knows, two years younger than his sister, Lao-Lo, then almost nine),
she bit the tip of his ear, not with her teeth indeed, but with her
lips. The Emperor, who surveyed his beautiful progeny with
intense delight, was indulgent to this fault, and beckoning to me,
said, " I am to blame, Tsing-Ti ! In the fifth year of her age, I did
the very same to Lao-Lo : but," recovering himself, " it was not
in the *hall of audience.* Come along, come along, I may do the same
again in the little library, and before thee, for Lao-Lo is the light
of my eyes, and makes it sweeter to be a father than an emperor.
I have sent for my children," continued his majesty, " that they
may be amused by thy narrative ; for nothing is so delightful to
the youthful mind as voyages. But prythee do not relate to them
any act of intolerance or inhumanity. The young should not be
habituated to hear or see what is offensive to our nature and derogatory to the beneficence of our God. Surely *all* the absurdities of
those mischievous priests are not inseparably mixed up with blood

and bile. Follow me ; for the children must be very dull when there are only books about them."

Suddenly the Emperor stopped, and made a sign to me to look toward the pond. Lao-Lo was standing with her arm upon the golden balustrade and looking at Min-Psi, who, from time to time, gave her a pearl or two, which he was detaching, with all the force and agility of his teeth, from the border of her silver sash. No sooner had he succeeded, than she threw it to the fish. Those which swallowed one she called " sweet creatures," and those which detected the fraud " cunning old mandarins." When the baits were exhausted, and Min-Psi shook his head at the melancholy question, " are there no more ? " the Emperor drew back softly, and said to me, " We must give her time to smoothen her sash, and take care not to see it." Perhaps the same kindness moved Fo-Kien and Rao-Fa to begin a game at chess, not opposite each other, but both with the back toward the pond. Fo-Kien once or twice moved an eye in that direction, and smiled : but Rao-Fa told him he might smile when he had won, and never glanced from the chess-board. At the sound of the Emperor's feet they both arose and turned toward him. Min-Psi did not come quite opposite. I saw one ear, the left, and it was crimson, although it was not the ear that Lao-Lo had pinched with her rubies. He held down his head a little ; and Lao-Lo struck his hand with her sash, saying, " I wonder what in the world can ever make Min-Psi look as if he had been in mischief." His ear grew more transparent. Lao-Lo asked her father's permission to give him three kisses ; only three. The request was granted ; but Min-Psi ran behind me, and laughed at her vain attempts. As they were rather rough and boisterous with my robe, the Emperor said, " Lao-Lo ! do not you remember that you are in the presence of a mandarin ? " " Oh papa ! there are several not far off ; are there not, Min-Psi ? " said the child, " but is anyone so good as Tsing-Ti is ? It is impossible not to admire his beautiful dress, now we are in a part of the palace where we may admire anything we like." The Emperor seated himself, and waving his hand, the children bowed gracefully. He waved his hand a second time, and Fo-Kien made two steps toward Rao-Fa, who made likewise two steps toward him. He then made another step, slightly bending ; the princess had no other steps to make, but inclined her head somewhat lower, so that her hand came forward a little. The imperial prince supported her arm above the wrist, and she was seated. Min-Psi too performed with equal grace and gravity the same duties toward Lao-Lo, who looked as diffident as if she had never seen him until then. He, being the younger, bowed twice before her, which salute she returned by opening her hand each time. On this occasion her brow came a little forward, and, as was required by the ceremonial, much to Min-Psi's contentment, her lips were quite closed. He then bowed twice to Rao-Fa, on whom it was not incumbent to open her hand, but merely to make a like movement with her fan. Her beautiful lips parted for a moment to compensate him for the difference, and her eyes looked tenderly upon the courtly child.

There are many, in the Celestial Empire itself, to whom these statutes of the imperial court are unknown, although they have regulated the movements of each successive dynasty three thousand years. Hence that polish which is proof against contact ; hence that lofty urbanity in every member of it which separates them widely from all other potentates ; hence that gentleness and obliging demeanour which render domestic offence impossible, and throw additional charms over every affection and every endearment. No unkind, no unpleasant word ever was uttered in these chambers ; where the wisdom of royalty, receiving fresh tributes in almost every century from inborn sages, has given form and substance to fairer imagery than poets and visionaries have dreamed. No duties are so punctilious as to be troublesome to a well-regulated mind, which always finds complacency and satisfaction in executing perfectly the most complex and difficult ; while rudeness can never do enough for its gratification, and grows continually more uneasy and untoward. I say these things, because what I am writing may, peradventure, be carried by ships into lands where such reflections have seldom fallen, and where scratches and buffets are thought more natural than courtesies and caresses.

I related to the imperial children much of what I had seen in the several countries of my voyage. " But do tell them a few tricks of the sorcerer," said his majesty, " and what are called the mysteries." Accordingly I began. Their laughter was interrupted by questions, and their questions by laughter ; for both were permitted in the small library. One absurdity struck Fo-Kien particularly : it related to numerals. The princesses sate with their eyelids raised, perhaps in doubt of my correctness, either as to judgment or to fact : Min-Psi counted his fingers, first on one hand and then on the other, and looked hard at me ; I fancied he was uneasy. Fo-Kien asked me whether the English too believed in this, being thought such good accountants. My reply was, that, " Although they had rejected, in great measure, the practice of Christianity, yet they retained the dogmas ; and this among the rest."

" I wonder then," said he, " that the merchants of Canton do not often sell their tobacco for opium, and a pound for a quintal, since they appear to be ignorant both of substances and numbers. I do not wonder they are so cheated by those who manage their affairs at home as we hear they are."

" Methinks," said his majesty, " they must nevertheless have some calculators among them, else how could they become such good astronomers ? "

" I have heard," said Lao-Lo, " that these astronomers pick up stars every day like cockle-shells. Tell us about it, good Tsing-Ti ! can it be true ? what can they do with so many ? must not they leave them where they find them ? are they not all in the sky ? "

" Excepting some few," said Min-Psi, " that fall into the canals."

His majesty the Emperor was graciously pleased to inquire of me whether the English retained the same confidence as formerly in judicial astronomy. I acknowledged my ignorance of the fact, whether they were stationary in that science, or had latterly made any improvements in it.

" Certain it is," said I, " that, under the guidance of the stars, they are steadfast in their observance of lucky days."

" It is only grown-up men that ever see unlucky ones," said Min-Psi, " unless it rains."

A soft vibration of a gong was audible in the corridor. The children rose from their seats, performing the same ceremonies as before, each saying, in turn, after a pause,

" May Tsing-Ti be blessed with health and happiness ! "

Then they kissed the hand of their imperial father, and requested he would grant them an appetite for their pilaw ; which his majesty most graciously conceded.

" Go on, Tsing-Ti," said his majesty, " about the observations of the astronomers in the White Island."

TSING-TI. There is scarcely an hour in the twenty-four of any day throughout the twelvemonth, on which I have not requested, from the wisest men I know among them, the solution of my doubts on theological topics. The answer was invariably,

This is not the time for it.

Turning over many newspapers—a strange improper name! for the editors call one another rogue, turncoat, &c., which is no news at all, and report speeches made in parliament, the purport of which is always known beforehand, it being the custom for every man to carry his mind into the house, and his money out——

EMPEROR. Tsing-Ti! Tsing-Ti! put the hyphen to thy parenthesis : thou art giving me a rather long elucidation of what is *no news at all.*

TSING-TI. I received the same declaration from the political leaders as from the theological. When a reform of any abuse was proposed, no denial of its existence, none of its multiplicity, none of its magnitude, none of its intensity, was resorted to : the objection was,

This is not the time for considering it.

Were the people quiet, it was a strong subsidiary ! were they turbulent, it was a stronger ; were they between both, it was the very worst season of all to agitate the question.

Were the people in a state of famine, and were a reduction advised in the national expenditure, whether of sums voted for racehorses or brilliants, for pensions or services of plate, the adviser was counter-advised not to render the people dissatisfied by reminding them of their hunger, and was assured,

This is not the time.

In fact, the English are religiously, not to say superstitiously, scrupulous in that one matter, and perhaps the rather for having rejected all other kinds of religion : and the higher orders seem to be more so than the lower. The bishops and chancellors sit watching for the auspicious hour, and have watched for it above half a century : and although they declare they are tired of sitting and watching, and it would do their hearts good if they could see it, yet, in their honesty and forbearance, they never have pretended or

23

hinted that the discovery was made by them. Such patience and modesty are unexampled.

EMPEROR. Dost thou verily think, Tsing-Ti, that these chancellors and bishops are in earnest ?

TSING-TI. They appear so. I never heard of anyone among them caught stealing on the river, or riding off with another's horse or ass, or setting fire to houses for plunder, or infesting the high-road.

EMPEROR. Calm and moral as they are, I perceive that much more lying and shuffling is required and practised in their government than in mine. England is all mercantile, from the pinnacle of the Temple to the sewer of the Exchange. Our dealers may be as thievish as theirs : our mandarins, praised be God, are better. Although they feel at seasons a superficial itch for lucre, they are not blotched and buboed with its pestilence : they do not lead their children to be fed out of the platters of the poor, nor make the citizens, who have idols of their own, worship theirs, and pay for it.

His majesty then rose from his seat, wiped his mouth, and went away.

FOURTH AUDIENCE

The third audience may appear to have been shorter than the first, but in fact was longer by much. The imperial children asked me such a variety of questions, which I think it unnecessary to repeat, and made such a variety of remarks on my answers, that the hour allotted for their pastime in the small library wore insensibly away. They puzzled me, as children often do, and made me wish they would have turned their inquiries toward the sea, or toward men and manners, or toward anything intelligible and instructive. His majesty too puzzled me almost as much as they did.

However, on this my fourth audience, he rewarded me amply for every toil and perplexity. The first words he uttered were, that he admired my judgment and ingenuity, in passing through so many lanes and turning so many corners, without a rip or a soil on my garment. He was graciously pleased to add, that he would never have allowed any other than myself to display before his children such fantastic mysteries ; that, however, I had gone far enough into them to disgust an ingenuous mind with their darkness and doublings, and to render a lover of truth well contented with the simple institutions of his forefathers.

" My children," said his majesty, " will disdain to persecute even the persecutor, but will blow away both his fury and his fraudulence. The philosopher whom my house respects and venerates, Kong-Fu-Tsi, is never misunderstood by the attentive student of his doctrines ; there is no contradiction in them, no exaction of impossibilities, nothing above our nature, nothing below it. The most vehement of his exhortations is to industry and concord, the severest of his denunciations is against the self-tormentor, vice. He entreats us to give justice and kindness a fair trial as conductresses to happiness, and only to abandon them when they play us false. He assures us that every hour of our existence is favourable to the sowing or the gathering of some fruit ; and that sleep and repose are salutary repasts, to be enjoyed at stated times, and not to be long indulged nor frequently repeated. He is too honourable to hold out bribes, too gentle to hold out threats ; he says only, ' satisfy your conscience ; and you will satisfy your God.' But antecedently to the satisfaction of this conscience, he takes care to look into it minutely, to see that it hangs commodiously and lightly on the breast, that all its parts be sound, and all its contents in order, that it be not contracted, nor covered with cobwebs, nor crawled over with centipedes and tarantulas."

EMPEROR. I am so well satisfied with thy prudence and delicacy, O Tsing-Ti, in the explanation of things ludicrous and ferocious, that I do not only grant unto thy father, Nun-Pek, who is dead, a title of nobility, making him mandarin of the first class, but likewise the same to thy grandfather who died long before ; so much hast thou merited from me ; and so much have they merited who begat thee. Thy grandfather's name I well remember was——

TSING-TI. Peh-Nun ; may it please your majesty !

EMPEROR. Who else could have been the grandfather of Tsing-Ti ? From this moment he has yellow slippers on his feet, and he makes but one prostration in my presence. And now inform me in what manner do the kings of the White Island mark the deserts of their subjects.

I bowed my head several times before the throne, to collect from my memory as much of this matter as was deposited within it. At last I said,

IMAGINARY CONVERSATIONS : ORIENTAL

" O Emperor ! light of the East ! since nobody in England is
fond of talking of another's deserts, here my store of intelligence is
scanty ; and the king of the country seems to have found himself
in the same penury. For it is not the custom of his mandarins to
approach him with such narrations ; and none are proposed to his
majesty as worthy of advancement to high offices, or even of bearing
such titles as exalt them a span above the common class of citizens,
unless they have slain many or ruined many ; such are soldiers and
lawyers."

EMPEROR. No quieter ornament of his country, none whom future
ages will venerate, must raise up his head in his own ? Is this thy
meaning ? He may irrigate the garden of genius ; he may delight
in the fruits that will grow from it ; he may anticipate with transport
the day when his enemy's children, united with his own, shall repose
under the tree he has planted : glory never breaks in upon his
labour ; applause never disturbs his meditations ! Is that the state
of England ? Tell me ; how could these lawyers find admittance
to the king ? Have they nothing to do in their tribunals ? Will
nobody employ them ?

TSING-TI. Not only do they find admittance, but they come near
enough his person to throw some sacred dust in his eyes out of
certain ancient parchments. When they have done this, they tie
his hands behind him, loosing him only when he has given them
titles for themselves and children, who are also created great lawyers
under the royal signet.

EMPEROR. Art thou mad, Tsing-Ti ?

TSING-TI. I thought I was ; but the madness, I was glad to find,
was merely reflected.

EMPEROR. The kings of England do this ? they reward the
children for being begotted by clever fellows ? and never for making
them ? Now indeed may we believe that the soles of their feet are
opposed to the soles of ours. Didst thou tell me they delegate to
their servants the granting of distinctions to worthless men ?

TSING-TI. Too true, in eleven instances out of the dozen.

EMPEROR. Well then may the English be called regicides ; for he
who lowers the kingly character spills the most precious blood of his
king. Go home : I must ponder on these subjects. Methinks I
have caught thy old sea-sickness, my head turns round so, and everything seems so disproportioned and confused.

26

EMPEROR OF CHINA AND TSING-TI

On my return the following day, his majesty took my sleeve between the tips of his imperial thumb and finger, and said blandly, " Thou, being in thy heart a Christian, shalt now enter more deeply with me on that religion. Albeit, I see nothing but a quagmire in it, bearing unwholesome weeds on the surface, and unfathomable mud within. Another swarm of insects hath recently been hatched on it, some of which, my mandarins inform me, have been blown over into Canton. They style themselves *Good-news-mongers*. By the accounts I have received of them, they resemble a jar of tamarinds with little pulp and no sugar. I apprehend they will do small credit to their master in heaven."

TSING-TI. Whose blessed name, O Emperor! be praised for ever. He came before the arrogant, firm in meekness. He said, " Abstain from violence, abstain from fraud : be continent, be pure, be patient : love one another."

EMPEROR. How happy would men be universally, if they observed these precepts ! Life would bring few wishes, death few fears. We should come and go, jocund as children enter and leave a garden, entering it to play in and leaving it to sleep. Alas ! they do not toil to earn repose at the day's end : but the whole occupation of their existence is to make the last hour solicitous and restless.

We are friends, Tsing-Ti ! for we both have listened to the words of wisdom, and in youth, and together. Recollections such as these unite the high and the humble, and make benevolence grow up even where the soil is sterile. Sterile it is not with thee ; but yielding a hundredfold. Come then freely to me every day, as thou wert wont formerly, and let us exchange, what alone can make both of us the richer, our thoughts and knowledge. Thou hast travelled afar, and art master of many things which none have laid before me. I will turn them over, partly for curiosity and partly for acquisition, like those who enter the house of the jeweller.

I am wearied with the inconsistencies and shocked at the irreligion of the islanders. At some future time I may perhaps have leisure and patience to examine them more minutely. At present I am more desirous to take a view of their literature. My father of blessed memory planted poetry in their island : does it flourish ?

27

IMAGINARY CONVERSATIONS : ORIENTAL

TSING-TI. From the specimens I purchased, it appears to me, O Emperor! that the English may become poets, and reach nearer to the perfection of the Chinese than any people of the West; for I observe that a greater number of their verses end in monosyllables.

EMPEROR. Indeed! are they arrived at that? Bring me to-morrow a few of the least heavy from among thy volumes, and such as by their nature may, with skilful comments, be the most intelligible to me. At the same time thou wilt be able to render me some account of those who read their verses at the king's bedside.

TSING-TI. His majesty is a sound sleeper: none are called in.

EMPEROR. At his table then.

TSING-TI. None recite verses there. The fictions of poetry are not exactly those which find the readiest admittance into the palaces of the West. The ornaments of style and composition are thought in England to denote a vacant mind. If flowers exhale their fragrance from a silver vase, the English doubt at once whether it is silver. Their princes are no cultivators of poetry and eloquence; which is the more remarkable, as they are fanciers of old porcelain, and can distinguish and estimate it almost as correctly as our best dealers. They are likewise so judicious in paintings, that they invariably buy from Dutch artists such pieces as bear the nearest affinity to ours.

EMPEROR. Then, by degrees, Tsing-Ti, their nails will lengthen and their feet contract. We shall be all one people, as the oldest sages have foretold.

TSING-TI. Alas, sire! the youngest will never live to see that day. No sovran in England ever conversed an hour together with poet or philosopher; many for days and nights with gamesters and other pickpockets, especially the king now reigning.

EMPEROR. I have heard some such reports: I have also heard that there are fewer of like character in the island than on the continent.

TSING-TI. The English, although they have lost their religion, are still in many of their dealings the most honest and abstinent people in the world. I have walked by the side of a canal in the vicinity of the capital, and I have seen rats, cats, dogs, very delicate sucking kittens, and the tenderest plumpest puppies, and even fine long snakes, green and yellow, of several pounds each, enough to give an appetite to an opium-eater at day-break. I have seen them, sire, killed upon the banks, without a man or a woman or a child to guard them : and I have waited in vain, for hours together, in the hope of making a contract for a quota of the stock, the proprietor never appearing. In some instances it has happened that they remained there until they rotted. Such is the fertility of soil, and the scantiness of population in proportion to it. Even frogs are neglected as articles of luxury. I have noticed some lying dead by the side of ditches, having been stoned by peasants, who would have been banished to the extremity of the earth for attempting to kill a granivorous bird, or for stealing a sour apple.

EMPEROR. Do the English offer up sour apples in sacrifice ? do they worship birds ?

TSING-TI. In public, no : what they may do privately, in the present state of religion among them, it is difficult for a traveller to ascertain. Certainly they think differently on these subjects from what we read in the history of more ancient nations which worshipped brute animals. These selected for preservation the creatures that benefited the husbandman, by devouring the reptiles and insects, or by rendering him some other good service. The English nobles preserve foxes, that kill his lambs ; hares, pheasants, partridges, that consume his corn ; and, instead of remunerating him for exterminating the pests of agriculture, confiscate his property, condemn him to die of famine, or, when the sentence is mildest, remove him for ever from that land which he has enriched with the sweat of his brow.

EMPEROR. Tsing-Ti ! it was in a moment of irritation, it was when the rebels had sorely vexed me, that I was malicious enough to think of sending such Christians as these among the Tartars.

TSING-TI. On the imperial footstool I lay the few pieces of poetry I have collected in England. Wishing to procure some specimens of elegant handwriting, I went to my tailor and intreated his recommendation. It was not particularly for his honesty that I selected him, but because I had found him the most acute reasoner I had met with. My first acquaintance was contracted with him by desiring him to mend a rent in my dress. It appeared to me that his charge was exorbitant, and I asked him whether he did not think the same.

" Certainly I do," replied he.

" But, my friend, the price of a new vest would not exceed this demand."

" Certainly not," replied he, with equal calmness. " To cut the thing short, as we tailors are fond of doing," said he before I could go on, " it is an easier matter to make than to mend : try at a speech, try at a teacup, try at a wife."

" Excuse me," answered I, " we may have trials enough in this world without that " ; and gave him the sum demanded. He told me to take his arm (a strange unwieldy custom of the English), and conducted me into an alley, where I found a middle-aged man, in a grey coat, employed in transcribing what he told us were *sermons*.

EMPEROR. Hold, Tsing-Ti ! What species of poetry may that be ?

TSING-TI. None whatever, O Emperor ! but religious exhortations, religious explanations, or religious damnations, for they all come under these three heads.

EMPEROR. And pretty bulky heads too.

TSING-TI. The grey-coated man was sedulous in transcribing them from printed books, into a book covered with black. He told me that no other colour was serviceable in church (church means pagod), and that it would be shameful for a preacher, expositor, exhorter, or damner, to preach another man's words without making it appear that they were his own. He was to receive a dollar for each sermon, from a priest who had three *livings*.

EMPEROR. Tsing-Ti ! do the rogues pretend to have found out the Elixir ? Three *livings* ! one man hold three *livings* ! Have I any horse that can eat in any three of my stables at a time ? Have I any that can carry me along three roads at once ? It is difficult for the best and wisest man to perform his duty of exhortation and admonition to the near and to the few : how then shall he perform it to the distant and the many ?

TSING-TI. Those about the king have sons and brothers, of whom it is easier to make priests than to make poets, and who would rather receive twenty thousand golden pieces annually, than the two-hundredth part only.

EMPEROR. If this immense wealth belongs to certain families, as appears to be the case, yet the king might command them to expend a portion of it on canals and roads, or, if there are any poor in the country, on the poor.

TSING-TI. A tenth of the produce of the land, and of all the money spent on it in manure and culture (for these are considered as nothing by the priesthood), is paid annually to the successors of the Christians. Out of which tenth, anciently, a fourth was set apart by the Christians for the maintenance of the poor. No law whatever has alienated this portion from its destination. Therefore on all benefices, which have not regularly paid it, there exists a just debt of the arrears.

This statement was submitted to the consideration of the king's ministers, and farthermore that parliament should be called upon to enforce it. The ministers, who courted the people where the courtship was uncostly, were very disdainful against the author of the proposal, and declared that he was no better than a robber.

EMPEROR. Could that be their real objection to him ?

TSING-TI. They declared him a robber who would plunder their relatives of their possessions, and their children of their inheritance.

EMPEROR. Perhaps he was as they said : for robbers are clear-sighted, as we find in cats, rats, weasels, and the like. And it is not probable that there should be in the country any notorious one quite unknown to them.

TSING-TI. It was found, on examination, that he had only robbed himself; to which they, recovering their courtesy, said he was very welcome.

EMPEROR. I do not wonder that they are loth to alienate the rich possessions of the crown, which it appears they share, under the pretext of religion.

TSING-TI. This is not the pretext : the pretext is, that they can not in their consciences bear to hear of *organic* changes. Such is the expression : I am unable to divine what it means.

EMPEROR. Tsing-Ti ! is it then so long since thou leftest thy country ? hast thou quite forgotten thy music ? Dost not thou remember that the organ creaks and grunts, when the foot presses the pedal and the wind has no direction ? But organic changes, as the affected fools call them, require skilful hands ; if they have not them, let them get up and give the seat to those who have.

TSING-TI. Sire ! the instrument is a noble one. Children and madmen have played upon it, and its treasure of rich tones lies within it still. Not a pipe is impaired ; not a key is loosened ; but there are impudent idlers, who insist on putting their hats and gloves on it ; and the audience, ere long, will throw them over the rails of the gallery.

EMPEROR. That were violent : let them promote them, by an elevation of the foot, quietly downstairs, and break no bones.

Thy estimate of the sacerdotal domains, and royalties annexed to them, must be erroneous.

TSING-TI. May it please your majesty ! on this subject my information, I venture to affirm, is both ample and correct.   There are yet remaining in the White and the Green Island, a dozen of priests each of whom receives a larger sum than all the poets and philosophers of both united have received in two thousand years.

EMPEROR. Prodigious ! computing that one thousand years have produced one philosopher and one poet.

TSING-TI. A priest of the first order, on which it is not incumbent either to preach or sing, either to pray or curse, receives an emolument of which the amount is greater than the consolidated pay of a thousand soldiers, composing the king's body-guard.

EMPEROR. Did they tell thee this ?

TSING-TI. They did.

EMPEROR. And dost thou believe it ?

TSING-TI. I do.

EMPEROR. Then, Tsing-Ti, thou hast belief enough for both of us.   It is not usually a kind of dust that travellers are apt to gather.   There is, on the contrary, much attrition of it, in general, unless the wheels are guarded and greased.

But what is the business then of these priests ?

TSING-TI. Chiefly to lay their hands, through a sack, on a row of children's heads, to keep them firm and steady in the new faith.

EMPEROR. I doubt whether, when the hand is taken off, the heads do not rise up again, like the keys of the organ we talked about, and retain as little of the music.   He must very soon have the same to do over again.

TSING-TI. No, no, no ; that would spoil all.

EMPEROR. This is incomprehensible ; the salary incredible.   I am afraid, Tsing-Ti, thou hast set thy face against the priests, for no better reason than because thou couldst not find thy favourite Christianity among them.   In what manner, out of what funds, and by whom, are they remunerated ?   For to suppose the stout farmer will let them carry off his tenth sheaf, would be silly, let the farmer be as learned as he may in theology, and as zealous to promote the study of it. Come, tell me this, and allow them their deserts.

TSING-TI. O my Emperor! I do indeed, with all humility, still adhere to that humane and pure religion ; and I may peradventure be disappointed and displeased at finding its place made desolate, its image thrown down, and what was erected for its support rendered the instrument of its destruction.

The priests of the establishment which has been substituted for it are not rewarded in proportion to their learning, their virtues, their zeal, or the proficiency of those whom they instruct.

EMPEROR. Bad! bad! bad! how then?

TSING-TI. In proportion to the fertility of the land around them.

EMPEROR. There spoke the honest man, the true sage, the genuine Tsing-Ti. I approve of this dispensation : labour should be thus remunerated. Such an example, set by an order of men who are not always the most industrious in mind or body, must produce an admirable effect on the people.

TSING-TI. They labour not, but punish the labour of others by severe and unrelenting exaction. In proportion as the farmer works, he pays the priest. In proportion to the one's industry rise the means of the other's idleness. Whether the English believe fertility to spring from the sacerdotal presence, I have never ascertained. Some, I apprehend, are doubters. But this scepticism is become more dangerous than any merely on theological points. The performer has warmer partisans than the composer of the music, of which truly the theme is lost among fugues and variations. I would not however strip the better sort of the priests of their deserts, or call them all idlers. Many are far from it, and the earth owes them a portion of her fruits. I myself have seen them diligent in clearing the fields of birds and vermin : I have seen several on horseback——

EMPEROR. Priests! priests on horseback!

TSING-TI. In that posture, O my Emperor! have I seen them ; and farthermore, in pursuit of wild animals.

EMPEROR. Conscientious men! these at least would earn their stipends.

TSING-TI. Even the fox hath not escaped their scrutiny. Some, I am told, are not afraid of handling a gun, and have been known to kill birds upon wing, at the distance of many paces.

IMAGINARY CONVERSATIONS : ORIENTAL

EMPEROR. Cormorants are vast and heavy birds, but are they so tame in the north ? and kites and hawks do they fly like ours ? Well, if the priests actually perform these things, they are more useful than I fancied. These must be of a different sect from those who despoil the farmer.

TSING-TI. The very same.

EMPEROR. Ah Tsing-Ti ! ah my friend ! thou art shrewd, thou art observative ; but either thou hast confounded two objects, or thine eyes are not long enough to comprehend at once the extremities of these strange creatures, which vary so widely in their parts.

[Thus spake the Emperor, and it was my duty to be in the wrong.]

EMPEROR. I tell thee plainly, O Tsing-Ti ! that I was puzzled how to sow dissensions among the Tartar tribes, unless I could introduce Christianity among them. But thy discourse hath convinced me that, weakened as it is in virulence, enough of it remains in Europe to serve my purposes, if they should rise up again in arms. It will be worth my while to order a cargo by the next East India fleet. I will breathe upon these troublesome marauders such a blast from that quarter, as shall cover and hide for ever the names of Khu-Li-Chang and Chin-Ki-Se-Han.* What an advantage to our Celestial Empire, not only to abolish all combination and concord from the tents of our enemy, but likewise to decimate his cavalry, his curds, and whey ; to throw the soldier out of the stirrup, and toss the priest into it ! Thou shalt indulge in thy own fancies, and none shall ever molest thee, for thou art kind and quiet. Christianity makes such men even better than they were before. Like wine, it brings out every humour. The ferocious it renders more ferocious, the exacting more exacting, the hypocritical more hypocritical, the austere more austere ; and it lays more gracefully on the gentle breast the folded hands of devotion. Such are the observations of our forefathers on the Jesuits and their disciples, whose religion (they pretended) was founded on Christianity. I know not whether, in theirs, there were more than four things which diverged from it : they lied, they sought riches, they persecuted, and they murdered. These are the principal divergences from the ordinances of Christ ; several others were proved against them, but rather as private men than as a public body, and prevalent in other religions

* Kouli Khan and Gengiz Khan.—W. S. L.

34

to nearly the same extent. I never could discover how long the Christian continued in any part of Europe. In Asia the habits and institutions of men are of much longer duration : there, in one extremely small part indeed, we know from good authority, it existed (we can not say flourished) about six centuries. Every other had lasted longer, and that which succeeded it has continued double the time, and with much less deviation.

Tsing-Ti. Yet a purer law was never laid down, gentler maxims never inculcated, better example never given.

Emperor. How then could the religion pass away so soon ?

Tsing-Ti. For those very reasons. Religions may differ, but priests are similar in all countries. They will have blood, they will have mysteries, they will have money ; they will threaten, they will persecute, they will command.

Emperor. Not here.

Tsing-Ti. For which reason the empire has lasted long ; fathers, and princes who resemble them, are respected ; and the nation, though surrounded by barbarians, by predatory and warlike tribes, has enjoyed more peace and prosperity than any other. Industry and quiet, charity and hospitality, cleanly and frugal habits, are always in exact proportion to the poverty and paucity of the priesthood. This is the only important truth I have learned with certainty in my travels.

Emperor. Strange indeed ! that neither English nor Americans have betrayed the secret, that Christianity was extirpated from among them.

Tsing-Ti. The establishment or abolition of a religion is a less matter in the view of an American, than the sowing of a corn-field, or the killing of a snake. The English have better reasons for their silence. The Christian priests had rich possessions : people still dress and read and preach like them, and call themselves by the name, and drag any man into a court of justice who says they are not Christians. They hold the lands of the ancient priests on this tenure ; which priests, before they were ejected, made a joke of the vocation, as they called their trade ; but ejection is a bitter antidote to jocularity.

Emperor. I do not wonder that those who occupy the places of the priests, and dress and speak like them, should be angry at being called by any other name than that under which they hold their property : my wonder is, why the conditions should have been imposed, since the nation has no taste for any particle of the old religion.

Tsing-Ti. There are some occasions on which it is thought decorous to relax a little in the pertinacity of adherence to the name. For instance, they do not expect you to call them by it, and are almost angry if you do, when they are dancing or drinking or dicing, or riding in pursuit of foxes, or occupied in the humaner recreation of unappropriated girls, of which there are as many in the streets of London, as we hear there are of dogs unappropriated in Stamboul.

Emperor. Well governed and abundant country must be Turkey, wherein even the poor can see dogs about the streets, and yet abstain from filching a cutlet or an ear.

Tsing-Ti. The dogs must be very old and thin, or the Turks must fear that poison has been given them by the Franks ; for human forbearance hath its limits, and Hunger hears neither Ulemah nor Kadi.

Emperor. As thou didst not travel far beyond the limits of London, which, according to the map laid at the feet of my father by Mak ArTni, the mandarin, occupies only a small portion of the British isles—but first, is that true ?

Tsing-Ti. Perfectly.

Emperor. I ask the question, because a Frenchman would persuade my minister, in the name of His Most Christian Majesty, that although London is nearly the whole of Britain, and encroaches far upon Ireland, yet it might be contained in the court-yard of His Most Christian Majesty, Lu Is the Eighteenth.

Tsing-Ti. No, nor in his belly, capacious as he was, and worthy of reigning. But the French have always undervalued the English, since the English conquered and rendered them tributary : and the Englishman has always looked up to the Frenchman, since he threw the Frenchman down and tied his wrists behind him.

Emperor. I was about to ask thee whether thou art quite certain, O Tsing-Ti, that some latent spark of Christianity may not possibly be found under the ashes, in the remoter parts of the country.

Tsing-Ti. I have heard it, and do believe it.

Emperor. Imaginest thou that thou canst computate, by approximation, the number of Christians now existing in the world ?

EMPEROR OF CHINA AND TSING-TI

TSING-TI. I believe the number of Christians in the world is about the same as the number of Parsees. These two religions are the purest in existence. That of the Parsees was always good, always rigorously observed ; and those who followed it were always temperate, hospitable, and veracious. It does not appear that the followers of the Christian were remarkable for these qualities, first or last ; yet certainly they were much better than those who have succeeded to their houses and dresses, and who (in England at least) seize for their own use what the Christian priests gave partly to the infirm, partly to the poor, partly to the traveller, and partly to the stranger. Before I had heard of the revolution in religion, my heart bounded at the pleasure I expected to communicate, in taking a frugal repast with a minister of Christ. I desired the captain, who was much my friend, to conduct me, not mentioning to him the purport of my visit, and happy to hear that he must return when he had knocked at the door for me, I being unwilling to trouble the religious man with a second guest, who was neither poor nor a stranger in the land. A female of pleasurable aspect opened the door, and complimented me on my facility in the language, and examined my dress not less attentively with her hands than her eyes. Her master heard her, and cried " What the devil does that fellow want ? " looking at me all the while.

" I am come," said I, " to break bread with thee, O minister of Christ ! "

" *Thee !* " cried he, with anger and disdain : for in England and France every man must be addressed as four or five ; in other parts of Europe, as a young lady. He took me violently by the collar and threw me out of the house ; and a few minutes afterward a more civil person came up to me, desiring me to follow him, and to answer for myself before a justice of the peace. My heart again bounded : what delightful words, *justice ! peace !* I told him I had no complaint to make. " Come along," said he ; and I rejoiced at his earnestness. I was brought before a member of parliament, whose father (I heard) was as famous for flogging boys, as the member is for torturing men. He heard me without deigning to answer ; and said to my conductor,

" Take the fellow to the treadmill."

I do not regret my inability to give an account of this place, since it appears to be a place of punishment. At the door I met my captain, who was introducing another inmate for theft. He asked me what I was doing there. I replied that I believed I was about to have the honour of dining there with a member of the church, and a member of the parliament ; the dignity of the latter having been imparted to me on the road. After some explanation from me in the presence of the miller, he prevailed on that worthy tradesman to allow me a chair in his parlour, and, in about an hour, returned with an elderly man, also a member of parliament, who heard me in my defence, and laughed heartily. In fine, I was constrained to order my dinner in another place, having first thanked the captain, and expressed a wish that we might meet again.

"Not here, I hope, Mr. Tsing-Ti!" said my friend : "I like dancing upon my own deck better than upon yon fellow's." He shook my hand, and went away : I never saw him after.

EMPEROR. I wonder the King of England does not introduce a few specimens of better precepts and better religions. If he has never heard of ours, and those of Thibet, there are some very excellent in his own dominions of India.

TSING-TI. The people about his late majesty frightened him ; telling him that, if he pulled down an altar at the extremity of his kingdom, his throne would fall at the same moment, and that he would fracture a thigh at the least. This was whispered to me ; so was what shall follow. Being corpulent, as becomes his station, he greatly dreaded a broken thigh, and paid several carpenters, whom he maintained in an old chapel, to knock nails every year into the altars throughout the country, and to lay their rules stoutly, and occasionally their hammers, on the backs of those people who would over-curiously try whether the said altars are upright, and what timber they are made of. The carpenters are at once the greatest chatterers and the greatest rogues in the whole community, and enjoy the privilege of exemption from the payment of their debts.

EMPEROR. From what province are they ?

TSING-TI. From all : every city sends to the old chapel, for the king's service, those whom the citizens are afraid to trust for mutton and beef, or to leave too near their wives and daughters, making each one promise he will furnish them with nails and chips, and little reflecting that for every nail they must give an iron-mine, and for every chip a forest. At last the king's majesty chose a proper fellow to superintend his business. A clamorous old ringleader,

38

who worked upstairs, was desired to walk down. He begged, with tears in his eyes, permission to stay half an hour longer, and spent it in picking up pins on the floor. Unbending his back from this laborious function, he groaned heavily, went home, and prevailed on his wife, after a long entreaty, to promise him two sheep-tails to sit upon, as he had been used to a cushion of wool. His wife bought only one sheep-tail, apprising him that, cutting it cleverly through the middle, it would serve the purpose of two. He threw up his eyes to heaven, and thanked God for inspiring her to save the family from ruin, when his thoughts were distracted by his tribulations. Carpenters, who formerly were criers in the courts, were clamorous in their assembly. An old soldier walked among them with the look of an eagle : he made no reply, but (it is reported) he opened a drawer, and showed them a Peruvian glue, admirable for sticking lips together : the very sight of it draws them close. He has promised to all those who work under him a continuance of their wages, but threatens the refractory with dismissal.

EMPEROR. I fancied the English were intractable and courageous.

TSING-TI. To others. Dogs know that dogs have sharp teeth, and that calves have flat ones. The man who has the purse in his own fist, has the sword in his servant's.

EMPEROR. Proverbs, O Tsing-Ti ! prove one man wise, but rarely make another so. Experience, adversity, and affliction, impress divine lessons deeply.

TSING-TI. Then the English are the most learned people upon earth. Those they have conquered leave the table of the conquerors without bread and salt upon it ; those they have protected strip off them the last shirt ; and, while they sit and scratch their shoulders, they agree to praise in letters of gold, and on monuments of marble, the wisdom of such as misguided, and the integrity of such as ruined them.

SIXTH AUDIENCE

EMPEROR. I am curious of any fresh and certain information, about a country which appears to be separated from others more widely in character than in locality. May we not surmise, that a fragment of a star hath dropped, with two or three of its inhabitants, on this part of our globe ?

TSING-TI. Highly probable. Even yet there appears a strange

39

disinclination in the English to associate with those of other regions. Their neighbours meet a foreigner with a smile and a salutation : the English withdraw from him staring and frowning, as if the fright of the fall were recent, and the intent of the stranger worse than uncertain. The rest of the Europeans give indications of good will or good manners, by an embrace, or an interchange of the hand, or by insertion of their noses into that portion of the hair which grows between the ear and the chin, and which, being to them what the interior of the tail is to dogs, they nourish for that purpose. You must bruise an Englishman's face into the figure and dimensions of a football, ere he can discern to his satisfaction that he ought to recognise you as a friend. To this obliquity and perversity I must attribute it, that every ordinance of Jesus Christ hath been cast aside by him, having first ascertained the fact, that everyone hath been thus rejected, on the authority of a public preacher. He sat in a sort of tub or barrel, over which was suspended by a chain (not without some support from the hinder part of the barrel) the cover of a winepress, at the height of about two feet above his head. He smiled at his auditors ; called them his brothers, though there were before him more of the female sex than of the male ; and assured them that, according to the *Book of Glad Tidings*, the greater part of them must inevitably go to the devil, and gnash their teeth eternally. Upon which, he and his audience began to sing and ogle ; and I saw among them several sets of teeth which I thought too pretty for their destination ; and several mouths, on the contrary, which never could pay the penalty denounced. A young person sat beside me beating time, but beating it where it was impossible she should hear it, and seeming to provoke añ accompaniment. A sallow man under the preacher, a man with watery eyes, not unlike a duck's in form and colour, and with nostrils opening and shutting, and with a mouth semicircular in front, and drawn upward at the corners, caught me by the elbow as I left the temple, and told me the labourer was worthy of his hire. I did not comprehend his meaning, and perhaps might have stared at him for an explanation, when an agriculturist came up between us, to whom I bowed, and said, " He means you." The agriculturist made me no answer, but said to the other, " He looks like a Dutch sailor in his holiday suit." And turning to me, " Master, I say, tip him five shillings : he comes but once a quarter, and damns the parish, he and his parson, at a reasonable rate." Then winking, "If you sleep at the Green Dragon, he will see that your bed is warmed to your wish, and sing you a stave at the opening of the service." In fact, such was the good man's gratitude, he brought me his daughter at dusk ; which is often done in London, although not so often, we may suppose, as in the time of the Christians. I wish the young woman had profited by the father's example, and had rather asked for money than run off with it.

The love of the generous man expands and displays itself in the sunshine of his liberality ; the love of the wise man reposes in the shade of his discretion. Neither of these was left to my choice ; and, O Emperor ! friend of my youth ! I lost at once my money, my watch, and my silk trousers.

EMPEROR. I can hail and rain and overflood with money ; watches I have many as stars are in the firmament ; and with silk I can array the earth, and cover the billows of the ocean. Money take thou from my coffers with both hands. Take forty-four robes from my closet, called the closet of ambergris, all worn by the members of my imperial house, some by the bravest and most ancient of our ancestors, and many flowered with verses and proverbs. Take likewise what watches thou needest and approvest, from the wall of any edifice in my gardens, in most of which there are hundreds to relieve the tiresomeness we suffer from the rude obstreperance of the birds in spring.

TSING-TI. O Emperor ! friend of my youth ! one watch suffices, and be it any one plain and good. In the vestments I would make a selection ; not taking what the bravest or most ancient of our Emperors have sanctified, nor much regarding the literature impressed on them, which I am afraid the moths may have divided into somewhat too minute paragraphs, and dramatised with unnecessary interjections.

EMPEROR. Thou shalt then have forty-four newer : twenty-two of them flowered with gold, sixteen hung with pearls, and six interwoven with my father's verses.

TSING-TI. These six will never wear out : the others too will preserve through many ages the odour of my gratitude, and the richer fragrance of my prince's love.

EMPEROR. It is much to be regretted that the better religion of the English was little durable.

IMAGINARY CONVERSATIONS : ORIENTAL

TSING-TI. Religions, like teas, suffer by passing the salt water.

EMPEROR. Kong-Fu-Tsi wrote not this.

TSING-TI. He wrote it not.

EMPEROR. Write it thou on the blank leaf at the termination of his sayings, in that copy which my ancestor, Chow-Hi, of blessed memory, bought at the expense of a rice-ground in Wong-Wa, and of the tea-cup called Chang-Chang, transparent and thin as a white rose-leaf, though a soldier's span in diameter, and little short of a lawyer's ; and so smooth, that (it is written in our chronicles) flies have broken their legs in attempting to climb it.

TSING-TI. They must have been young ones, or very decrepit.

EMPEROR. The chronicles of my ancestors do not commemorate that particular, nor offer a conjecture at their ages.

TSING-TI. History is much improved of late, and chiefly by the sedulity of the English. In England we should have known all about it to a day, and some duels would have been fought, and many calumnies and curses dealt reciprocally in the outset. For although their denominations in hostility are much longer and much more ponderous than ours, they cast them with great dexterity and velocity. The English historians are double-handed.

EMPEROR. So are ours.

TSING-TI. But theirs keep one hand for history, the other for controversy ; the one being blackened with ink, the other with gunpowder. Their favourite words anciently were *saint* and *hero ;* the present in fashion are *rogue* and *rebel.* One of their kings ordered the bones of his father's enemies to be disinterred, long after their burial. This monarch seems to unite more suffrages from the modern historians than any other, and their works relating to his reign are enriched with more sermons, and pleadings, and opinions of counsel, and depositions of witnesses.

EMPEROR. Such histories, with their depositions, must be as unsavoury as the oldest street in Canton : and, with their sermons and pleadings and opinions, must be equally long and crooked.

TSING-TI. The English, like the ants, follow one another in a regular line, through wet and dry, their leaders choosing in preference those places which have a pungent odour.

EMPEROR. Nay, nay, Tsing-Ti ! thou dislikest them for disappointing thee in thy favourite religion.

TSING-TI. Certainly I do not like them the better for it : but I

42

love my country and my emperor the more when I return and see
the toleration of every sect and creed. What a strange institution
is prevalent in Europe ! Christianity is known and confessed to be
so excellent and divine a thing, that no man is permitted at once to
be a Christian and to call himself so. He may take which division
he likes : he may practise the ordinances of Christ without assuming
the name, or he may assume the name on condition that he abstain
from the ordinances. However, it is whispered that several whole
families are privileged, and neither deny that they are Christians,
nor abstain with any rigour from the duties enjoined. I was but a
year in the country : I say only what I have heard. Often that
which is beautiful at a distance, loses its effect as we approach it.
The cloud whereon the departing sun pours his treasures, which he
invests with purple and gold, and appears to leave as a representative not unworthy of himself, fills us with gladness, pure and
chastened, from the horizon ; but is the mountain it hath rested
on less dreary and less sterile the day after ? I was a Christian
when I quitted my native land : I return to my native land, and am
a Christian. My tears fell abundantly, genially, sweetly, on first
reading the sermon of the blessed Teacher to his disciples. How I
wished to press my brow upon the herbs below him, in the midst of
that faithful and fraternal multitude ! How I wished to humble it,
even unto the insects, and so quiet my heart for ever by its just
abasement !

When I had resided a short time in England, I began to suspect
that some few sentences were interpolated by Act of Parliament ;
such as,

If any man will sue thee at law, and take away thy coat, let him
have thy cloak also.

And again, speaking of prisons,

Thou shalt by no means come out thence till thou hast paid the
uttermost farthing.

I saw several poor soldiers in the streets, who had been in Egypt
about the time (I suspect) when Christianity was breathing her last.
They were holy men, but somewhat more addicted to the ancient
part of the Bible than to the newer, calling often upon God to
confound and damn this person and that. However they had

43

observed with punctuality the hardest of the more recent commandments ; which is,

If thine eye offend thee, pluck it out and cast it from thee ; for it
is profitable for thee that one of thy members should perish, and not
that thy whole body should be cast into hell. And if thy right hand
offend thee, cut it off and cast it from thee.

The precept is plain ; the reasons, I imagine, are parliamentary.
However, there were many who thought them quite sufficient, and
who not only cut off the hand but the arm likewise. Wonderful in
how short a time so complete a change was effected !

I myself did not aim precipitately at this perfection, but, in
order to be well received in the country, I greatly wished the favour
of a blow on the right cheek. Unfortunately I got several on the
left before I succeeded. At last I was so happy as to make the
acquisition of a most hearty cuff under the socket of the right eye,
giving me all those vague colours which we Chinese reduce into
regular features, or into strange postures of the body, by means of
glasses. As soon as I knew positively whether my head was remaining on my neck or not, I turned my left cheek for the testimony of my
faith. The assailant cursed me and kicked me ; the by-standers,
instead of calling me Christian, called me Turk and Malay ; and,
instead of humble and modest, the most impudent dog and devil
they had ever set eyes upon. I fell on my knees, and praised God,
since at last I had been admitted into so pure and pious a country,
that even this action was deemed arrogant and immodest. Seeing
a Jew on my return (as I soon found he was) who had several things
to sell, I asked of him whether he had any medicine good for the
contusion of my cheek-bone.

" Come along with me," said he.

We entered an alley ; he unlocked a door in the narrowest part
of it, and conducted me to the summit of the house. His wife and
children ran out to meet him ; and a little girl had caught him by
the hand before any of the party saw that a stranger was behind ;
for the stairs were narrow and dark. The exuberance of pleasure
was repressed. The little girl did not loose her father's hand, nor
did the mother draw her back, although she held her by the arm.
The little girl looked steadfastly at me, and then loosed her father's
hand and turned her back toward me, and placed her finger, I
conjecture, to her eye. But the mother was excusing her dress,

44

and her ignorance how to receive such a personage, when the child, impatient that her signs were ineffectual, cried, " O mother! can not you see how he is bruised ? "

The words had scarcely escaped her lips, before the father brought a white liquid in a teacup, and said calmly, " Rachel! put down your hands from above your head, and neither grieve nor wonder, but help." I imagine I had been detained on the outside of the door, until several things were removed from the crowded and small apartment, in which the air had by no means all the benefit it might have had from its elevation. When I entered it and came fully into the light, every face, excepting the husband's, expressed the most tender pity. Rachel had scarcely touched me with the cooling remedy, ere she said she was sure she hurt me. The little girl said to me, " Let me do it," and " It does not hurt at all. See! I have put some on the same place in my own cheek," and then whispered in the mother's ear, " can not you encourage him better ? does he cry ? "

Then escaped me those words, O my Emperor and friend! those which never before fell from me, and which I do believe are original, " Yes, a wise man may marry."

The husband did not confine his inquiries to the cause of what he called the quarrel; and on my saying that I never could have expected so little of commiseration, so little of assistance, from Christians, " Why not," cried he abruptly. " Are Turks more cruel ? " " I can not speak of the Turks," said I, " but I could wish that so pure and so pious a sect as the Christians were humaner."

I then began to ask questions in my turn ; certainly not, whether he was among the professing or the acting ; but how long ago it was forbidden that the same person should be both ? He began to feel my head, unceremoniously, in places where there were no bruises, and thought it would be better for me to lose a little blood, as an ugly blow might be unlucky to the brain. The wife made signs to him, but could not stop him ; and her anxiety that he should desist, only urged him to explain and defend himself. The little girl slipped away!

" We children of Abraham," said he, " have our law and keep it ; while every year some new fungus, whiter or blacker, more innocent or more poisonous, springs from the scatterings of the old dunghill, forked up and littered and trimmed within the walls of

45

Rome. Persecution has not shaken us nor our fathers : we hold fast by their robes, and are burnt or stoned together."

The wife lifted up her hands, and said nothing : but a boy, about five years old, seeing her hands lifted up, knelt under them and asked her blessing : she gave it, shedding tears over him. The husband too himself was moved ; for nothing rouses the soul like another's patient suffering. He likewise was moved ; but less with tenderness than indignation.

" They have burned, yes," cried he, " they have burned even such as thou art, O my Abel ! "

Here he entered into historical facts, so horrible and atrocious, that the princes of Europe thought it expedient to unite, and to exert their utmost authority, in order that two of the perpetrators might be kept on their thrones, against the reclamation of their subjects ; these two having repeatedly committed perjury, and repeatedly attempted parricide.

EMPEROR. And the other kings aided and assisted them !

TSING-TI. All, all : never were they unanimous before. These kings, it is reported, are of different sects ; yet they most formally agreed, and most solemnly protested, that parricide and perjury are legitimate in princes. In England there are some who doubt it, but they are deemed shallow and insufficient ; and though indeed they think more rigidly than the rest, they are called *free-thinkers*.

EMPEROR. High compliment !

TSING-TI. Far otherwise in the opinion of the people ; the word *liberal* is the only word more odious.

EMPEROR. Tsing-Ti ! Tsing-Ti ! art thou quite sure that this contusion may not have jolted and confounded and estranged thy memory ? for, although men change their religion, or lose their principles, a reminiscence of right and wrong must remain. That any should voluntarily lay impediments on the operation of their minds, is really incredible ; that they should hate you for smoothening the way before them, and for leaving it open, can only be attributed to the worst depravity, or to insanity the most irremediable.

TSING-TI. Things less enormous may be more easily forgotten. The blow on my cheek-bone rather improved than impaired my memory : at least supplying it with another fact for its store-house.

EMPEROR. I would more willingly hear again of the Jew than of the princes : he seems much honester and much wiser. The distance in rank between us is the same, therefore the same would be my sympathy with them as with him, if they deserved it. I can, however, show no countenance to such execrable wretches as those who not only held alliance with perjurers and parricides, but who abstained from bringing them to punishment. Indifferent and heedless am I what religion they profess or hold. Some is requisite; since imbecile men (and such are those princes) can only learn morality under the rod of fear.

TSING-TI. The English treat theirs as the Malays we see in China treat their serpents, first drawing their teeth, then teaching them to dance to one certain tune. But these serpents, whenever they get loose, make off toward other serpents and join them, forgetting the wrist and tabor, and preferring any holes and brambles to the level well-brushed ground upon which they received their education.

When I pressed the Jew to join me and become a Christian, he declared he had no aversion to the precepts of Christ, who had given a strong testimony for his nation.

" I am sorry that, by the laws of the land," said he, " so humane and devoted a creature was condemned to death. But the laws of our land, in this instance, were not more rigorous than the laws of others. The public men endured him longer than the public men of any other country in the world would endure one who excited so pertinaciously the populace against them. Scribes, publicans, pharisees, are for ever in his mouth, mixed with much bitterness. What government could go on regularly and securely in the midst of mobs and invectives? Yet he received for many years far less molestation than he gave. These scribes, these publicans, these pharisees, were the richest, the most powerful, and the most enlightened men in the country. Call the judges, and the bishops, and the secretaries of state in England, by such names; point them out for hatred, for abhorrence, for indignation, in the same manner; and your personal liberty, instead of remaining three or four years, would not be left you, my friend, so many mornings."

This is true; and I attempted to evade it: for, though many men like truth, there is always something they like better. Victory is so sweet a thing, we not only shed words but blood for it; just as the wild men did in the first ages on record.

" Where! " cried I, with an air of triumph (for an escape is

47

often one), " where does Jesus Christ bear testimony in your favour ?
he often bears it against you."

He replied calmly, " In these plain words : ' Think not I am
come to destroy the Law or the Prophets : I am not come to destroy,
but to fulfill : for verily I say unto you, till heaven and earth pass,
one jot or one tittle shall in nowise pass from the law, till all be
fulfilled.' "

He confounded me : I thanked him and his wife for their courtesy, and, not knowing what to do with my fingers, wrapped up
in a piece of coarse paper a ring, taken from my little one, and
requested the good Rachel to give the contents to her daughter,
when she happened to have a cough. I escaped the formulary of
acceptance or refusal which she might have employed had she
discovered them.

Every day showed me the vestiges of a religion in ruins. The
Teacher and his disciples and apostles taught not only the justice
but the necessity of enjoying all things in common : and those who
disobeyed, were declared guilty of the crime against the Holy Ghost.

EMPEROR. In the name of wonder, what crime can that be ?

TSING-TI. One indeed not very clear in its nature, but manifest
enough in its effects. Those who sinned against it were instantly
stricken dead, particularly in that said article concerning the community of goods. No other crime whatever was punished so sum-
marily, or with such severity, as the holding back a particle of
property. And yet perhaps the warier might reasonably have had
some scruples and perplexities about it, seeing that one Judas
Iscariot, a special knave, who betrayed the Teacher to crucifixion,
had been the treasurer.*

Women were forbidden to attend the churches in fine clothes.
The women of England, at the present day, turn up their noses at
anyone who does not put on her best upon the Sunday ; and the
principal part of the service seems to be a most rigid examination
how far this necessary compliment is paid to the anti-christian
priest.

The Teacher orders men to pray little, and in private.† One
who had persecuted him, and afterward came over to his party,
one Saul or Paul, could not in his conscience let him have his own
way in everything, and told people to pray publicly. The day of

* *John*, xii. 6.—W. S. L.   † *Matthew*, vi. 6.—W. S. L.

my arrival in London, I wished to accommodate myself to the habits
of the nation, and having read in my Bible, " If any be merry, let
him sing Psalms," and thinking that a peculiarity of pronunciation
is disguised more easily in singing than in talking, I began to sing
Psalms through the streets.   The populace pelted me ; the women
cried, " Scandalous ! " the boys, " Let us have some fun ! " and proof
was made upon me with many eggs, even after I had declared I
could perform no miracles with them, and had plainly proved I
could neither catch one in my mouth, nor restore to life the chicken
that had long ago died within it.   An anti-christian priest of great
austerity, with legs like a flamingo's, asked me whether I was not
ashamed of my profaneness, in singing Psalms along the public
walks ?   Another, who was called his chaplain, and rode with him
in his coach, cried, " My lord, drive on ! Coachman, drive on !
Send the son of a —— to Bedlam."   Extensive as are the commercial relations of the English, I was astonished that a chaplain,
which means the priest that prays for another (none of consideration
performing for himself so menial an office), should (never having
visited China) have known so much of my mother, and should designate by so coarse an appellation the concubine of a prince.   After
a time, I acquired the intelligence, that no woman in England is
exempt from it who forms an alliance, unsanctioned by marriage,
with any except the king.   The lady in that case is styled the king's
favourite, or, more properly, his *mistress*, having the appointment of
his ambassadors and his bishops, the stocking of his fish-ponds, and
the formation of his ministry.   In fact, she alone has the care of
his dignity and of his comforts and of his conscience, and may tickle
his ribs and make him laugh, without being hanged for it.

EMPEROR. Prodigious privilege ! in a country where two hundred
other offences are subject to that punishment.

TSING-TI. The heads of the law bend before her, the gravest of
them and the most religious, even those who would punish with
death the adultery of a queen.

EMPEROR. Tsing-Ti ! Tsing-Ti ! that blow upon the cheek-
bone ! those rotten eggs ! that flamingo perch ! that odd dignity
emblazoned on thy mother ! surely they have wasped thee ! The
lowest in the land may be guilty of such baseness, the highest may
be guilty of such cruelty ; but even crimes have their classes and
their lines betwixt : the worst man in the worst nation of the earth

never could be guilty at once of crimes so different. What freezeth may burn, what burneth may freeze, but not at one moment. Thou hast indeed had some reason for displeasure ; but how much greater wouldst thou feel, O Tsing-Ti ! if thou camest from it on the thorns along the precipice of falsehood. No, my friend, thy words were always true ; and what is there, or should there be incredible, of a nation where justice is more costly than violence, and religion more rapacious than theft ! I would hear farther upon this, and what thou hast to say in defence of Saul or Paul, who gave an ordinance in contradiction to his master's. He must have put strong weapons into the hands of the anti-christians.

TSING-TI. I can not understand the anti-christians at all, and the Christians not much better. These last extolled him highly, but perhaps at the time when they thought of becoming anti-christians, as giving a sanction to disobedience and persecution. He had many strange by-ways of doing things. For instance now : Satan is god of blasphemy : he stands opposite to the Creator.

EMPEROR. Why does the Creator let the rogue stand opposite ?

TSING-TI. I know not : he does however stand eternally in that position, and breathes fire and defiance at him, dividing the universe with him, taking the richer and more beautiful to his own share. Finding the wife of the unhappy man in whose house I lodged ill-humoured and sullen, though much addicted to her Bible, I repeated to her from it,

" Let the woman learn in silence with all subjection."

She stared at me ; and when, to make her easy, I would have given her the kiss of peace, as commanded us, she cried, " You canting hound ! I will give you a cuff in the muzzle ! " It came almost too quick for a promise. Nor did it end here. The husband, who was present, said, " Master Orange-face, your pocket shall sweat for this," and took me to *Bow Street*, so called from the numbers of fashionable men resorting there, and *bowing* to the magistrate. A pickpocket was before him, who, while he raised one hand to heaven in protestation of his innocence, robbed me with the other of all the money I carried for my acquittal.

EMPEROR. How then didst thou escape ? Thy situation was deplorable.

TSING-TI. I was in prison three days.

EMPEROR. My mandarin ? by what law ?

EMPEROR OF CHINA AND TSING-TI

Tsing-Ti. I can not say by what law : I can only say it was for preaching the clearest text of Paul, and for practising the best ceremony of the church. A short time afterward, I sat at table one day with a young lady of exquisite beauty, and of equal modesty. Her mother had invited me to dinner for my love of the Bible. The gentleman who sat next to me on the right hand (his lady was on the left), observing me very diffident in my conversation with her, wished to give me a little more courage, by entering with me into the concerns of his family.

" Angelica," said he, after a while, " has an independent and ample fortune ; and yet I will dare to say before her that I married her for love. She will not flatter me by making the same confession." Angelica blushed and looked happy ; and said her mother had wished her to marry again, and she had thought it her duty to comply. I found she was in her twentieth year, and had one daughter by her first husband, dead about eighteen months. This information was given me the following day by the mother, in whose face I looked earnestly as she spoke. " What ! " cried I, " unhappy woman ! did you acquiesce in it ? did you sanction it ? did you wish it ? " " Why not ? " said she. " And does your Angelica read the Bible ? and dares she take a second husband in spite of Timothy and Paul ? ' having damnation because she hath cast off her first faith.' " * Knowing that the English are superior to other nations in a species of wit denominated *quizzing*, and that they consider it a particular act of politeness toward a stranger, I suspected they were beginning to initiate me in some of its ceremonies, and I resolved to make further inquiries of the mother ; and the more, as both exclamation and text were intercepted by an elderly gentleman in an arm-chair, who shook the loose skin of his cheeks at me, and told me, some questions were to be asked and some not. Therefore, when she and I were alone, I did not repeat the passage, but showed it in the book. She replied gravely and circuitously.

" Mister Tsing-Ti—pardon me—perhaps I ought to address you as Sir Tsing-Ti—for I can never think a person of your appearance, moving in an elevated sphere——"

Emperor. What ! like a parrot in a gold wire-cage from the ceiling ? Well, go on.

Tsing-Ti. " —would be long without a recommendation to his

* Paul, 1 *Tim.* v. 12.—W. S. L.

majesty, that he might be graciously pleased to confer on you the dignity of knighthood or baronetcy."

EMPEROR. My eyes are as long and narrow as most men's, thanks be to God! yet I can not slip them into the crevices of thy discourse. Proceed.

TSING-TI. " For his majesty," continued she, " is growing old, poor man! and takes nothing in hand so often as the sword : and when he is tired of making knights, he makes a baronet or two, in order to laugh and get a good digestion, by discussing the merits and genealogies of the new-created."

EMPEROR. New *created!* Hast thou eaten opium? Tsing-Ti, continue.

TSING-TI. She apologised, and protested she did not mean to insinuate that anyone could make merry with mine, the worst Chinese families being older than the best English.

EMPEROR. I must smell thy breath, Tsing-Ti. I fear thou hast acquired bad habits : no : no ; upon my faith! I am satisfied. Conclude the story.

TSING-TI. At last I brought the lady to the point ; and finding her sincere in her belief, and extremely angry to prove it, I went through the whole passage, word for word. It puzzled her ; she could only say, " The apostles very often differ apparently—*apparently*, Sir Tsing! for nobody in his senses will presume to say they do really. Indeed the words sometimes are widely at variance : but so are the passages in the finest music ; and without them the composer would lose all pretence to harmony."

I looked at the elderly gentleman, who had entered the room in the midst of our conversation : he took a pinch of snuff and offered me one. I frequently have observed in others, although I never could experience it in myself, that snuff, as compounded in Europe, hath wonderful properties. Sometimes it matures a reply, as straw does apples : again it turns an argument to a witticism, or a witticism to an argument : and I have known even a rap on the box-lid bring over and convince a whole party. The elderly gentleman, when he had offered me his snuff-box, and I had taken a pinch in a manner to give him a good opinion of me, drew his chair still closer, and, surveying both my face and my body, seemed to signify that he thought me not unfit for the reception of reason. Placing his hand with extreme gentleness on my wrist, he said in an under-tone, " Our religion is to us what your gum-elastic is to you. It is rounder or longer, thinner or thicker, darker or lighter, as you leave it or pull it : we rub out whatever we will with it, and, although some dirt is left upon it, we employ it again and again. There is much demand for it in the market. No wonder ! Severe as the apostle was to the young widow, in prohibiting her to dry her tears on the pillow where another head had rested, he was liberal in letting men eat what they like, although he had agreed with the other companions of the Teacher that nobody should eat strangled animals or their blood. The diviner part of his character (for what is most different from ours may even in him be called the diviner) was toleration and forgiveness."

EMPEROR. Did the Christians at any time observe this law ?

TSING-TI. Never ; not even the apostles. Saint Paul prayed God to execute vengeance for him : and Saint Peter used the sword, which God commanded should be sheathed for ever, and used it with much intemperance and little provocation. We believe that the Holy Spirit was always present in their councils ; and nothing is more difficult for us than to reconcile the precept of Paul with the decision of the rest, and the action of Peter with the command of his master.

EMPEROR. In other words, with the inspiration of what you Christians call the Holy Ghost. Indeed I do think you must strain hard to bring them close.

TSING-TI. It perplexes us.

EMPEROR. The more fools you. There are many things of which it is shameful to be ignorant ; and more at which it is shameful to be perplexed. Did thy eating these meats ever hurt thy stomach ?

TSING-TI. Never.

EMPEROR. Did thy eating them ever hurt thy neighbour's ?

TSING-TI. Fountain of wisdom ! how could it ?

EMPEROR. Did thy eating them ever make thee wish to partake of human flesh ?

TSING-TI. Horrible ! Surely not.

EMPEROR. Draw then thy own conclusion. Produced it on any man one of these effects, him should my finger bid abstain.

TSING-TI. The old Christians slipped aside and feasted heartily on a noosed hare or black pudding.

EMPEROR. What ! even the old ones ?

TSING-TI. Alas ! even they, for the most part.

EMPEROR. Tell me no more about these disagreements, but rather how the oral doctrines of the Teacher himself were taken.

TSING-TI. There is one of them which I apprehend was never believed in, since a community of goods was abolished. " It is easier for a camel (or cable) to pass through the eye of a needle, than for a rich man to enter into the kingdom of God." If this be true, and what is God's word must be, the softest bed that ever rich man died on, supposing him a true believer, was more excruciating to him than if he were corded up within a sack of vipers.

EMPEROR. Thou sayest well ; but who believes, or ever believed it ?

TSING-TI. All Christians.

EMPEROR. Do not wonder then that Christianity has existed so short a time ; so much shorter than any religion upon record.

TSING-TI. O Emperor ! my light and leader ! there are acute and wary men in Europe who can penetrate through all our objections and explain all our difficulties. I heard it reported of an old lady, one of the last Christians left in England, that she ate some hemlock in mistake for celery, her eyes being too dull and her vinegar too sharp for the discovery. She told her children and grandchildren not to fear for her, since, among the signs of those who believe, it is written that " they shall take up serpents ; and that if they drink any deadly thing it shall not hurt them." A quarter of an hour after this exhortation she died in excruciating agonies. The priest who attended her in her malady, caught her last breath and requested his bishop to remove his inquietude. The bishop answered,

" The matter is easy. She did not drink the deadly thing ; she ate it."

" My Lord, suppose it had been a liquid—God forbid I should doubt or question, but is it certain—so very certain, I would say ? "

" Her faith might have staggered, during its operation, and then could not save her. The slightest doubt, the slightest fear, forfeits the reward."

" But, my Lord, we may take up serpents."

" You are no such fool ; Saint Matthew says you may take them up ; but where does he say they won't bite you ? Brother Grimstone ! the greatest of follies is, for old people to play young tricks ;

and the greatest of sins is, to tempt God. Exhort your parishioners, as they value their salvation, never to tempt him in this way."

I myself went to the learned expositor, and consulted him.

EMPEROR. So then thou wouldst cling to Christianity after the loss of thy watch and silk trousers.

TSING-TI. I would ; knowing that my emperor loves a man with a religion as well as a man without, and hath no partiality for a mandarin because he eateth of the same dish, but would quite as willingly see him dip his fingers into another.

EMPEROR. Rightly said : kings and emperors should think so.

TSING-TI. The distiller, who gains his livelihood by his distillery, may be displeased if a basketful of yellow lilies be brought to him for a basketful of white, and may throw the lilies and the basket at the bearer, in much anger ; but the possessor of a spacious garden, in which are clusters of lilies, both white and yellow, finds a pleasure in the smell of the one and in the colour of the other, and loves to see a portion of that variety which the Creator's hand implanted.

EMPEROR. Thou speakest well. Emperors should have wide eyes and broad nostrils, and should never turn the diversity of things to their displeasure ; all being God's, and they his guests, invited to partake and to enjoy the entertainment, and not to derange and discompose it. Thou rememberest my father's verses :

> The narrow mind is the discontented one.
> There is pleasure in wisdom, there is wisdom in pleasure.
> If thou findest no honey in thy cake,
> Put thy cake into honey with thine own right-hand,
> Nor think it defiled thereby.

About what didst thou consult the expositor ?

TSING-TI. Being a mandarin, and possessing no mean inheritance, the camel or cable, of which I spake, bore heavily upon me. The expositor is one of the richest men in the kingdom, and moves lightly under it.

EMPEROR. He must have laughed at thee.

TSING-TI. Not a muscle in his cheek was altered. He received me, and heard my question graciously ; and he rang the bell with his own hand, and ordered his servant to show me the door, bowed to me, and even gave me a piece of silver called a shilling. Whether my pride was raised too high by so refined a piece of courtesy, as his insinuation that a man of exalted rank or philosophical character

55

should be deemed incapable of finding the door himself, or whether it was to contend with him in liberality, when I kissed the shilling and deposited it in my bosom, I presented to him a broad piece of gold, elaborately worked with many figures, in a case of ivory, carved by an artificer of skill. He begged my pardon, and actually pushed away the present. I kissed his hand and wept upon it ; the true Christian's ! the humble man's ! Declining my gold and ivory, he entreated me to be seated, and asked me how he could serve me, with more than Asiatic politeness. In vain I besought him again and again to accept the tribute of his slave, and to shower on me the dew of wisdom. He was inexorable as to the offering, but appeared to be very well pleased with my expressions. I had soon discovered that those which Christ used, and received, were now thought unfit for the lowest of his ministers, even for such as sweep the temples and ring the bells, and were not only obsolete, but offensive. The expositor said he could perceive I was a person of distinction, and must have moved in the highest circles.

EMPEROR. Again ! what canst thou mean ? Do the principal men educate their children with parrots and monkeys and squirrels and marmosets ? Hast thou translated those words correctly ?

TSING-TI. Quite correctly.

EMPEROR. The strangest expression I ever heard in my life-time ! So then really those short coats, and buttoned vests, and cases of all kinds, were invented to give them in some measure the advantages of animals. I would rather see gold-fish in glass globes. Surely it is only when they are very young ; only to teach them kindness toward these creatures, held by them in captivity. Well, the idea is not so irrational as it appeared at first.

TSING-TI. Whatever may formerly have been the custom of the country, the expression, I believe, is metaphorical at present. The bishop himself was said universally to move in the higher circles ; yet I could see neither globe nor cage in his house, nor any hook in the ceiling. His lordship said he would attempt to solve my question according to his poor abilities, if the best scholars were unanimous on the signification of the text. I answered that it seemed plain enough.

" By no means," replied he ; " some translate the Hebrew word by *camel*, some by *cable*."

" Either will do," said I.

" God forbid," cried his lordship, " that we should be indifferent or lukewarm on the conditions of our eternal bliss ! Whenever the passage is clear, we will discourse again upon it. Everything is not yet manifested : let us wait in patience."

As he sighed, and appeared to be much out of spirits, I thought it indecorous to press him farther, and took my leave. On the morrow I saw him going to court ; but there were so many servants about him, and the dresses stood out so with golden lace and embroidery, he could not well see me : otherwise I would have requested to be present at the sacrifice he was about to offer ; his dress being purple, to hide the blood, and his shirt-sleeves being tucked up in readiness. The cable or camel, whichever it was, made me uneasy ; and I continued in agitation for several days. At last I saw another anti-christian, who loudly professed Christianity from a table in a field, and who familiarly asked questions, and winked and laughed and told stories, and advised his audience to laugh on that day, because after two or three more they would, with few exceptions, be burned to eternity. He then cried, " Answer me ; answer me : or ask me, and I will be the answerer."

Although I thought his reason for laughing in some degree inconclusive, I was persuaded he had better in store on other points.

" Sir," said I, and there was instantaneously a universal silence, " Sir, permit an ignorant man to ask one question."

" Babe ! " answered he blandly, " come and suck."

I then related to him my visit, my inquiry, and the reply.

" Tough chewing ! hard digestion ! camel or cable," cried he to the crowd. " So, in God's very teeth, he dares call a camel a cable ! Look ! my brethren, is here the cable or the camel ? " opening the book. They all groaned. " I could have taught the wilful man better," said he, " but the Lord has taken the words of wisdom from above his tongue, and has put them under ; and they are as uneasy to him as an ear of barley would be. There they are, and he makes a wry face over 'em, and can never get 'em out."

An elderly lady, fresh, fat, with flowers in her bonnet, and some few pimples in her face, seemed much affected, and cried, " What shall I do to be saved ? "

" Sister," said the preacher, " let our brother Dick (I would say Richard) support your head upon his bosom, now that he has alighted from behind the carriage. Hide not, O sister, your head therein, as one unworthy; but turn your face hitherward, as one yearning for the truth. There is no cure so easy for any malady as for the disease of wealth. You may scratch it off with a nail, and it returns no more, although it leave a little soreness in the place. Now to the text. Camel is the word; and none but camel for me! Suppose there were a drove of 'em: do you believe that our Lord, if he pleases, can not make a drove of 'em—a drove, I say, hunched and mounted and laden, pass, not in line, but in squadron, through the finest needle you ever bought at Whitechapel? And, if he pleases, will he not do it? And, if he pleases, will not the rich man enter the kingdom of Heaven? Sister Kattern! be of good faith! the words are, *rich man;* not *rich woman.* And even rich men may lay aside what is onerous and dangerous in riches, entrusting them to the servants of the Lord, who watch and pray." " O rogue and vagabond!" I was ready to exclaim, " though indeed thou art not red-legged, thy claw and thy craw are the same as the flamingo's."

Among my acquaintance was a barrister, who belonged to neither of the sects, and evaded my inquiries, by saying they did not belong to his profession. Wishing to pay him a compliment, I studied the law with assiduity, and felt great satisfaction when I had seventy-four questions for him, on difficult points in the English juris-prudence. I had often called on him, and he was out, which I ceased to regret, on finding the catalogue of my interrogatories swell out so copiously. At last I caught him on the staircase, and gave him my pocket-book. " A flaw in the second word!" cried he, " *English jurisprudence!* " He took out the remaining inch of pencil and wrote *statutes.* " Of these we have plenty," said he, " of that nothing. Honest Tsing! your studies have lain elsewhere since your arrival; otherwise this neat pocket-book of yours, instead of the seventy-four questions, which fill only four pages, would have others drawn out over *charades* and *sonnets* and *dresses for the season;* and this delicate green binding would look as if it were covered with ants, by holding its share of your little black letters; and even this fine steel clasp would be displaced to make room." " Can you speak thus lightly," said I, " on such imperfec-tions in your profession? " " Dear Tsing," said he, smiling, " you have sometimes enriched me with a proverb: I have but one of my own, and will give it you freely. ' On the imperfection of law is built the perfection of lawyers.' I could not eat, drink, nor sleep, without 'em : they are my fish, flesh, and fowl ; they are my bread, wine, and fuel ; they are my theatre, friends, and concubines. Leap into my carriage with me : I am going to Maidstone ; I will open to you some new commentaries on our religion——"

" Will you indeed ? " cried I——

" Indeed will I," said he : " and what is more, I will introduce you at a ball."

I had never seen an English dance ; the amusement is forbidden by law to the poorer and middling classes, and I arrived in London when the richer and gayer were departing. It was now Midsummer. Great was my surprise, as we approached the town of Maidstone, at seeing a procession, accompanied by spearmen and announced by trumpets. After it there came in a carriage, drawn by four horses, an old man with a pinkish face, not unlike veal fly-blown and putrescent. He wore over each shoulder the tail either of an Angola goat or Cashmere sheep, of which the upper extremity was fastened on his head. Whether a part had been consumed by time, or rubbed away by the carriage, I know not ; but it was neatly mended by a piece of black silk, about the size of that which is applied to a part less visible, when it suffers by riding. The rest of the person was covered with a scarlet robe. I asked my companion who it could be ? " The judge," he answered.

" Judge of what ? How can he be a judge of anything, who wears a thick scarlet vesture in the middle of July, and perhaps all his other cases under it ? Nay, he has fur upon it, two palms thick ! "

" Friend Tsing ! " replied he, " neither our laws nor the dresses of those who decide on them are changed according to the times and seasons. What was, is ; and it must be, because it was."

I attended the court of justice three consecutive days, and could not but admire the patience and ingenuity of the rulers, to rid the country from all remains of Christianity. Not an edict or sentence but ran counter to it. Some were punished for disobeying the Bible ; others for obeying.

EMPEROR. Great impartiality !

TSING-TI. The very men who were to pronounce on the guilt or innocence of others, began to fit themselves for it by breaking the law of Christ. He says, " *Swear not at all.*" They all swore ; twelve of them : every witness swore. Several offenders were brought forward in their chains, for striking and stealing.

EMPEROR. Properly enough ; and punished, no doubt.

TSING-TI. Certainly ; but with somewhat less severity than others for capturing wild animals, birds, and fishes.

EMPEROR. They were idle fellows.

TSING-TI. Some had caught so many that they could not be called idle : it was their trade. I suspect they were treated with the greater severity for following the law of Christ.

EMPEROR. Law ! what ! these rogues !

TSING-TI. Christ ordered men never to reap, never to sow, because the fowls did neither.

EMPEROR. Tsing-Ti ! I love thee from my soul ; but beware ; let no man utter this in China.

TSING-TI. He ordered men to take no thought of what they put on ; and indeed not to clothe at all ; assuring them that God would clothe them, as he clothed the grass of the field ; and would much rather clothe them than the grass.* Interpretation of what is commanded is less censurable in its strictness than in its laxity. Those who obeyed God's word undoubtingly ; those who obeyed it to the letter ; those who obeyed it both because it was his, and because he had condescended to give his reasons for their obedience, in the birds namely and the grass ; were strangely persecuted. I saw a man tortured for taking as little care as the grass did about his raiment ; and I am assured, if he had gone into a corn-field, and had satisfied his necessities as the birds satisfy theirs, his religion would have led him into greater difficulties. On the whole there were about fifty criminals. Most were condemned, like this believer, to the torture, by means of wire twisted about hempen ropes, and employed as scourges : ten were hanged. The bells rang merrily ; and the ladies danced all night. I thought they had looked prettier in the morning.

There was another court open, wherein few causes were decided. My friend assured me, that several being civil, would last for years.

" How ! " exclaimed I, " and thirty men tortured, and ten hanged, at one sitting ! "

EMPEROR. I hope the King of England hangs gratis.

TSING-TI. To my shame be it spoken, I did not ask. The English are far from explicit in their elucidation. I inquired how it happened that, having wholly rejected Christianity, and being

* *Matthew*, vi. 30.—W. S. L.

ashamed of following the plainest and easiest ordinances of Christ, they are almost unanimous in calling themselves Christians ? Most of those present were angry at the question : some asked me what I meant ; others swore they would make me explain, forgetting that I came for explanation. The gentler and more moderate said I quite mistook the spirit of Christianity ; that it altered its form and features as was required by the time or the people ; that it was no less easy in its operation than salutary in its effect.

" I am quite convinced it is," cried I ; " and it being so easy to abstain from war, from strife, and from evil-speaking, it is grievous that those unequivocal commands of the Teacher are disobeyed by the most conscientious of his followers."

The man is a Methodist ; the man is mad ; the man is more knave than fool ; the man is a jesuit ; the man is a radical : were the opinions formed upon me.

EMPEROR. Of these expressions there are some requiring elucidation : we will have it another time. For the present let me assure thee, O friend of my youth ! that, among the reasons of my affection for thee, is this. Whereas many who change their religion are proud of displaying the fresh plumage, and zealous to bring others after them, and noisy and quarrelsome against those who stay behind ; thou didst long conceal thy discovery of antiquated impostures, long worship in secrecy thy purer God, long permit thy parents (best of all in thee !) to imagine thy faith unalterably like theirs, and lookedst not upon their idols with abhorrence or with disdain.

TSING-TI. My emperor ! my friend ! my father ! I would not make uneasy the last years of anyone who loved me ; no, not even to be thought by future ages the most acute, the most eloquent, the most philosophical of mankind.

SEVENTH AUDIENCE

The last was a most graciously long audience.

Every day the Emperor my master was pleased to demand my attendance. But the discourses he now condescended to hold with me were usually on subjects not at all connected with my travels. Suddenly one morning he stopped me in the *walk of cassowaries ;* and holding my arm, said condescendingly,

IMAGINARY CONVERSATIONS : ORIENTAL

" I forgot, O Tsing-Ti ! to question thee about thy ten days'
visit to Frenchland. It can not much interest me, seeing that he
who was called the cleverest among them, was caught in a fray by
the most ignorant and stupid of the Tartar tribes, and that he never
had acquired the knowledge how a man may eventually die by frost
or famine. As for religion, it produced such evil fruits in Frenchland, it was wisely done to root it up, provided they had levelled the
ground about it, and made it fit for something better."

Perceiving that his majesty had paused, and waited for an answer,
my first words were these :

Tsing-Ti. Imperfect as is my acquaintance with the language of
that country, and short my residence in it, I fear to offer any opinion
on what I heard or saw. Although I carried with me the advantage
of introductory letters, both from my friend the poet, whose manuscript I purchased, and from my friend the lawyer, and did derive
all the benefit I expected from them, my observations are unsatisfactory to myself : what must they be then to the clearer and more
searching sight of your majesty !

Emperor. More tolerable : we never let things puzzle us at all,
nor interest us much. So go on, Tsing-Ti, from thy embarkment.

Tsing-Ti. Of my two servants one was an Englishman, the other
a native of Malta, a small island in a great lake, conquered by the
English from the French. He entered at that time the maritime
service of England, and served aboard the ship which landed me
there. He understood three languages, the French, the English, and
the Italian : he could also write legibly. He was a pagan, but not
strict nor superstitious. This I discovered soon after he entered my
house ; for while he was on shipboard I knew not of what religion
he was, or whether he was of any. The hour I entered my apartments
I had occasion to call for something, and I found him with an idol
in his hand, and saying a prayer. He tossed the idol down, and
cried out in the midst of the prayer, " *Eccomi, eccellenza !* " Understanding not a syllable, I thought he was angry, and had reason for
it ; so I said,

" Van ! [such being his name among the sailors, although at
home *Gio-Van-Ni-Pa-Ti-Sta**] Van, I am much to be blamed for
interrupting you in your devotions."

" *Cospetto ! Cappari !* " cried he.

* Giovanni Battista.—W. S. L.

EMPEROR OF CHINA AND TSING-TI

I drew out my purse, thinking his animation was anger, and that no concession of mine could appease him, or induce him to remain a day longer in my service. I was soon undeceived.

" Excellenza ! " said he, " I can neither pray nor swear in any but the older languages : do excuse me ! "

" Proceed," said I, " not in swearing, but in praying."

" As your excellency commands," replied he, " at the same time I can receive and execute your lordship's wishes." He recommenced his prayers, and in the midst of a sentence (as it appeared by his abruptness), " but your excellency has forgotten the orders." " No, Van ! " said I, " when your oration is completed." He went on with a few syllables more, looking at me all the while. " Command me, Excellenza Singa ! we are losing our time. The devil is in me if I can not say my prayers and hear my master too." He then went on with a little more, and stopped suddenly. I turned and left the room, but heard, as I was passing through the door, the words, " Ah poor heretic ! he knows nothing of religion ! "

Van was however the most ingenious and the most accomplished man aboard, private or officer. Beside his knowledge of three languages, he played on two instruments of music, and he could pray fluently in a language which not even the captain understood, nor Van either, nor perhaps his idols. My friend the lawyer had taken a great fancy to him, and declared to me he was the quickest fellow he had ever met with. His clerk likewise, who happened to be fond of music, offered to teach him short-hand, if Van in return would bestow on him a few lessons. Van was indefatigable, and told me that, when he lost the honour of serving me, he would become a professor of short-hand, and make " a *deafening, stupefying, overwhelming* fortune." " Those English," said he, " who have no talents, get on very well, but those who have any, know not what to do with them. They sit in a corner and mope, while the others eat the sausage."

Your majesty is too gracious in listening to such recitals, but really all I can relate is owing to my servant. He wrote down in short-hand whatever passed in Frenchland, and on board the vessel which conveyed us thither. And perhaps in this passage there occurred as much to interest a hearer, as during our residence the whole ten days on the continent. The two factions in England retain their ancient appellations, having interchanged principles.

63

IMAGINARY CONVERSATIONS: ORIENTAL

A Whig and a Tory, as they are called, were on board ; probably there were many ; but these two held an argument, of which I have the honour of laying a copy at the feet of your majesty.

EMPEROR. No, no, you have laid enough and a superfluity before my feet already, and I doubt whether I shall ever get through it : for things that are laid before royal feet seldom mount much higher. Take it up again and read away, Tsing-Ti. What I may catch of it, is all clear gain, and I can afford to lose the rest without repining.

TSING-TI (*reads*). " *Whig*. Shall a king of England be as intolerant as a monk of Sassoferrato ! Shall he withhold from Englishmen and Irishmen what he has bestowed on Bremeners and Hanoverians ? We fear danger, it seems, to our laws, from the event of a Catholic majority in our parliament. The Catholics will never constitute a tenth of it, reckoning both houses. Nothing but coercion keeps them together. Brave and honest and wise men are Catholics, because they are persecuted for it, and because it would be cowardice and baseness (and therefore folly) to recede before aggression. Where there are sounder creeds and more liberal institutions, Catholicism may long be a party cry, but can not long be a religion. It will retain as little of its old signification as Whig or Tory. Gentlemen will disdain an authority which rests upon equivocation and prevarication, which is convicted of frauds and fallacies, and which insists that falsehood is requisite to ensure the concord and tranquillity of nations. The fever is kept up by shutting the door. Open it, and the sufferer will walk out with you, enjoy the same prospects, and engage in the same interests and pursuits. While the Catholics are in a state of pupilage, the priests will continue to lead them : no longer. Perform the act of justice they demand, and what difference in any great political question can divide the Catholic from the Protestant ? Can the Pope persuade the Irish to hazard their houses when we have made them comfortable ? Hold nothing back from any man that is his ; and least of all urge as a reason for it, that you hold it back now because you have been holding it back many years. Be strictly just and impartial, and the priest may poison his affections and paralyse his intellect, but will never shake off his allegiance to legitimate authority. Construct the Catholic church in Ireland as you find it constructed in France and Germany ; and then, if the Pope fraudulently enters it, and stands at the door and threatens, seize him wherever he may run, and punish him severely for his impudence. No power in these days would interfere in his behalf; for however some may resist the *oppressing*, none can stand up against the *avenging* arm of Britain. We have given proofs of it, age after age, and I trust we need not whisper in the gallery of the Vatican what we proclaimed so lately from the summit of Montmartre.

" *Tory*. The Whigs have inherently so little of liberality, that another party has carried off the title. Englishmen have been deprived of the elective franchise; and by whom? by Whigs. Voters may give directions, may give orders, to representatives; but representatives can neither give orders nor directions to voters. How much less then are we to suppose that they shall, in law or reason, sign a mandate for the extinction of as many as they please, in order to become, not the representatives and executors, but the arbiters and rulers of the rest! Representation can not be changed or modified in this manner while a constitution is standing. When a constitution is thrown down, and another is about to be erected, the people may then draw narrower boundaries for the exercise of its power, in the hope (rational or irrational) of being more peaceable and secure.

" *Whig*. But we drew wider.

" *Tory*. You excluded some, and made a distinction in franchises. It is a solemn and a sacred thing to draw a new line for the *pomœria* of a state. When septennial Parliaments were decreed by you Whigs in place of triennial, I wonder that not a jurist, not a demagogue, told the populace that Parliament had inherently no authority for it. I wonder that all the counties and all the boroughs in the kingdom did not recall their betrayers, and insist on the preservation of their franchises. This invasion, this utter overthrow of the English constitution, was the work of our enemies, the Whigs. Whenever they have among them an honest sentiment, they borrow it; and when they have done what they want with it, they throw it aside. Faction in other countries has come forward in a fiercer and more formidable attitude; none ever growled so long and felt so little anger; none ever grovelled so low and expected so little benefit; none ever wagged its tail so winningly and earned so little confidence.

" *Whig*. It is idle to speculate on the irremediable, or to censure the measures of the extinct: beside, we were talking not of curtailment but of concession.

" *Tory*. The coronation-oath opposes it.

" *Whig*. Parliament, that can place clauses and inabilities before kings, can certainly remove them. Some have indeed been mad enough to deny the right of the English people to check or regulate the royal prerogative ; but nobody was ever mad enough to deny the right of removing an impediment to the exercise of the royal beneficence. If I exact an oath from you for my security, I may absolve you from it when I feel secure without it.

" *Tory*. Kings may have their scruples.

" *Whig*. Some people wish they had more. But when the scruples are about our safety, if we feel perfectly safe, and they persist in telling us we can have no such feeling unless we are insane, they grossly wrong and insult us.

" *Tory*. Harsh words ! very harsh words !

" *Whig*. Words are made harsh by what they fall on. The ground gives the fruit its flavour.

" *Tory*. Excuse me, but you are a very young man, sir ! and although I am well aware that your merits quite correspond with your reputation, yet, pray excuse me ! I can not think the opinions you have delivered are altogether your own : certainly the language and the manner are not : for, really and truly, my dear sir, the last sentences, in my humble opinion, were somewhat short and captious, and not quite so applicable to the subject as a close consistent reasoner might desire.

" *Whig*. I resign them to your discretion, being unable to ascertain the author ; and conscientiously believing they were mine. If wiser men have delivered them, they must appear worth your consideration : if unwiser, what am I to think of arguments, thus urged by reasoners of less ability than my own, and yet such as you, so acute in ratiocination and so superior to sophistry, can not grapple with and dare not meet ?

" *Tory*. Any fair plain question, any intelligible proposition ! But young birds take long flights, and there is no coming up with them. If there were nothing to fight for but creeds, everybody would hold his private one quietly : but the Catholic priest is soured at the sight of old steeples above new sounding-boards, and stamps for his own again.

" *Whig*. I would not have ventured on the remark. Should it be just, people may perhaps, and before twenty years are over our heads, hang the cat on this side of the door and the dog on the other, and end their difference with one string.

" *Tory.* God forbid ! But better twenty years hence than now. May I never live to see the day when we concede an iota to the people of Ireland ! We have given them too much already.

" *Whig.* Certainly ; if you never intended to give more. You showed your fears then, your injustice now, your obstinacy and perverseness ever. It is wiser to give freely than by force, and better to call forth their gratitude than their strength.

" *Tory.* We must treat them like brawn : we must keep them long over the fire, turn them out slowly, and bind them tight, or we can never slice them regularly and neatly.

" *Whig.* We may pay dear for the ordinary. No nation is likely to rely on the probity of France, after her ingratitude and falsehood to every ally on the continent ; to Spain, to Italy, to Poland. Nevertheless there is none that would not receive from her all the assistance it could, consistently with its own independence. At present, for a time at least, she makes no trial of strength by the tenacity of bondage, but would rather win, apparently, the affections of her subjects than control the consciences.

" *Tory.* She will soon see her error, if she goes much farther, and, let us hope, correct it : otherwise we must have another war against her in support of our constitution. For such principles spread like oil upon water, and are inflammable as oil upon fire. France may discover to her cost that we retain both our principles and our courage.

" *Whig.* Our principles, I trust, are out of danger ; and, in case of invasion, our courage too would be sufficient. But as our wars have usually been conducted, if every man in England had as much courage and as much strength as Samson, it would avail us little, unless we had in addition the *scrip* of his countryman Rothschild. Men like these support wars, and men like Grenville beget them.

" *Tory.* Not a word against that immortal man, if you please, sir ! This coat is his gift, and his principles keep it upon my shoulders. Your economists, the most radical of them, will inform you that, not money, but the rapid circulation of money, is wealth. Now what man ever made it circulate so rapidly ? All the steam-engines that ever were brought into action would hardly move such quantities of the precious metals with such velocity. England is England yet.

" *Whig.* In maps and histories. After her struggles and triumphs, she is like her soldiers in the field of Waterloo, slumberous from exhaustion. The battles of Marlborough were followed by far different effects. The nation was only the more alert for its exertions : generous sentiments prevailed over sordid, public over selfish : the Tory showed that he was a gentleman, and the Whig that he was ready to become one.

" *Tory.* Where are all these promises of his ?

" *Whig.* Partially, if but partially, fulfilled. Come, we have been dragging our net long enough over weeds and shallows : let us each pull in our end of the cord, and see what we have caught.

" *Tory.* Admirable proposal ! The debates of parties always end in this manner, either by word or deed.

" *Whig.* My meaning is different.

" *Tory.* My version is best.

" *Whig.* Perhaps it may be : you have many adherents. All things in this world have two sides and various aspects. Sensible men, after fair discussion, come into one another's terms at last. Position gives colour to men as to cameleons. Those on the treasury-bench are of a fine spring-green ; those on the opposite are rather blue."

Thus terminated the discussion ; and Van, striking his thigh, cried out in his own language, " Corbezzoli ! Sant-Antonio ! I thought we had rogues in Malta."

EIGHTH AUDIENCE

His majesty could understand so much of the foregoing debate (interrupting it often to ask me for explanations) as made his royal countenance gleam with smiles. When they fairly had subsided, he said compassionately,

" I pity a people that has always a thief at each pocket, and is doomed at once to hear their blusterings and to suffer their spoliations. The only respite is, when the left-hand thief is taking the right-hand thief's place. Let me hear no more about them ; but rather say something of your descent on Frenchland."

Tsing-Ti. It was happy, most happy. No sooner had I landed

than I had the good fortune to save the life of a fellow-creature. In the city of Calais there are many women who, for various offences, are condemned to carry on their heads pyramidal towers of nearly the same height as themselves. The French have invented, with wonderful ingenuity, a process by which linen is tempered to the hardness of steel. Of such linen are these pyramidal towers constructed. Rushing toward me, under the weight of one, the unfortunate creature tripped. I sprang forward in time to save her ; otherwise a swing-gate of the material, which swing-gate is called a *lappet*, turning under the chin as she stumbled, must inevitably have cut the head off. My first impulse was to rush into a church and render thanks to the Almighty for the interposition of his providence. But the woman, in an ecstasy of joy, kissed me again and again, twirled me round, and danced a religious dance ; in which, to the best of my ability, I joined. The people of this city are devout. Innumerable parties were instantly formed about us, and the rejoicings at so signal a delivery were loud and universal. Indeed, now I speak of loudness, I never was five minutes, from sunrise until sunset, in any place so solitary, that some loud voice, human or animal, did not reach me : yet several times I was afar from cities, and, as I thought, from habitations. When the people sing, they sing to the utmost pitch of their voices ; the children cry and scream and despair as loudly ; the dogs themselves think growling lost time, and unworthy of their courage, and bark vociferously. I wondered to find the women in Calais of darker complexion than ours in Canton ; not only the condemned, and others exposed to hard labour, but nearly all. The population in general of this province is much uglier than any I visited in my travels. The men forcing their wives and daughters to live exposed to the sun, and to work hard, may account for the brownness and the wrinkles of the skin, but I am unable to form any conjecture on what causes the hideousness of their features. My servant cried out at three who ogled him, " O my sweet Marzia-Paolina ! are these *spettacoli* of the same *pasta* that thou art ? " and, crossing himself, spat upon the ground. He then ran into every term of admiration for the beauties of Italy. " There," said he, " they are what Domine-Dio made them ; natural, liberal, sweet-tempered, and sincere. In Italy they let you see what they are ; in England they wish to make you fancy what they ought to be. Capriciousness will not permit *them* to be

69

tender ; and tenderness will not permit *ours* to be capricious : ours are mutable without immodesty, and love you again for letting them go free."

" I would have driven him away with stripes," said the Emperor, " if he had given me such a description of women—so far off. We must think no more about them, for we have not here the castellated saint of Calais to preserve our equipoise. I am anxious to find thee safe at the capital of the country."

" Glad was I, O my Emperor ! to reach it. Every bone in my body was in pain, as if dislocated. No public road in England or China is kept in such a wretched condition as the road from Calais to Paris. The poorest states in Europe would be ashamed of such a communication of village with village. I had been undressed at Calais by the king's officers ; I was undressed again at the barrier of Paris."

" I did not expect such an honour would be paid to my subject," said his majesty the Emperor, " as his undressing by the king's own officers."

" It was not intended," said I, " as any peculiar mark of favour ; for the same undressing was performed by the same agents on the persons of several men and women."

" How ! " exclaimed his majesty.

" Under pretext," replied I, " of examining the dresses, lest anything contraband should be concealed within them, but in reality to extort money from the men and blushes from the females. A blush in Frenchland is a rarity, and must be imported. I never saw one on any native face ; but then I visited only the capital and some smaller cities, and remained there only ten days. Travellers are apt to form too hasty conclusions : I would avoid it. Yet surely if blushes were either inherent or transferable, some must have made their appearance at the theatre. The brothel and the slaughter-house seem to unite their forces to support the Parisian stage : Civilisation and humanity stand aghast before it : Honour is travestied and derided. Without any knowledge of the language, I might have been mistaken in the dialogue, but fortunately Van Ni procured the pieces in print, and translated them into English. He himself was greatly shocked at the scenes of selfishness and dishonesty which signalised the principal personages in the drama. These however were applauded by both sexes. He sought relief in his devotions, and went to perform them in the principal church. No sooner had he begun his prayers, than two young men, who had been walking up and down the church, the one with a small monkey on his shoulder, the other with a poodle-dog half-sheared, stepped before him, and remarked in more than a whisper, that, being an Italian, he must certainly have assassinated somebody, otherwise on the right side of forty he never could have fallen into such imbecility and decrepitude. Van Ni hearing the word *assassin* applied to him, cried, ' Stay there, Excellencies, and, by Cosimo and Damiano ! when I have said another five *ave-marias*, I will give you soap to lather your faces with.' He hurried through them, and spinning on his legs, cried, ' Now, Excellencies, you porkers, this being holy church, come out, and meet a gallant man, who will make tripe of you.'

" He came up close to them, so close that the monkey sprang upon his head. Whether he feared a bite or was startled at the suddenness of the action, he struck the animal off ; and the poodle, not having formed any friendship with it, seized it, shook it by the throat, and tossed it into the side aperture of the confessional. Van Ni was struck with horror, and exclaimed, ' See now what you have done ! O Santa Orsola ! Santa Apollonia ! I am disembowelled with desperation ! That scurvy animal will die in the confessional ! O Giesu-Maria ! and the *asinaccio* of a father, whoever he is, has taken away the key : Giesu-Maria ! ' The two young men, who had been storming and lamenting, now burst forth into immoderate laughter. Finding that, in despite of his displeasure, the young men continued in their irrisory mood, Van Ni admonished them a second time, and with greater seriousness.

" ' Excellencies ! ' said he, ' how is this ? Is it convenient to turn into mockery a gallant man ? and before the saints ? Holy Virgin ! if you make any more of those verses at Gio-Van-Ni-Pa-Ti-Sta, I will show you what you shall see, and you will favour me by letting me hear what you feel. What ! again ! Mind me ! I have killed rats as good meat as your Excellencies, and where your Excellencies (pest on such porkery !) dared not come—on board a British ship, you cullions ! Remember now the words of Gio-Van-Ni-Pa-Ti-Sta, and bear him respect another time. Cospetto ! Signori ! you go laughing on. If you will only step out of this church, where I would not commit a *sproposito*, by the martyrs !

you shall laugh in laugh *minore*, and shake and quaver to my instrument. Eh ! Eh ! Eh ! but hear another word. I have tossed over the fire better omelets than your Excellencies. And now you know who I am.'

" The young persons screamed aloud with merriment, and left the church.

" Van returned to me with tears in his eyes, related the whole occurrence, and begged leave to run into another church, and make confession. ' Yonder two towers,' said he, ' are solid as Malta and Gozzo ; but Domine-Dio guard me from ever walking under them or within reach of their shadows ! That cursed monkey will have died in the confessional ! No arm can reach down to him ! Santa Vergine ! A pretty story to be told up there in Paradiso ! Was the fault mine ? Did I throw him in ? I ask ye all, all : have ye the faces to say it ? O Misericordia !—I wish I were fairly out of the country, after this ; particularly if, before I go, I could meet those two gentlemen who caused so much heart-breaking and scandal. San Cristofano ! '

" He continued quite uneasy for several days : at last he found a master, who was going into Italy ; but he declared his resolution to continue with me until my departure, although he should lose his place. My regard for him would not allow this. I rewarded his services more largely than he expected, and his tears fell together with his kisses on my hand. I reminded him of his resolution to make that stupendous fortune by his short-hand. ' *Non pensi ! non pensi ! lasciami fare !* ' said he, confident and contented.

" I was resolved to visit the temple so calamitous to him. It was full of people ; but before the altar I could discern two figures kneeling in rich dresses. The one was a man with a face like a horse's, the other was a woman with a face like a wolf's. I thought they had come thither to offer up prayers and supplications that their ancient visages might be restored to them, with any other feature of lost humanity which their dresses might conceal. No such thing. They were the heirs to the crown ; and the female was prostrate before her favourite idol, to entreat she might have a child. The idol, I was told, only promised her a man, and did not perform even that. On the very next day was the horrible rebellion which drove the reigning dynasty out of Frenchland. No repast was brought me at the usual hour, nor indeed had I any appetite for it.

But toward the same hour on the day following I grew hungry, and was about to ring the bell for the waiter, when Van entered the room and threw his arms about my neck.

" ' Heavens be praised ! ' cried he.

" I was greatly moved at his affection, and assured him I rejoiced in his safety as heartily as he rejoiced in mine.

" ' Ke ! Ke ! ' said he, ' that is all well ; but what do you think, Eccellenza Singa ? the monkey is alive and safe ! The confessional pure and holy ! *Bestiaccia !* how it moved my entrails.'

" Van had been present in the midst of the carnage, and heard a laugh close to him. Active as he was in the combat, he turned his eye to that quarter, and saw the two young men fighting most valiantly. He bowed to them, and they cheered him. The fire of their opponents now began to slacken, and they came up to him and shook him by the hand.

" ' Excellencies ! ' said he, ' I bear you no ill-will, for a Christian has no malice in his heart, but you and that monkey have put my soul in peril, and it is right you should know it. The money that ugly beast used to cost you in feeding him ought to go to the priest.'

" ' I could not find a more legitimate heir,' said the owner ; ' but he may make his own will yet.'

" ' He lives then ! he lives ! ' cried Van Ni. ' The saints be praised ! I shall not want your money for masses, should the worst befall me.'

" Van Ni, knowing my state of inanition, ran to the nearest cook's shop for a dish of meat, telling me that his master had escaped from Paris, and had left a note, the purport of which was, that he would write to him again when he had found a place of safety in Switzerland or Tyrol. On this day I did not perceive any difference in the cookery, and although I did perceive it the day following, I said nothing. However at last I remarked it : whereupon Van Ni said, ' Eccellenza ! I quite forgot to tell you that he who was pamphleteer and gazetteer, and critic and cook, is now become, or about to become, prime minister.' " [1]

When I had recited so much of my narrative to his majesty the Emperor, he laid his imperial hand benignly on my shoulder, saying,

" O Tsing-Ti ! the occidental world orientalises rapidly. Anything farther about this dexterous lucky slave ? "

[1] Thiers, first ministry, 1836.

" Little more," answered I. " On his elevation a Parisian poet wrote some complimentary verses ; but the ancient idiom of the French language, which he chose, is beyond my comprehension : permit me therefore to lay before the footstool of your Majesty the scroll containing them.

> Dic sodes, animose, dic Thiersi !
> Tantus quum fueris domi forisque,
> Illâ denique natione cretus
> Quæ jacentia, quæ minuta, verbis
> (Nôsti) magnificis solet vocare ;
> Dic, quum sis patre major in culinâ
> (Nec pater tamen infimus coquorum)
> Cur, tanto ingenio unicè maligni,
> Te Galli vocitent tui *Coquinum?*
> Quare te minuant ita, O Thiersì ? "

His majesty the Emperor cast his eye on them as they were lying on the carpet, and said gravely,

" The characters are European, but several of the words I discover to bear a close affinity to the Kobolsk Tartar."

His majesty is an etymologist.

" I have been thinking," said his majesty the Emperor, " how that ancient French resembles the loftier language under the rising sun. I regret that thou hadst not leisure to acquire some knowledge both of the ancient and the modern."

" I regret it also, my Emperor," said I ; " not because the nations of Europe agree to converse in the modern as being central, but because it contains our Fables, told in a manner far more delightful than with us. No language in Europe is said to be so scanty or so inharmonious : but there being so little room in it, you can not get out of your way. Precision is its merit. As in England the belief of Christianity is allowed to one sect and the profession to another, so in Frenchland the written language is one thing, another the spoken. There is however a faint similitude, which may be discovered even by a learner. I took but seven lessons, yet could perceive it when it was carefully pointed out. My teacher was an impostor, who wished to keep me long under his hands. Not contented with asserting that the authors of Frenchland are superior to the best of England, of Italy, of Germany, of Spain, and that the language is softer and more flexible than the Russian and the Swedish,

74

he attempted to persuade me that *et*, *est*, *ez*, *ex*, *oie*, *ais*, *oit*, *aix*, and many more, had all the same sound. This was evidently to save him trouble, and to make me ridiculed——"

" That can not be a language," said the Emperor, " of which the sounds are reducible to no rules ; unless as we apply the term when we say the *language* of birds and beasts. Letters and syllables were not made to be thrown away or spit out. Every sign, every symbol, denotes one thing, and only one. The same finger of a direction-post can not show twenty roads. Having now the advantage of thy servant again, I hope thou enjoyedst by his means the opportunity of conversing with the learned, and greatly more to thy comfort than if thou hadst been under the guidance of a teacher so mischievous and malicious."

" Yes," answered I, " the moment my fears abated, I was conducted to visit a few of them, carrying with me my letters of introduction. I had none for scientific men, of whom there are several in Paris of the first eminence. Works of genius, apart from science, there are few, and, by what I heard, of quite another order. There are however two poets of some distinction : one raises the enthusiasm of the vivacious and the liberal by the energy of his songs, the other is more in esteem with the devout, which compensates for the want of vigour and originality. I thought I could not conciliate the lover of liberty more readily than by comparing its triumph at the previous day with its suppression under the iron hand of Napoleon. ' He abolished your republic, he devised a catechism for your children, by which unquestioning and blind obedience was inculcated ; he forged the glorious arms of your patriots and defenders into chains long and strong enough to hold everlastingly in thraldom all their future progeny.'—' Sit down, sir,' said the poet, ' and hold your tongue. Don't repeat in this house the eastern dream of an opium-eater. We are warm with the unsetting glory of France.'

" Perceiving that I had given offence, and suspecting that I had mistaken the house, I returned home, and, when his speech was interpreted to me, I looked in my dictionary for the word *glory*. I found it often meant the glitter that painters put over the heads of idols ; and this was truly its most intelligible and its most common acceptation. Knowing to a certainty that the devouter poet was attached to the king of the last week, I condoled with him on the disaster of a monarch so pious and unfortunate. He bowed. The

75

only comfort I could offer him was, that talents had never lost their value in Frenchland, through all the vicissitudes of thirty years ; and that scarcely Prussia or Russia was more admirable for the advancement of literary men.   He bowed, and answered in an undertone of voice, ' I really do not pretend to know anything of those people : I only know that our houses are degraded at every step that his majesty has been constrained to take.   All ranks and orders are confounded, and the high sense of honour which was peculiar to Frenchland, and which formerly made the meanest Frenchman's heart leap impatiently out of his bosom, lies prostrate and half-extinct.'

" I thought I had been listening to a Montmorency (French for *old noble*) ; but on inquiry I found I had not been guilty of that mistake.

" Out of respect to the ancient nobility, such at least I presume is the motive, many young persons in that country, whether of the commissariat or the coach-office, are grave and taciturn when privileges or privations are mentioned.   They draw themselves up into the stiffness and concentration of mummies, and from their swathings and cases stare us into stone.   These however are civil and distant ; and perhaps their distance is the best part of their civility.   Another set is less tolerable : it assumes the name of *Young France*.   Whatever can be conceived of insolence and audacity is put into daily practice by these troublesome and restless barbarians.   I could not refrain from making the remark to a gentleman of philosophical cast, who came to visit me, adding, that surely all the abuses of the extinct nobility, with all the absurdity and injustice of its hereditariness, were less intolerable.

" ' The older creation of the nobility,' said he, ' like the older of animals lately discovered by the geologists, is more ill-constructed and ill-favoured than the recenter ; so that it pleased God to put an end to it, and to try such other forms as might be convenient to carry his designs into execution.   But either is, as you say, better than this ditch-spawn.'

" Finding him a calm and reasonable man, I ventured to congratulate him on the near prospect of peace and tranquillity in his country, and on the enthusiasm his new king excited.   He bowed to me, and answered,

" ' We have at last a chance of it.   These forty years past we have had our Goddesses of Liberty, Goddesses of Reason, Goddesses of Theophilanthropy, Goddesses of War, screaming and pulling caps in the Place de la Concorde. We have had white feathers, red feathers, eagle's feathers, cock's feathers, and at last no feathers at all. We have gone kingless, breechless, lawless, and constitution-less : we can not be well less at present. We have gone booted into every drawing-room on the continent, and our spurs have torn off every flounce and train. Finally, we put them on ourselves, and swaggered about for a while with much theatrical effect. One unlucky day the first actor, who never could walk straight nor see three inches before him, caught his own long-tailed robe with his spur, and being an impetuous man, gave such a plunge that it fell off his shoulders, and left the whole of him as bare as the back of my hand. The inferior actors were scandalised at the disgrace brought on the profession, but no one had the dexterity or presence of mind to pick up the long-tailed robe. At last it was claimed by a fat man, who drew it across his belly, and made the ends meet as well as he could ; but much was wanting. When he died, the priests seized upon it, and cut it up in pieces to put under their wine-cups. But you were speaking of our happy acquisition. Depend upon it, the present king is no such a novice in the trade as some about him would persuade him. He is fitter to govern us than any man we have seen for two centuries. He will never have a minister who is not taken from the ranks ; never a man of genius, never an honest man ; but secondary and plausible. The reason is, that whenever they dis-please him, their removal will only render him more popular. Added to which, it is always gratifying to the populace, and by no means offensive to the middle classes, to see low people raised. In one word, Louis-Philippe is the only person of ancient family in France who may not justly be reproached with degeneracy. I do assure you, he is as honest a man as his father, and farthermore, has learned the secret of keeping a wiser head on his shoulders. He has the shrewdness of Richelieu, the suppleness of Mazarin ; all their rapacity, all their pertinacity ; the arrogance of both, the vanity of neither. Whatever there is about him tells for something ; and we must pay its value to the uttermost. His royal foot rests so assuredly on well-beaten and levelled France, that the telescope with which he looks leisurely on the world around him is not shaken a hair's breadth. I will answer for him, there is no potentate in

77

Europe whom he has not already convinced of his loyalty and good intentions ; and when you return to China you will find that he has offered your Emperor to assist him in putting down the refractory spirit of the Tartars, being well in harmony with his brother the Emperor of Russia, who is equally ready to exert his kind offices to the same effect.' "

EMPEROR. It is unhandsome to sue for such generosity until the time of need, or to take every word to the letter.

TSING-TI. I was not aware of the existence of such a sect as Young France, until I was shoved off the pavement by a stripling, who was troubled with a hairy mole on the nether lip. Not being his father, the misfortune could nohow be attributed to me. I had acquired enough of the language to enable me to ask him to what dignitary I had the honour of surrendering my station. " I represent the *Young France*," cried he.

I bowed profoundly, and was constrained to answer in English, for my French failed me at so long a breath. " I shall be most happy in the opportunity of congratulating the *Young France* on her having learned by heart the first lesson of politeness."

He raised his arm to strike me ; but a German, of about the same age, who happened to be passing at the time, said to him calmly, " Remember, sir, we have fired at the same academy, and my ball usually went nearer the bull's eye."

Young France recovered at once his memory and his temper. I returned home in perturbation : for, O my Emperor ! I have not yet outlived all my passions. God has been pleased to grant me a lively consciousness of my existence, by implanting in me deeply the fear of losing it.

My servant was not alone when I entered. In his walk homeward, hearing his native tongue in the streets, he accosted the speakers : " Excellencies ! " cried he. " We are no excellencies ; we are exiles," answered one of them. " The better ! the better ! " said honest warm-hearted Van Ni. " I dare invite you then to my house. Come along : pardon me if I walk before you."

Hearing voices in my apartment, I halted at the door, and caught what I was afterward told were these words, which Van Ni wrote down : " We have no right to complain of our fortune, young or old. Was not Tasso chained to his bed-post ? Was not he half-starved in the house of Cardinal Scipione ? Was not he driven out

78

of it ? Was not he defrauded of his own cottage ? Would his best friend lend him the few crowns which, he said, might save him from starvation and distraction ? Princes, you see, did much against him; but not all. The manly breast can bear any blow unless from the hand it cherished." He who was listening now struck his forehead, and groaned aloud. " 'Tis there ! " cried he, " and that blow reaches me in this chamber." " I," said the exhorter and comforter, " I can only pity you then. No balm grows in those deserts ; no dew falls there ! Alas, my friend ! if only persecuted genius were pouring forth his lamentation, I could soar above him and bring him airs from heaven. I would point up to Dante in the skies. Was not Dante an exile ? was not Dante in danger of being burnt alive ? was not that sentence passed against him ? A republic did it ; his own republic. Italy is beautiful yet, and once was glorious ; but the nurse of genius is older than she. Brought up and fostered in the soft clime of Syracuse, she breathed her last in the palmgroves of the Ptolemies."

I took advantage of this pause, and instantly told my servant to be seated again and to call his friends. " Eccellenza ! " said he, " how is it possible ? how is it possible I can be so wanting to my duty ? These gentlemen are my countrymen, and in tribulation."

Meanwhile they were standing, and making many apologies.

" Persons of your worth and misfortunes pain me more than sufficiently," said I, " without the trouble you are taking in these explanations."

" I invited them to my house, Eccellenza ! " said Van Ni. " Now, Signori ! do not servants in Italy always use the expression, *my* house ? We should think it more presumptuous to say *our* house ; because it would seem to indicate that we placed ourselves on an equality with our masters." They acknowledged that the expression was universal in their country, and had only to regret that by its misrepresentation it had caused me such an inconvenience.

I could not but compare their manners with the French, very greatly to their advantage, and fancied that even the English might learn something from them. Certainly the islanders are thick-rinded and rather sour.

No persuasion of mine could induce the exiles to remain. They fancied I was an Englishman from the East Indies, and hoped I would exert my influence for the delivery of their country.

IMAGINARY CONVERSATIONS : ORIENTAL

" If my master were an Englishman, he would feel it his duty,"
said Van Ni ; " for Englishmen threw you, bound hand and foot,
among the dogs."

His majesty the Emperor asked me whether the Italians were
not from that country which pretended to the monopoly of religion.
I was not quite sure, and told him so.

" I have a suspicion," said his majesty, " that the old sorcerer
lay somewhere thereabout."

I believe he was near the mark ; but my memory failed me. He
then asked about the causes of the insurrection and revolution in
Frenchland. My reply was, that the king had been persuaded by
his courtiers to take away some things which he had given ; and his
people said that he had given them what was theirs before ; that it
was an indignity to offer it at first ; that it was a defiance to seize
it again ; and that he had no right to stand above the laws.

" It is the glory of princes," said his majesty the Emperor, " to
stand the foremost under them."

END OF THE ORIENTAL CONVERSATIONS

IMAGINARY CONVERSATIONS

VARIOUS

I. KING OF THE SANDWICH ISLES, MR. PEEL,
MR. CROKER, AND INTERPRETER [1]

(*Imag. Convers.*, iv., 1829 ; *Wks.*, 1846 ; *Wks.*, vi., 1876.)

KING. I receive with satisfaction the royal sons of my brother the King of England, whose noble nature and high exploits have filled the whole space between him and me, and are become familiar to my people as fish and bread-fruit.

PEEL. Sire, we dispose indeed of his family and of his subjects universally ; but we are not the sons of our most gracious King.[2]

CROKER. Blood and 'ounds ! Why tell the fool that we are not his sons ?

KING. You are then the high priest ?

PEEL. Not exactly that neither, Sire ; but I make him do and say what I order. I dictate the forms of prayer [3] and appoint the chief priests.

KING (*to* CROKER). And pray, mighty lord, by what appellation am I to address your celestiality ?

CROKER. I am principal of the admiralty.

KING (*to* INTERPRETER). What is admiralty ?

INTERPRETER. The ships and captains and admirals.

PEEL. His majesty seems faint.

CROKER. He stares at me like a stuck pig.

---

[1] The visit to England took place in 1824. The King's consort died in England in July of that year ; the King himself died, in the Adelphi, a year later. Landor's too favourable view of the King's deportment would seem to be derived from the *Examiner*.

[2] 1st ed. reads : " King, illustrious as are our families and the titles with which we are invested. CROKER," etc.

[3] 1st ed. reads : " prayer, tell him when to use them, when not to use them : when he dies I appoint a successor. KING," etc.

IMAGINARY CONVERSATIONS : VARIOUS

KING (*to* INTERPRETER). I can not, with my ideas of propriety, fall down before him, but anything short of that. Would he permit me to take his hand ?

INTERPRETER. I can not answer for him. Time was, he would have been ready to take mine—with a dollar in it.

KING. The other high lord governs the King's family and people ; but this governs the King and the airs and the waters and the world. Dog, dost grin ?

INTERPRETER. I will tell your Majesty another time how mistaken you are.

KING. No other times for me : tell me now. I must know, as other kings do, the men I deal with.

INTERPRETER. Ah Sire ! your former mistake was nothing to this. As other kings do ! One must cross the widest of the seas to find them : they lie among coral, and clothe in feathers, or are in buff.

KING. High and mighty, land-and-sea-and-sky lords ! in order to render the honours due to your rank and dignity, I, a stranger to you——

PEEL. Sire, we are come only to announce to your Majesty the pleasure his Majesty the King of England will experience on receiving your Majesty at his court.

KING (*to* INTERPRETER). Is it the custom of the land to interrupt a person who is speaking ?

INTERPRETER. It is the custom all over Europe, excepting Turkey, where manners are more decorous.

KING (*to* INTERPRETER). How do they do in their parliament ?

INTERPRETER. The same thing perpetually, unless the orator has something to give them. In that case there is no other interruption than applause.[1]

KING. Tell your King, O king's-family-and-people-feeder, that I forerun his wishes, and will be present at his court to-morrow.

PEEL. Dear Croker, do inform him, for upon my soul I have not the face, that he must pull off that odd dress of his, and order a court one.

---

[1] 1st ed. reads : " applause ; and the wit of a college scout, a mail coach driver, or a quack's assistant upon a cart, is the finest in the world. KING. Man, that is not the Sandwich tongue : I do not understand half the words. (*To Peel.*) Tell," etc.

CROKER. What have I to do with plucking and trussing the creature ? Tell him yourself ; it lies within your office.

PEEL.[1] Sire ! I am sorry to announce——

KING. He says he is sorry : I understand all that. Try to comfort him. Bring out a skinful of delicate whale-oil : or, in the urgency, persuade him to smell this little slip of salt ling, which I always carry about me.

INTERPRETER. Put it up, put it up : do not let them see it. The word " *sorry* " means in general quite the contrary : when it does not, it means nothing at all. Among the last letters I received is one beginning " I am sorry to inform you that your father is dead, but am extremely happy to add that he has left to you the whole of his little property, your elder brother having been unexpectedly taken off after twelve days' severe suffering from his unfortunate duel."

KING. You have taught me a great deal of English in a little time.

Well, king's-feeder and high-priest-maker ! what dolorous event impedes your enunciation ?

(*To the* INTERPRETER.) Surely nobody has told him that his father is dead ; for he really looks quite concerned.

PEEL. Sire, I am sorry to announce to your Majesty that your Majesty can not be received in any but a court-dress.

KING. Oh ! I know it, I know it well : I have brought with me fifty court-dresses.

PEEL. Permit me to explain, Sire : I mean to say, the court-dress of the Court of St. James.

KING. I have not one. Apparently [2] St. James requires as much buckling as a coach-horse ; and one would fancy his votaries have broken knees. I saw several well-looking men bound in that joint ; and doubtless by the ablest surgeon. They were going to thank the Saint for the commencement of their recovery, and they mounted the palace-stairs as briskly as if nothing had happened.

PEEL. I will send a tailor to your Majesty, with [3] your Majesty's royal permission.

KING (*to* INTERPRETER). What is that ?

---

[1] From " PEEL " to " looks quite concerned " added in 2nd ed.
[2] From " Apparently " to " happened " added in 2nd ed.
[3] From " with " to " permission " added in 2nd ed.

INTERPRETER. One who makes court-dresses.

KING (*to* INTERPRETER). In truth no king was ever received with more hospitality, kindness, and distinction, than I am. All the first dignitaries of the state attend me. The court-tailor holds, I suppose, the third rank in the kingdom.

INTERPRETER. There are some between, not many. He however is next to the King himself, or rather his copartner, in conferring distinctions. Without him the greatest [1] and highest man in England would be nothing. Silk gowns swell little men into great ones, and silk ribbons elevate the lightest up to the most conspicuous station.

KING (*to* INTERPRETER). Perhaps the silk is a charm too against anger and thunder.

CROKER. What a bore ! I am out of all patience.

PEEL. I regret that your Majesty should experience anything like delay or disappointment ; but the etiquette of our court requires a strict compliance with custom, in matters of dress.

KING. Pray, how many dresses has your King ?

CROKER. Don't answer the rascal. These barbarians are always inquisitive.

PEEL. Sire, I can not exactly tell your Majesty how many his Majesty possesses, not having the honour to preside over his wardrobe ; but of course on gala-days he always wears a new one.

KING. Gala-days I suppose are the days when he wrestles and tears his clothes. For in this cold climate I can well imagine the richer may wrestle drest. But your King must have many suits. I am sensible of his affability and liberality, and shall be quite contented with such distinction as it may please his Majesty to confer on me ; but among men of equal rank, unequal as is the power, treaties may be formed, compacts settled——

CROKER. A slice of Sandwich, I trust, may come to us thereby ; ay, Bob !

KING (*to* INTERPRETER). The great whale, the admiral-feeder, the navy flint, is prouder and fiercer than the wizard-feeder and prayer-

---

[1] 1st ed. reads : " greatest would be where I am ; and many a breech is an unkicked one because it has silk about it. KING. No wonder. The English laws, as captains have told me, talking about wives and such things, make you pay for the damage you do. A judge looks at the hole you have made in the woman ; an innkeeper at that in the bread and cheese ; both make you pay accordingly. But perhaps I have misunderstood you : perhaps the silk," etc.

pointer, disposer of the King's family and subjects while dry-shod and upon the dirt. The latter is the civiler, but if features tell me anything, cold, smooth, slippery, and hard to hold as a porpoise.

INTERPRETER. The [1] other looks as if he would pick a quarrel; he would quite as readily pick a—— but your Majesty does not wear one.

KING. Pick-a! pick-a! pick-a! What dost mean, word-eater-and-voider?

INTERPRETER. Your Majesty's fine language does not supply me with the word, and if I made an adequate sign of it I might be hanged.

KING. My language is the richest in the world, and the very best. I have two or three words for one thing.

INTERPRETER. Sire, we have twenty. *Roguery* for instance. We box the compass and come quite round to *honesty* and *honour;* but some writers (not many indeed) make a distinction, and put an *s* to the latter.

KING. We kings are very nice upon higher points, but not upon these. There are in my islands some men who understand all sorts of words, native or imported: I take them as they come. If people are good, let them be easy in speech and free in action: let everyone roast his fish as he likes, and catch it as he can.

CROKER. Your Majesty was saying something of treaties and compacts. If I can serve your Majesty in the interpretation of your royal wishes, you may command me.

KING. I have an interpreter here I can trust better.

CROKER (*to* INTERPRETER). He never said that, sirrah. He has good manners.

INTERPRETER. Then, Mr. Croker, do not omit such an opportunity of acquiring them. Do not wait for Lieutenant White to propose to you again an excursion through the window, for telling him to " moderate his impertinent vulgar Irish," when the gentleman had spoken most respectfully, under a sense of injury, and when in his father's house yours would not have had the assurance to be seated.

CROKER. Sir, I remember no such occurrence.

INTERPRETER. Wonderful indeed! Such occurrences are the only

---

[1] 1st ed. reads: " The one . . . quarrel, and the other as if he would quite," etc.

ones that usually make a deep impression on such people. The lieutenant held up a fist, not made to crack a Croker, or anything of the kind, but able to split a cocoa-nut on a pincushion. Not remember it indeed !

CROKER. Peel, have you no prison, no treadmill, for such fellows? We are here upon the King's service.

PEEL. In England, though.

KING. I request of that minister's celestiality that he will not light his match where there is no gun. What faces these Europeans have ! they can fire them when they please. The Great Spirit has in his wisdom appointed all things for the countries in which they exist. What a blessing in these cold climates, where water is turned into dust and rock, and the feathers that fall from heaven's birds and winged genii are colder than sea-shells, that the higher and nobler part at least of the inhabitants can conjure up into their eyes, and between their cheeks, such a quantity of flame and heat.

PEEL. Was that for us ?

INTERPRETER. No, sir.

PEEL. If your Sandwichian Majesty is graciously disposed to enter into any treaty with his Britannic Majesty, my royal master, I am empowered by his aforesaid, to wit, his Britannic Majesty, to receive, consider, and lay it before his said Majesty, for his Majesty's further consideration, by and with the advice of his Privy Council.

KING. The very thing for his Privy Council. His Majesty sticks a new and brighter and loftier plume in my hair at every word of your discourse with me. On the court-day, in presence of all his nobility, male and female, I would decorate his Majesty with a noble dress, suitable to his dignity, with my own hands, declaring upon my royal word that I have worn the same dress twenty times on the greatest ceremonies of religion and state, and that I slept in the lower part of it the night of my nuptials. Now I request from his Majesty, I being a less powerful king, a dress which his Majesty shall have worn only twice or thrice on public festivities, and once only in dalliance with some favourite ; and that his royal hands shall invest me with nothing more of it than that part which the most active man in the world could not leap into by himself, and which no other nations than the most civilised and ingenious have discovered the means of putting on : this being the principal, if not the only distinction between the polished and the rude. After the surmounting of such a difficulty in science, I do not wonder that you can count the stars, and measure their sizes and distances, which I think I could do myself, if I had leisure and they would wait for me.

CROKER. Does the beast quiz us ? He looks in earnest.

PEEL. He really is serious, and expects an answer.

Sire, I will communicate to his Majesty the heads of your Majesty's communication, and I entertain no doubt that his Majesty will most graciously pay that attention which is due to so ancient and faithful an ally, and which is conservative of the harmony that happily exists between the two nations.

II. QUEEN POMARE, PRITCHARD, CAPTAINS POLVEREL AND DES MITRAILLES, LIEUTENANT POIGNAUNEZ, MARINERS [1]

(*Wks.*, ii., 1846 ; *Wks.*, vi., 1876.)

POLVEREL. Mr. Pritchard, I have desired your presence, as a gentleman of great influence and authority.

PRITCHARD. Sir, I know not exactly in what manner I can be of service to crews of vessels which invade this island.

POLVEREL. The island is in a state of insurrection. We come opportunely to aid the legitimate Power in quelling it. Among the natives there are many discontented, as you know.

PRITCHARD. The very men who apparently ought to be the most contented : for they not only enjoy the fruits of French principles, but also of French manufactures, and they possess many luxuries which the others never heard of.

POLVEREL. Is it possible ?

PRITCHARD. They have displayed, most ostentatiously and boastingly, knives, cutlasses, tobacco, brandy, rum, plates, dishes, mirrors, and other articles of furniture and luxury, which a generous magnanimous ally, ever devoted to their welfare, ever watchful over their prosperity, has munificently bestowed.

POLVEREL. Mr. Pritchard ! every word you utter raises my wonder higher. We are both of us philanthropists : let us then, dispassionately and amicably, talk together on the present condition of these misguided people, so mysteriously deluded.

PRITCHARD. Our conversation, I suspect, would alter but little what is predetermined.

POLVEREL. Mon Dieu ! What can that be ?

PRITCHARD. Evidently the subjugation of the natives.

---

[1] The events dealt with in this Conversation occurred in 1843, when Queen Pomare, on protesting that she had been coerced into agreement with the French, was deposed by them, and Pritchard was deported. France eventually made partial reparation to Pritchard.

QUEEN POMARE, ETC.

POLVEREL. Mr. Pritchard! your language is quite unintelligible to me. France never subjugates. She receives with open arms all nations who run into her bosom for protection : she endows them with all the blessings of peace, of civilisation, of industry, of the sciences, of the fine arts.

PRITCHARD. Certainly no arts are finer than the arts they receive from that bosom of hers, at once so expansive and so stringent.

POLVEREL. Ah, Mr. Pritchard! Mr. Pritchard! you know my humour, my temperament, my taste, by intuition. I enjoy a joke, no man better.

PRITCHARD. Especially such jokes, M. le Capitaine, as you utter vivaciously from the mouth of your cannon, and which play with lambent light about your cutlasses and bayonets.

POLVEREL. We have done with war, totally and for ever done with it. France, having conquered the confederated world, desires only peace. She has subdued and civilised Africa. The desert teems with her harvests. Temples and theatres rise above and beyond the remotest tent of Moor and Arab. The conquerors of Spain implore the pardon of France. The camel bends his arched neck and falls on his flat knees, supplicating the children of mothers from our beautiful country to mount the protuberance which provident Nature framed expressly for the purpose, and to alight from it in the astonished streets of Timbuctoo. We swear he shall alight in safety. Yes, we swear it, Mr. Pritchard!

PRITCHARD. You have sworn many things, M. le Capitaine, some of which were very soon counter sworn, and others are unaccomplished : but in this, impracticable as it appears to me, I heartily wish you success.

POLVEREL. Consider it as done, completely, irreversibly.

PRITCHARD. Population is increasing rapidly both in France and England : industry should increase proportionally. By conciliating and humanising the various tribes in Africa, you enlarge the field of commerce, in which the most industrious and the most honest will ultimately be the most successful. It might be offensive to you if, in addition to this, I mention to you the blessings of religion.

POLVEREL. Not at all, not at all. I have given proofs already that I can endure very dark reflections, and can make very large allowances. Our soldiers will relieve the poor devils of Mahometans from the grievous sin of polygamy. If any one of them is rich enough to keep a couple of wives or concubines, he is also rich enough to keep a confessor, who will relax a little the bonds of Satan for him, and carry a link or two of the chain on his own shoulders. Seriously, for at bottom I am a true believer and a good catholic, we must establish the mass both there and here. France has recovered her fine old attitude, and can endure no longer the curse of irreligion. Asia now lies at her feet, but intermediately the Pacific Ocean. It shall roll its vast waves before her with due submission, and every one of them shall reflect her tricolor.

PRITCHARD. Sir, you promised that we should converse together amicably, and that neither of us, in the course of our discussion, should give or take offence.

POLVEREL. A Frenchman's word was never violated : a grain of dust never could lie upon his honour.

PRITCHARD (*aside*). Certainly not without the cramp, if dust could catch it.

POLVEREL. I perceive your mute acknowledgment. Speak then freely.

PRITCHARD. How happens it, M. le Capitaine, that having sub-dued such restless and powerful tribes, and thereby possessing such extensive territories, so fertile, so secure, so near home, you covet what can bring you no glory and no advantage ?

POLVEREL. The honour of France demands it.

PRITCHARD. You promised you would retire from Barbary when you had avenged the insults you complained of ; and Europe believed you.

POLVEREL. The more fool Europe.

PRITCHARD. And the more what France ?

POLVEREL. No remarks on France, sir ! She is never to be questioned. Reasons of state, let me tell you, are above all other reasons, as the sword is the apex of the law. We often see after a few steps what we never saw until those steps were taken. Thus my country sees the necessity of retaining her conquests in Barbary. England is reconciled to what she could not prevent nor resist.

PRITCHARD. She destroyed those batteries which you occupied.

POLVEREL. Exactly so. She is always so complaisant as to pave the way for us, either with her iron or her gold. She has in some measure done it here ; but neglecting to support legitimate power, the task devolves on us of protecting the queen from the violence and artifice of her enemies. We offer the *Entente Cordiale* to Queen Pomare as we offered it to Queen Victoria. The one is unsuspicious ; the other would be if evil counsellors were removed from about her. I have difficulties to surmount, if indeed, where Frenchmen are, difficulties can be.

PRITCHARD. Certainly there are fewer impediments and restrictions in their way than in the way of any other men upon earth.

POLVEREL. Bravo ! M. Pritchard ! I love an enlightened and unprejudiced man, rarely found (if ever) among your countrymen.

PRITCHARD. We have indeed our prejudices : and although we are perhaps more free in general from suspicion than might be expected in a nation so calm and contemplative, yet, if armed men landed in England, and demanded terms and conditions, and on protecting those who refused their protection, we should suspect a hostile disposition.

POLVEREL. On this remark of yours, M. Pritchard, I declare to you, as a man who have studied my profession in all its parts, and who am far from ignorant of England and of her present means of defence, we could at any time land twenty thousand men upon her shores, and as many on the coast of Ireland.

PRITCHARD. Nelson saw this before steamers were invented : and the most intelligent and far-sighted of our engineers, General Birch,[1] has recently warned the nation of its danger. Wooden heads still reverberate the sound of *our wooden walls :* we want these : but we also want such as render France secure on every coast. Beside which, we require a strong central fortress, not indeed so extensive as those of Paris, but capable of protecting a large body of troops in readiness for any quarter of the island. Birmingham, which may be considered as our grand arsenal and foundry, is unfit : but Warwick, united to it by canals and railway, is so situated that all access to the town may be inundated by three or four brooks, and the river and an artificial piece of water, broad and deep, render it a place admirably suited for an entrenched camp.

POLVEREL. You talk, M. Pritchard, of places which may hereafter be defended, but which at present are without defence. Our generosity alone has spared you.

PRITCHARD. Doubtless, the King of the French, so prompt to gratify the humour of his Parisians for hostilities with us, which

[1] General John Francis Birch, R.E.

this wanton aggression fully proves, would have invaded Ireland, were it not for the certainty of insurrection in various parts of his own kingdom. All the liberals and robbers and rabble are republicans : half the poorer tradesmen and ignorant peasants are royalists, in favour of the ejected dynasty.

POLVEREL. Insurrection indeed ! Do you Englishmen talk of insurrection ? you whose whole army is wanted, and would be insufficient, to keep it down in Ireland.

PRITCHARD. It must be acknowledged that all the atrocities of France are fewer and lighter and more intermittent than ours in Ireland. In that country, not one in eight is of the religion whose priesthood all are equally bound to maintain. And to maintain in what manner ! Far more sumptuously than the favourites of the Pope are maintained in Italy. I could mention ten bishoprics in the Papal and Neapolitan states, of which the united emoluments fall short of a single protestant one in Ireland. The least reformed church is our reformed church. But I see not how one injustice can authorise another in another country. We refuse to the Irish what we granted to the Scotch. And we are in danger of losing Ireland in our first war, whatever may be our enemy. The people are justly exasperated against us : and they will throw up many advantages rather than continue in the endurance of an indignity.

POLVEREL. I am charmed at hearing a man speak so reasonably, especially an Englishman : for I respect and esteem you in such a degree that I would rather have the pleasure of fighting you than any other people upon earth.

PRITCHARD. I am apprehensive the pleasure you anticipate is not remote. For certainly, ill able as we are at present to cope with any enemy, the people of England will never bear your interference with a nation they always have protected, and have taught the advantages of peace, commerce, morality, and religion.

POLVEREL. Religion ! Never shall the poor Tahitians lose that blessing by any interference or any negligence of ours. I have brought over with me a few gentlemen of the *Company of Jesus.*

PRITCHARD. In these latter ages the company kept by the blessed Jesus, much against his will, as when he was among the scourgers and between the thieves, is a very different sort of company from what he was accustomed to meet by the Sea of Galilee and at the Mount of Olives.

POLVEREL. Between ourselves, they are sad dogs. If ever we land, which is possible, I fear my sailors and they will speedily come to blows about certain articles of the first necessity : and the Jesuits are the least likely to be the sufferers.

PRITCHARD. It is not because I am a missionary, and profess a doctrine widely different from theirs, that I adjure you to abstain from giving any countenance to the turbulent and the traitorous. It is already well known at whose instigation they became so : and not only the English, but also the Americans, will promulgate the disgraceful fact. If war (which God forbid !) is to rage again between the two nations which alone could impose eternal peace on the world, let it never spring from wanton insolence, but rather from some great motive, which must display to future generations how much less potent, in the wisest of rulers, is reason than resentment and ambition. We have been fighting seven hundred years, nearly eight hundred, and have lately breathed longer between the rounds than we ever breathed before : we have time and room to consider how little has either party gained, and how much both have suffered.

POLVEREL. M. Pritchard ! I really beg your pardon : I yawned quite involuntarily, I do assure you.

PRITCHARD. What afflicts me most, is the certainty that my countrymen will be confirmed in their old prejudices and antipathies, by this aggression in the season of profound peace, and that they will call it treachery.

POLVEREL. The ignorant call that treachery which the wiser call policy and decision.

PRITCHARD. And by what name do the virtuous call it ?

POLVEREL. I carry no dictionary in my pocket. We can discourse more intelligibly on the condition of Ireland.

Parbleu ! I believe there neither is nor ever was anything similar in any other country under the sun. We must invade Ireland ; I see we must. My ship is in readiness to sail into the bay of Dublin : my brave crew has already planted the tricolor on the castle-walls. I see the Atlantic, the Pacific, California, China, India. We have been too merciful, M. Pritchard ! we have been too merciful to you ; but we must correct that error.

PRITCHARD. It is a foible, sir, in you, of which few beside your-selves have complained. If others had shown as little of it, I should not at this moment have had the honour of conversing with you on the protectorate of Tahiti.

POLVEREL. We fear and respect no power that omits its opportunity of crushing an enemy. You have omitted this, and more. America and France, justly proud of free institutions, have each its *National Guards*. Where are yours ? You ought to have in England at least two hundred thousand of them, beside forty thousand artillerymen and engineers ; and in Ireland half the number. If there is in England any class of men which apprehends the danger of such an institution, you must instantly annihilate that class, or submit to annihilation. Have you any reply for this ?

PRITCHARD. I wish I had. More temperate men than yourself entertain the same opinion. You happen to be governed at the present time by the wisest king that ever reigned over you, or perhaps over any people ; his wisdom would render him pacific, if his power and popularity consented. But our negligence is a temptation to him. There are many who would not tear a straw-bonnet off the head of a girl wide awake, yet would draw a diamond-ring from the finger if they caught her unprotected and fast asleep. We must fortify all our ports and roadsteads in both islands. To conciliate popularity, every minister is ready to abolish a tax. We should never have abolished one : on the contrary we should have quoted the authority of Nelson on the dangers we have escaped, and on the necessity of guarding against them for the future. My own opinion is, that a less sum than twenty millions of pounds sterling would be inadequate. But in twenty weeks of the last war we expended as much : we may now disburse more leisurely.

POLVEREL. We shall at all times be a match for you.

PRITCHARD. As a minister of religion, and an advocate for whatever tends to promote the interests of humanity, of which things peace is the first, I can not but regret this commencement of hostilities, so unworthy in its object, even if the object be ultimately attained.

POLVEREL. Sir, after such strong language, so derogatory to the dignity of France, I must inform you that I merely sent for you in order to let you know that I am not ignorant of your designs.

PRITCHARD. You have greatly the advantage over me, M. le Capitaine, I remain in profound ignorance of yours, if you intend no aggression.

QUEEN POMARE, ETC.

POLVEREL. I come by order of his Majesty the king of the French to protect the queen and people of Tahiti, from rebels, incendiaries, and fanatics.

PRITCHARD. Namely, those who have risen in all quarters of the island to escape from the protection you offer.

POLVEREL. At your instigation.

PRITCHARD. It required no instigation from me, or from any other man, native or stranger. For many years, indeed ever since we discovered the country they inhabit, they have lived peaceably and happily, subject to no foreign laws or controul. Under the guidance of disinterested men, men contented with laborious poverty, they have abandoned their ancient superstitions, immoral and sanguinary, and have listened to the promises of the Gospel.

POLVEREL. It is now their duty to listen to ours, more positive and immediate. We have nothing to do with Gospel or with missionaries : we come to liberate a people crushed by your avarice.

PRITCHARD. Of what have we ever deprived them ? what taxes, what concessions, what obedience, have we ever exacted ? They never fought against us, never fled from us, never complained of us.

POLVEREL. How dared they ?

PRITCHARD. Yet they dare attack men so much braver.

POLVEREL. M. Pritchard ! I perceive you are a person of impartiality and discernment. You bestow on us unreservedly the character we claim and merit. The rabble is not to be consulted in affairs of state : and the rabble alone is in insurrection against us.

PRITCHARD. I did imagine, sir, that the word *rabble* had no longer a place in the French language.

POLVEREL. It never had for the French. But these wretches must be taught obedience to the laws.

PRITCHARD. What laws ?

[DES MITRAILLES *enters.*]

POLVEREL. Permit me to present to you M. le Capitaine Des Mitrailles, and to take my leave.

DES MITRAILLES. On my entrance you were asking what laws the people of Tahiti are to obey : the answer is easy and simple : ours, and no other.

PRITCHARD. The answer is easier than the execution.

[DES MITRAILLES, *clenching his fist.*]

PRITCHARD. I am a man of peace, M. le Capitaine, and a servant

95

of God. But if any impertinent arrogant outrageous aggressor should strike me, I might peradventure wipe the dust off the wall with his whiskers : so take care. King Louis-Philippe, I imagine, issued no orders to bestow on so humble an individual as myself an earnest of his Protectorate by a blow in the face, which is a ceremonial he reserves for the defenceless, in order to establish the glory of his navy. You begin it with a priest, and (no doubt) you will end it with a woman.

DES MITRAILLES. If that abominable hag Pomare were present at this instant, I would strike her to the earth, were it only to irritate the English.

PRITCHARD. You would succeed in both exploits. Our queen must be enamoured of your king's gallantry, when she hears that his officers have executed his commission so delicately.

DES MITRAILLES. The queen Pomare has concealed herself.

PRITCHARD. How! From the Protectorate she solicited so earnestly ?

DES MITRAILLES. Find her : bring her in : or expect the confiscation of your property, and a prison.

PRITCHARD. Find her ! bring her in ! I am no bloodhound.

DES MITRAILLES. Unless she comes forward and acknowledges our Protectorate, I dethrone her in the name of Louis-Philippe, king of the French.

PRITCHARD. Europe may not see with tranquillity the execution of such violence.

DES MITRAILLES. We have a long account to settle with Europe, and our quarrel must commence with her Paymaster-general.

PRITCHARD. I hope he does not reside in Tahiti.

DES MITRAILLES. You understand me better.   ·

PRITCHARD. Until now there has been little discord in the island, no insurrection and murder. He who first brings war into any country will be remembered and execrated by all others to the end of time. Can Englishmen believe that a king who hath seen so much suffering, and hath endured so much himself, will ever enjoy a phantom of power rising up over blood and carnage ? This happy people want protection against no enemy. Our mariners discovered their island, and have continued to live among them not as masters, or what you call protectors, but simply as instructors. We do not even exercise the right which is usually conceded to discoverers : we are unwilling to receive, and more unwilling to exact, submission. Improbable then is it that we should let another, under any pretext, usurp it.

DES MITRAILLES. We are aware of that sentiment ; otherwise my frigate would not have sailed at present to the South Sea. I shall act according to my orders.

PRITCHARD. Consider, sir, the responsibility. What is now occurring in this obscure little island, may agitate the minds of the most powerful in the present age, and of the most intellectual in the future. What were once the events of the day are become the events of all days. Historians and orators of the first order have founded their fame on what at the beginning raised only a little dust round the market-place.

DES MITRAILLES. You have the presumption and impertinence, sir, to reason and argue and dogmatise with me, and even to call me to account. I am responsible only to the king my master, and to the minister who gave me his instructions.

PRITCHARD. If that minister is a demagogue whose daily bread is baked on the ashes of ruined habitations ; if that minister is a firebrand of which every spark is supplied by the conflagration of the household gods——

DES MITRAILLES. Do not talk to me of households and gods.

PRITCHARD. Depend upon it there are men in England who can catch the ball with whatever force you bat it ; and you will not win the game.

You threatened to strike a woman to the ground, a defenceless woman, whom you avowedly came to protect.

DES MITRAILLES. We did come to protect her, and she insults our generosity by her flight. A Frenchman never threatens what he finds himself unable to execute. Were the wretch here, you should see the proof.

LIEUTENANT POIGNAUNEZ. My captain ! we have brought in the fugitive, the incendiary, the traitress.

DES MITRAILLES. Chain her, and carry her aboard.

PRITCHARD. I protest against either outrage.

LIEUTENANT POIGNAUNEZ. You protest ! who are you ?

PRITCHARD. British Consul.

LIEUTENANT POIGNAUNEZ. What are British consuls in the presence of French officers ? My captain ! with submission ! knock out at least a tooth as a trophy. I have set my heart on a couple of her front teeth ; they are worth a louis in the Palais Royal. M. du Petit Thouars, our admiral, has extorted his six thousand dollars ; are a couple of teeth above a lieutenant's share of the booty ?

DES MITRAILLES. Knock out one yourself ; it is not among the duties of a French capitaine de vaisseau. You may strike her safely ; she is so heavy with child she can not run after you.

LIEUTENANT POIGNAUNEZ. Madame, the queen ! I carry the orders of Monsieur le Capitaine, serving in the Pacific, by appointment of his Majesty Louis-Philippe, king of the French, to knock out a tooth.

[Strikes her in the face ; sailors hold PRITCHARD.

POMARE. O inhumanity ! Although I am a woman, a Christian, and a queen, and although you are Frenchmen, I never could have expected this.

DES MITRAILLES. Bravo ! bravo ! but rather lower, Poignaunez ! hit rather lower. How the tiger defends her breast ! Well ; the eyes will do. Again ! Bravo ! you have pretty nearly knocked out one.

POMARE. Spare my life ! do not murder me ! O brave captain ! can such be your orders ?

DES MITRAILLES. May it please your Majesty ! I bear no such injunctions from the King my master, or from Monsieur his minister of state for the marine and colonies.

PRITCHARD. Have you received or given orders that I should be seized and detained ?

DES MITRAILLES. Sir, I call upon you to attest in writing the perfect good-faith and composure with which we have acted.

PRITCHARD. Every man in England receives a slap in the face when a woman receives one in any quarter of the globe.

DES MITRAILLES. Queen Pomare did not receive a slap on the face.

LIEUTENANT POIGNAUNEZ. By no means.

DES MITRAILLES. She had only a tooth knocked out.

LIEUTENANT POIGNAUNEZ. My captain ! pardon ! you concede too much. The tooth is in its place, and in accordance with all the rest : it has merely undergone the declension of a few degrees toward the horizon.

DES MITRAILLES. Madame ! I am exceedingly concerned, and

intimately penetrated, that, by some strange unaccountable interpretation, so untoward an accident has befallen your Majesty.

LIEUTENANT POIGNAUNEZ (*to the crew*). Cry, you fools, cry !

SAILOR. I thought, M. le Lieutenant, we were to carry her off in
chains. Here they are.

LIEUTENANT POIGNAUNEZ. Presently, presently. But now deploy
your throats, and cry, rascals, cry " Vive la Reine ! "

CREW. Vive la Reine ! A bas les fuyards ! A bas les Anglais !
A bas les tyrans ! Vive le Roi !

III. JOHN DRYDEN AND HENRY PURCELL [1]

(*Fraser's Magazine*, 1852; not reprinted by Forster or Crump.)

DRYDEN. Well, Harry, so the fates have decreed that we should be once more associated on the stage. Betterton, our master, has issued his mandate, and we must again obey it.

PURCELL. His commands are not always welcome ; but when they compel my companionship with you, they cannot fail to be so : an association with Mr. Dryden would be an honour to any musician.

DRYDEN. And I understand you have attained a degree of musical eminence which now renders you my fit and worthy associate. I have no knowledge of your art, but the universal report, even of your brethren, places you at their head.

PURCELL. My worthy master Blow, and my well-instructed friends Wise, Humphries, and Clark, have restricted themselves to the service of the Church. It has been my fortune, from very early life, to apply my knowledge of music to the Church. You know that I was only a boy when I wrote my opera *Dido and Æneas*.

DRYDEN. Which, no doubt, recommended you to Betterton, and occasioned the alliance between us which is now to be further cemented by a new partnership.

PURCELL. I scarcely imagined you would condescend to ally yourself with an English musician after what you said of Grabu, in his opera, *Albion and Albanius*.[2]

DRYDEN. Well, perhaps I said more than I ought, but, after all, I rather echoed King Charles's opinion than gave one of my own. You know, Harry, I am no musician ; and therefore my opinion would be estimated only at its real worth by those that are.

PURCELL. True, and we Abbey-boys have had many a hearty laugh at it. But pray never again quote the late king as an authority

---

[1] In *Fraser* this Conversation was entitled : " Dialogue Between John Dryden and Henry Purcell, In The Year 1691, on the subject of their forth-coming ' Dramatick Opera of *King Arthur*.' "

[2] Libretto by Dryden, music by Grabu ; produced at the Dorset Gardens House in 1685.

in musical taste—he who silenced the organ at the Chapel Royal, and supplied its place with a band of French fiddlers.

DRYDEN. No great proof of good taste, certainly ; but I had many reasons for wishing to compliment him, and we poets are allowed licenses—besides that, we succeed better in fiction than truth. But come, to business. What is the immediate purpose of this visit ?

PURCELL. To settle, if we can, the terms on which we are to enter upon this joint-labour, and to come to some understanding as to the best way in which it can be accomplished.

DRYDEN. Why, that is clear enough. " 'Tis my part to invent, and the musician's to follow the invention."

PURCELL. What, at all hazards ? This might be sometimes inexpedient, and sometimes impossible. You know that when I set the music in your alteration of Shakspeare's *Tempest*, you adopted several of my suggestions. Mr. Dryden, you are a great poet, and no man, at times, writes more finely for a musician—but you are not always right. You are not aware that some lines and thoughts music can express finely, some imperfectly, some not at all.

DRYDEN. Well, well, " I am willing to be counselled, and will always follow a friend's advice when I find it reasonable, but I will never part with the power of the militia."

PURCELL. Suppose, in order that we may clearly understand each other's views, you give me your definition of an opera.

DRYDEN. Readily. " The opera is a poetical tale or fiction, represented by vocal and instrumental music. The supposed persons of this musical drama are generally supernatural, as gods, goddesses, and heroes. The recitative part of the opera requires a masculine character of expression and sound, the other, which (for want of a proper English word) I must call the songish part, must abound in softness and variety of numbers ; its principal intention being to please the hearing rather than to gratify the understanding."

PURCELL. It ought to aim at both ; but we will discuss this point afterwards. You have been describing the plans and rules of an Italian opera.

DRYDEN. No doubt ; " for whoever undertakes the writing of an opera, is obliged to imitate the design of the Italians, who have not only invented, but brought to perfection this sort of dramatic musical entertainment."

PURCELL. If you mean, that having chosen the lyric drama of Italy as our avowed model, undoubtedly we *are* bound to follow it. But I deny that we are *obliged* to do so—and I also deny that it is brought to perfection. Perfection in music, Mr. Dryden, we shall not have on this side heaven. " Our art is but in its nonage." I know enough of it to be assured of that. I see that its powers are capable of infinite extension and combination, and that those will be unfolded and called into existence in a way and to an extent to which we have no idea.

DRYDEN. But if you reject Italian authority, to what will you refer and appeal ?

PURCELL. Simply to nature ; experience and judgment in the selection of a dramatic subject, and in the employment of music, as connected with it. You say the Italians invented the Italian opera, as no doubt they did, but I need not remind so eminent a dramatic writer as you are, that music has been connected with the stage in this country before the Italian opera, according to your definition of it, was born. You speak of recitative : why, recitative is a thing of yesterday, first understood by Carissimi and poor Stradella, our contemporaries—men whom I hold in the highest honour.

DRYDEN. Well, Harry, you have looked into the history of your art more than I have had either time or inclination to do. You know I have confessed that I have no knowledge " either of the time when the Italian opera began, or its first author." My surmise as to its Spanish origin was perhaps erroneous. But what connexion with music and drama do you refer to ?

PURCELL. In the first place, to many of our masques, which were dramatic entertainments, into which music largely entered, and which were written before the Italian opera had been moulded into its present form ; and in the second, to the *Tempest*, which as Shakespeare wrote it, and independent of the large musical additions you made to it, never could have been acted without music. You know (nobody better) that music is a prime and potent agent in this play, and that the business of the scene often could not be carried on without it.

DRYDEN. Well, then, if I understand you aright, you mean to contend that we are free to construct an opera of our own.

102

JOHN DRYDEN AND HENRY PURCELL

PURCELL. To be sure I do—who is to hinder us? In fact, we have already exhibited our own views with regard to the connexion of music with the drama. Why are we to be bound by foreign rules which may justly apply to the language, customs, and habits of other countries, but are wholly unsuited to our own? Pardon me, sir, for saying that you have shown a slavish, and in you, an unbecoming deference to French models in the construction and language of your plays.

DRYDEN. Why, Harry, you know the Court sets the fashion, and as I write to live, I must fall in with its taste. Courtiers account Shakespeare a barbarian, and will not listen to him till he has been Frenchified. But I have given you my definition of an opera; it is time that I hear yours.

PURCELL. You shall have it. You know, perhaps, that my first opera was exactly conformed to your definition. The persons were classical heroes—the dialogue throughout in recitative; therefore I may be allowed to say it is not the want of ability, but experience and conviction, that led me to recommend to English hearers a different form of the lyric drama.

DRYDEN. What, then, would you give up the employment of recitative which the Italians regard as essential to the very existence of an opera?

PURCELL. By no means. There are times when recitative can accomplish what the best delivered speech would fail to effect. I don't like to quote my own humble labours, but in the opening of the " Conjurer's Song " in the play [1] which you and Sir Robert Howard wrote, even Betterton himself could not impart the force and the expression that I have enabled the singer to give. You remember, perhaps, Leveridge in the part.

DRYDEN. You mean, " You twice ten hundred deities." I wrote that song, and I own that I never felt the true power and force of recitative until then. But how comes it that you, who have succeeded so well in it, should wish to discard it?

PURCELL. I have no such wish. I only wish to employ it when and where I think, in our language, it ought to be employed. I would use it whenever any strong feeling or passion is to be expressed, but not to carry on the current dialogue of a play. Music is not merely an art and a science, (for it is both) but a language—to be

[1] *The Indian Queen*, Theatre Royal, and published, 1665.

used fitly, judiciously, appropriately. I have endeavoured to express my opinion of the position of the two arts in the dedication to my *Dioclesian*, and if I remember aright, it runs thus :—

Music and poetry have ever been acknowledged sisters, which, walking hand in hand, support each other. As poetry is the harmony of words, so music is that of notes—and as poetry is a rise above prose and oratory, so is music the exaltation of poetry. Both of them may excel apart, but sure they are most excellent when they are joined, because nothing is then wanting to either of their perfections.

DRYDEN. Prettily expressed, Harry, but I hope that my verses need not your help to give them acceptance and credit with the town.

PURCELL. No, sir ; they need no help of mine to win for them the position they have secured, and will retain long after you and I are no more seen. My remark, too, must be taken with certain qualifications. It had reference only to that class of poetry which would engender musical ideas. I should find some difficulty, for example, in setting your " Hind and Panther " to music.

DRYDEN. No doubt. But let us come to the point—our new play, for I will not call it an opera.

PURCELL Call it what you please ; the label is of little consequence if the quality and flavour of the wine be good.

DRYDEN. I have given you my definition of an opera ; now give me yours.

PURCELL. You have given me the definition of an *Italian* opera. My definition of an English opera (to adopt the name) would be " a play, of which music formed a frequent, necessary, and integral part, but of which the dialogue was spoken." If you mean your play to be sung throughout, you and Betterton must look out for another composer : and remember that you will lose all your best actors—you know that neither he, nor Kynaston, Montford, Mohun, nor Leigh can sing. But what is your subject ?

DRYDEN. The subject on which I intended and hoped to have written an epic poem—King Arthur ; but all thought of that is at an end, and I have now determined to bring out the play to which, as you know, my *Albion and Albanius* was merely intended as a sort of prelude. But times and dynasties have changed, and " not to offend the government which has hitherto protected me, I have been obliged so much to alter the first design, that it is now no more what it was formerly than the present ship of the Royal Sovereign, after so often taking down and altering, is the vessel it was at the first building."

PURCELL. Your *dramatis personæ*, then, are Britons and Saxons.

DRYDEN. They are. King Arthur, Merlin, the Duke of Cornwall, and his blind daughter, being the principal British characters ; to whom I have added Philidel, whose origin you will easily trace to Ariel.

PURCELL. Good ; and for whom I will write another " Come unto these yellow sands."

DRYDEN. The Saxons are Oswald and his followers, with Grimbald, an earthy spirit.

PURCELL. Well, well ; here are materials, if we can but work them up. I will adopt your own words, and give you " a friend's advice," which you will " follow only when you find it reasonable." How does your play open ?

DRYDEN. Conon and other friends of King Arthur describe the state of England and the impending contest between the Britons and Saxons. Emmeline and Arthur, her lover, will afterwards appear. The trumpet is heard, and Arthur prepares for the approaching battle, which——

PURCELL. Stop, stop, sir ; I will be ready for your battle when the time comes ; but we must not have recourse to music's most animating strains at first. Rather something of a graver kind, while the attention of the hearers is fresh. Your Saxons are heathens—what are the names of their reputed gods ?

DRYDEN. Woden and Thor.

PURCELL. Then interpose a sacrifice to them, with priests and their attendants, in order to invoke their deities' aid in the approaching conflict. Music will be here appropriately used, for without her aid you could not carry such a scene through. Always remember, Mr. Dryden, that there can be no combination of voices on the stage without you call in music. Destitute of her assistance, you can get no farther than a huzza. Give me words for solo and chorus, and I will answer for the effect.

DRYDEN. I will proceed with my outline. " A battle is supposed to take place behind the scenes, and the Britons enter victorious."

PURCELL. To do what—march off again ? No, no. Here give me a bold, martial song, that can be chorused by the whole army— something that breathes defiance.

DRYDEN. As much as to say, " Come, if you dare."

PURCELL. The very words I should like—I have the music for them in my head already.

DRYDEN. Then I have had a thought (taken from Tasso) of conducting my hero and his army through an enchanted forest, where he shall be assailed by good and evil spirits, under the command of Philidel and Grimbald.

PURCELL. For which you must and shall have the assistance of my art ; and without it you may strike out your scene. Troops of spirits, no more than congregations of priests, or battalions of soldiers, can open their throats together on the stage except by the aid of music.

DRYDEN. Arthur, like Rinaldo, is then to pass through a variety of temptations, and I have provided songs by syrens, nymphs, and sylvans.

PURCELL. For all of which I will furnish appropriate music.

DRYDEN. Then, according to custom, I mean to introduce a masque, in which Pan, Æolus, Venus, Comus, and other heathen deities will sing in praise of England ; winding up with a chapter of the order of the Garter, a song to " St. George, the patron of our Isle," and a compliment to our reigning sovereign.

PURCELL. And is it your real design to have this all sung— dialogue and all ? If so, I need not again remind you that you must discard all your best actors, since we have no singers equal to the performance of an opera written according to the Italian model. Adopt my idea of an English opera, discard all slavish adherence to rules, customs, and habits, which, if suited to a foreign nation and language, are not necessarily binding upon or suited to ours. Surely, Mr. Dryden, you are the person to give and not to receive the law. Do this, and I am with you heart and soul.

DRYDEN. But you know that I have committed myself to the opinion I have quoted.

PURCELL. True ; and so you did to the French rule, that tragedies should be written in rhyme ; but you had the sense and courage to confess yourself in the wrong, and pay your allegiance to nature and Shakspeare. I have not forgotten part of your

prologue to *Aurengzebe*, the last of your rhyming plays. The
lines run thus :—

> Our author has now another taste of wit,
> And to confess a truth, though out of time,
> Grows weary of his long-loved mistress—rhyme.
> Passions too fierce to be in fetters bound,
> And nature flies him, like enchanted ground.
> In spite of all his pride, a secret shame
> Invades his breast at Shakspeare's honoured name.

DRYDEN. I remember the lines, and the conviction that produced
them. But a man always feels some repugnance at avowing a change
of opinion. 'Tis a confession either that he had imperfectly studied
the subject on which he wrote, or that he was influenced by some
selfish or unworthy motive.

PURCELL. Pardon me, sir ; neither of these reasons apply to you.
Rather let me say it was a distrust of your own judgment and your
own proper position. Permit me to add, that my admiration of the
Italian masters of music is upon record ; and if it were not in words,
my anthem, "O God, thou hast cast us out," and my motet, "Jehova,
quam multi sunt hostes mei," would show that I had studied both
Palestrina and Carissimi ; but how far Italian rules for the writing
of an opera are applicable to our language and to our stage is quite
another question.

DRYDEN. Well, Harry, I believe you are right. I respect a man
who loves his art cordially and disinterestedly, as all the world knows
you do. I will take your advice, and from time to time, we will
confer together again on the subject of our—what shall we call it ?

PURCELL. What you please, sir. Good morning, it is time for
me to be at the Abbey.

IV. LORD MOUNTJOY AND LORD EDWARD FITZGERALD *

(*Literary Life and Correspondence of Countess of Blessington*, 1855 ; not reprinted by Forster or Crump.)

LORD EDWARD. My dear Mountjoy, I wish I could entertain the flattering hope, that you have granted me admittance to you, as much from your old friendship as from your invariable politeness.

MOUNTJOY. Such a wish is itself a proof to me that I was in the wrong, if I did not.

LORD EDWARD. Neither my knowledge of your easy temper, nor of your warm and generous heart, gave me all that assurance which I now receive from the pressure of your hand ; a diversity in politics, I need not tell you, has made several of my earliest friends, and nearest relations, turn their backs upon me.

MOUNTJOY. I hope I shall never turn mine on a good soldier, friend, or enemy.

LORD EDWARD. I will be sworn for you ; if the last spark of honour and chivalry is to be extinguished on the earth, it will be in the breast of Mountjoy.

MOUNTJOY. Lord Edward, let us leave off compliments, which, while they were in use, were used principally to display some grace in the person, or to conceal obliquity in the mind.

LORD EDWARD. Faith ! if that is the good of them, you have the best right of any man to vote them out of fashion : now to the business of my visit. The people, you have long been aware, my Lord, are highly exasperated against the government; I will not ask you whether you think they are so, with reason or without ; certainly, there is danger of an open insurrection.

MOUNTJOY. Lord Edward, when a dog is mad, I do not ask what

* Lord Mountjoy, the staunch and early friend of the Irish Roman Catholics, was slain by the people in rebellion in 1798. Lord E. Fitzgerald perished at the hands of authority in the same rebellion, he the head and front of its offending. —W. S. L.

drove him mad ? I defend my own dogs and myself from his fury as well as I can.

LORD EDWARD. Sometimes it is wiser to get out of his way.

MOUNTJOY. I neither can nor would get out of the way, gladly as I should see every root of grievance torn up from a country but too fertile in them.

LORD EDWARD. We were together in the association of Dublin volunteers, which, supported by others throughout the kingdom, was then strong enough to have set at defiance the battered and broken arms of our oppressor, and could have accomplished all that was wanting for the permanent good of Ireland. The English government no longer had money or credit ; the English people, exhausted by the expenditure of war, alienated by the misconduct of it, began at last to perceive and to acknowledge the justice of the American cause ; ours was the same under much longer and much worse irritations ; we had a larger and a better array to assert it ; more within our reach to confiscate justly for the support of it ; and we should have had the same allies. When we could have done every thing for our country, what did we ? we sat down again contented with paltry concessions and empty promises : England thought herself generous for granting them ; Ireland for her easy acceptance of the grant. In England every generosity is called a folly ; in Ireland, every folly is called a generosity. We are now told that too much has been done for us, and truly, I believe it ; since every thing is too much for us, which we do not for ourselves.

MOUNTJOY. Lord Edward, our country endures no injury to which I am not as sensitive as you are ; we differ only in the expediency of resistance ; we have lost the only opportunity we ever had of being the confederates rather than the subjects of England, or, what is yet better than confederacy, a part. Britons, Saxons, Danes, Normans, have united ; what hinders the Irish ?

LORD EDWARD. English policy.

MOUNTJOY. I see no reason why salt water, rather than fresh, should separate those whom affections and interests draw together.

LORD EDWARD. Nor do I ; but the wholesale butchers who have turned Ireland into their slaughter-house have so ensanguined the knot, that it will hold no longer.

MOUNTJOY. Nothing in the whole of our misfortunes is so deplorable, as that it should continue to be the policy of our rulers to bind us rather by restrictions than by generosity—a bad policy with any nation, but worse with the Irish than with any other, for, among the Irish, the very vilest and the most inconsiderate are brought over and attached to you by one kind action, and alienated by one effort of control. Who would imagine that the English aristocracy and the Irish democracy should be equally strenuous in producing the same result? Yet so it is; if you cannot lead the blind man, do not mock him, my dear Lord Edward. The trick may bring about the calamity. It now appears to be the intention of certain men, that we should throw ourselves into the arms of France, and thus render our country the arena for all the battles of the English with all their enemies.

LORD EDWARD. How much better it would have been, as you remarked, to identify the two countries, and to render every man in each, the neighbour of his neighbour. It seems an absurdity, a contradiction, an impossibility, that it should not be so; yet, where all men with equal wishes and knowledge may not aspire to equal rank and estimation, where a thought on God is a crime in the eyes of him who has another thought on the same God; where a son, if he follows his father, is stripped of his civic rights for it, and interdicted his natural; what hope, then, can we have of justice or what desire of reconciliation?

MOUNTJOY. I will not discourse with you on open war.

LORD EDWARD. But show me if you can, in all the records of history, a war of nation against nation more manifestly just.

MOUNTJOY. The cause of justice is but little forwarded by compromising the cause of humanity; we are hardly the people that can teach the English to be wiser, or that can compel them to be more equitable—I wish we were: we would then begin the first lesson to-morrow. As matters stand, by any attempt to resistance, we should only make the brutal more brutal, and the suffering more suffering; and the end of it would be, that every peaceable man would leave the kingdom by choice, and every brave man by proscription. I think it criminal to contend without a chance of success, unless it be where, by the sacrifice of our lives, as well as theirs under us, we can give time for others to come on, who may continue or renew the contest with better hopes. In that case our bodies may well fill up the straits, and the idlest of strangers will never write *fool* above our epitaphs. I see clearly the expectations of the

MOUNTJOY AND FITZGERALD

United Irishmen, and no less clearly the disappointment and delusion of them. The French and Irish can never cordially agree.

LORD EDWARD. Why do you think so ?

MOUNTJOY. Because the one will no longer be ruled by priests ; the other will be ruled by none else.

LORD EDWARD. It must indeed be a tremendous curse, that can render them endurable. We may want them for a time.

MOUNTJOY. Their time will be longer than ours ; hopes, fears, consciences, are tost about, and distributed by their hands.

LORD EDWARD. Too true ; throw in likewise a moiety of the wives, present and future ; they find spouses both for God and man, with good accommodation ; and not only do they bring about marriages, but they can make heavy ones light, and light ones heavy, and can put other horns above the devil's, in any doorway they have once entered.

MOUNTJOY. If England had the equity and wisdom to place Ireland by her side in the same level, and no lower ; if she would grant to the Irish all the rights of citizens, as she hath done to the Canadians ? *

LORD EDWARD. Which renders it the more galling, the more iniquitous, the more intolerable.

MOUNTJOY. Then, indeed, the priesthood could make no further appeals to the passions of the ignorant, and the contest for mastery would shortly lie between the people and it. Popery would lose her hold on the latter's ignorance ; for among the Irish, if the acutest sense is that of injustice, the quickest is that of ridicule ; the expression of which two feelings can never exist together. Ireland will grow more Catholic every day she continues to be oppressed ; less Catholic, every day after she is relieved from her oppression. Faction will cease within the first century of this real Reformation, which it seems wonderful that the Protestant clergy should be reluctant to bring about.

LORD EDWARD. Not at all ; the Protestant clergy leap from the goat-fold to the sheep-fold ; from the sheep-fold to the ox-stall, and being there, grow too lazy to budge. Who among them would not abandon parishioners for a vicarage, for a deanery, a bishopric for

---

* That such is not the case at present is quite certain ; on the authority of the Duke of Wellington, and of nearly all the principal men in the cabinet.— W. S. L.

an archbishopric, and the house of God for the house of Lords ? The government—be the party what it may—Whig or Tory, never wished our pacification ; a state of discontent, of discord, and of turbulence, kept up artificially and sedulously by them, is necessary as a plea to keep up likewise a large establishment here, both military and civil, and the people of England are induced to pay taxes for it, on which many hundred dependants of every administration rear their families. Were Ireland flourishing, as she must be under any other system, the rival oligarchies would lose a large portion of their patronage ; England wavers perpetually, in every branch of her policy, expecting this. The Horatii and Curatii, who contend for supremacy, instead of three, are about nine on a side, and in the families of these we are to look for the secret. Why, by their consent we are never to meliorate our condition : the people of England would gain some millions yearly by our freedom, by our mere equality with the French-Canadians. The means of keeping them in subjection to these ruling families would be lost, by leaving us unbound.

MOUNTJOY. The English would benefit in wealth by it quite as much as we should, and greatly more in the reduction of taxes ; all that they would lose would be the sentiment of contempt for the generality of us, and of hatred for the remainder.

LORD EDWARD. If they persist, my life for it, they shall lose one of these sentiments, and very soon.

MOUNTJOY. I see nothing but a divided people and a corrupt parliament.

LORD EDWARD. You shall see neither much longer. Those who separate themselves from the people are no part of it, and what is corrupt will drop off, or must be cut off—who could regret it ? Was there ever an association, even an assemblage in any lane of the worst city, or in any forest of the wildest country, so profligate and shameless, so barbarous and rapacious as our Irish peers ? *

MOUNTJOY. Little better, I confess it, than the Poles.

LORD EDWARD. In Poland everything is noble that is not a slave, in Ireland, every thing that is . . .

* Lord Edward Fitzgerald may be imagined to have formed this erroneous opinion on the Irish peers, whom (equally erroneously) he deemed actuated by corruption in the business of the Union ; he spoke unguardedly of all whom he thought rogues, and it would have been well for him, if he had been more suspicious than he was.—W. S. L.

MOUNTJOY AND FITZGERALD

MOUNTJOY. Our peerage, with the exception of six or seven.

LORD EDWARD. Take the six, give me the seventh, and I pay you down his weight in rubies; such scrapings from sugar-casks and tobacco wrappers never was flung among the mussel shells and skate tails of Kelvoc slugs of Flushing, so disorderly a gang of cut-throats and cut-purses never sate on the same benches in any galley of Tripoli or Marseilles. The poor are sent back to their parishes; it were greater equity to send back the rich, who, without some gross injustice, some intolerable grievance, ought not to live away. Have we no cart to carry, no constable to escort our packed pedlary: wonderful it must appear, that England, as a residence, is preferable to Ireland amongst those who, in the London gaming-houses, are liable to be mistaken for the candle-snuffers, whenever in the hurry of their rapacity, they forgot to put a star before them, for a light to steer by.

MOUNTJOY. Your estimation of our peerage is pretty correct, and you are as little to be accused of envy as of ambition; you yourself are likely to be, one day, the first nobleman in the empire; for where there is only one duke, surely that one is above any, where there is fifteen or twenty.

LORD EDWARD. I have never permitted the contingency to enter into my calculations. Were I a duke to-morrow, and everything went on well and prosperously, both with me and with our country, I declare, before you and before God, I would throw my dukedom off my back, if by doing so I could run the quicker, to raise up one honest and brave fellow from oppression.

MOUNTJOY. I believe you, and you are the only man I could believe who should make me a similar protestation.

LORD EDWARD. The better of the Lords are very hostile to me, not for what I think about the rest, but for what I would do in regard to all.

MOUNTJOY. No wonder.

LORD EDWARD. And yet, Mountjoy, such men as yourself, for instance, ought to rejoice at being no longer confounded with brokers and bankers, and bullock drivers; ought to rejoice at that personal distinctness, which alone is true distinction; ought to rejoice at that superiority as gentlemen, which is seen more advantageously, when people are not standing upon stilts about you. Is it not a shame to hold by favour, from another, what we can take to ourselves by right ? Reason has a long time lain fermenting in the canker of society, and must soon cast off the froth. The generous juice, I swear by God and my country ! shall be distributed by a hand both steady and unsparing.

MOUNTJOY. I will not irritate you, nor myself, by discussing the views of a political body so universally hated and despised, yet I hope, Lord Edward, you do not believe the invidious and spiteful story raised about them by the factions, that Mr. Pitt intends a union of the two nations, by means of their giving each member of the peerage a thousand pounds a-year, and other indemnities for loss of privilege.

LORD EDWARD. No, no, my lord, what I have said of them I think is pretty near enough the truth. The Irish would tear them in pieces, as betrayers ; the English would feed the eels of the Thames with them, rather than endure such blood-suckers on their shoulders. I am no visionary in evil ; I see enough of it. I know its proximity and magnitude ; I distinguish its form and colour. I want neither telescope nor darkened glass.

MOUNTJOY. Let us attempt to allay the passions of the multitude, and to enlighten the prejudices of the rest.

LORD EDWARD. The only chance of assuaging the multitude is in their being used to suffer. Weak as a hope, and weaker as an argument : and what are the prejudices of the rest ? and where do they exist ? Take from them the prospect of living on the plunder of their country, and what you call prejudices vanish. I came to your house, my dear Mountjoy, with intentions which I ardently wish may not be quite so fruitless. The people are more angry with those whom they know to be patriotic ; and yet, who will not join them when they are with the old stagers on the king's highway of oppression and peculation. Hence their love for you, which was unrivaled, is converted into acrimony !

MOUNTJOY. Whatever I could do, constitutionally and conscientiously, I have always done for them, and will do always. It would not become me to throw up my commission in the hour of danger ; would you yourself commend me if I did ? Your silence shows me, if anything were necessary to shew it, that my resolution is right.

LORD EDWARD. There are questions that might involve my

security, my life itself, which I could answer you at the first appeal ; this I cannot. Let me guard as warmly as I wish, and as effectually as I can, the safety of a citizen and a soldier more widely and more worthily esteemed than any other in Ireland. I need not inform you of armed bands in every part of the kingdom, I have already told you of their exasperation against you. Let me now come to that point which now pains me, and warn you that I have heard your life threatened, should you appear in any array against them. Why do you laugh ?

MOUNTJOY. What man's life is not threatened who appears in arms, and in the face of an enemy ?

LORD EDWARD. Faith, I did not think about life or danger in the common accidents of war ; but, in America, there began a custom which nothing short of national independence can ever authorize :— the custom of singling out officers !

MOUNTJOY. A high compliment, if hand to hand !

LORD EDWARD. But the rifleman is rude at compliments, and I should be grieved to the heart by your falling, be the cause what it may.

MOUNTJOY. I have little inclination to die just at present, and less to desert my station. If you heard any threats against my life, individually, you ought to have seized the threatener by the collar, and to have delivered him over to the laws.

LORD EDWARD. I chose to do what I believe to be more efficacious. The apprehension of one would excite a thousand to avenge him, by doing what he left undone. Should you be ordered to quell any disturbance, vain as I know it is to request you not to be the foremost, let me entreat you rather to be heard and known by your own men than by those opposite.

MOUNTJOY. Lord Edward ! both sides shall hear and know me. The service that is imposed on me is indeed most painful ; and, for this very reason, the discharge of it shall be complete and prompt. We are lost when our affections glide in between us and our duties ; and I perceive you do not like a moralizer, and look graver than one yourself.

LORD EDWARD. If all moralizers were Mountjoys, I could listen in the thickest of a sermon. In general, men are given to moralizing when their most ravenous desires are crop full ; and when they are determined to sit quiet and enjoy their sunny side of life, you take to it, for the first time, when you are resolved on more activity than ever, and are as ready to die as to live.

MOUNTJOY. Lord Edward ! in this I am confident we agree : that a glorious death is the best gift of heaven, and that an early one is not the heaviest of its dispensations.

LORD EDWARD. True, true ; God bless you, Mountjoy (*going*). I must not falter ;—but—are all the rest in the kingdom worth this man ?

APPENDIX TO IMAGINARY CONVERSATIONS

Vol. i. p. 64.   1st ed. has the following terminal note :

" The Persian despots contented themselves with debasing the souls of the nations whom they had enslaved ; but do not appear to have been very covetous of their purses.   Herodotus calls their taxation of the Ionian states a tranquillizing and pacificatory measure.   In this respect the world has grown wiser as it has grown older.   Appian states that Pompey imposed on the Syrians and Cilicians a *hundredth* of their income.   Hadrian was accused of great severity towards the Jews, for having somewhat augmented the rate which Vespasian had fixed, and which, according to Zonaras and Xiphilinus, was two drachmas on each (about eighteen pence). Strabo remarks that Egypt brought a revenue of one hundred and eighty thousand pounds to the father of Cleopatra, which sum Augustus doubled.   Paterculus says, that Gaul paid more than Egypt.   According to Suetonius and Eutropius, Cesar imposed on Gaul a tax of twentyfour thousand pounds, which Lipsicus thinks an error, and quadruples the amount.   He estimates the revenue drawn by Rome from Asia, Spain, Greece, Illyria, and the other provinces, at six million sterling.   He inclines to exaggeration. Plutarch, in the life of Pompey, informs us that he levied from Asia one hundred and ninetytwo thousand pounds.   Marcus Antonius exacted from the same country, at one time, the tribute of ten years, about three million six hundred thousand pounds, reproaching the nations that they had paid as much to Brutus and Cassius in two. When Augustus was declared commander-in-chief against him, the senate, according to Xiphilinus, ordered that all citizens and others should besides pay four oboli (sixpence) for each chimney.   Dion Cassius goes farther ; and adds that they also paid two oboli for every *tile* of their houses both in town and country.   Antonius and Augustus were the first that imposed a tax on slaves : it amounted to less than ten shillings for each.   When they imposed one upon wills, it caused an insurrection.—We are better subjects than they were, although they enjoyed under an *holy alliance* the benefits of regular government, and had been accustomed to the salutary discipline of proscription."

Vol. iii. p. 222. 2nd ed. reads : " price.[1] Shelley and Keats were neither less ingenuous nor less averse to disputation.

" LANDOR. It was not my fortune (shall I call it good or bad now they are dead ?) to know those young men who, within so short a space of time, have added [2] two more immortal names to the cemeteries of Rome. Upon one of them I have written what by no means satisfies me.

" ENGLISH VISITOR.[3] Pray let me hear it, if you retain it in your memory.

" LANDOR. I rarely do retain anything of my own : and probably you will never find a man who has heard me repeat a line. But here it is : you may read it for yourself.

" ENGLISH VISITOR.

> " Fair and free soul of poesy, O Keats !
> O how my temples throb, my heart-blood beats,
>   At every image, every word of thine !
> Thy bosom, pierced by Envy, drops to rest,
> Nor hearest thou the friendlier voice, nor seest
>   The sun of fancy climb along thy line.
>
> " But under it, although a viperous brood
> That stung an Orpheus (in a clime more rude
>   Than Rhodope and Hæmus frown upon)
> Still writhes and hisses, and peers out for more
> Whose buoyant blood they leave concreted gore,
>   Thy flowers root deep and split the creviced stone.
>
> " Ill may I speculate on scenes to come,
> Yet I would dream to meet thee at our home
>   With Spenser's quiet, Chaucer's livelier ghost,

---

[1] 1st ed. reads : " a key which the lawful proprietors cannot turn. [See p. 220, vol. iii. of the present edition.] It was not my fortune," etc.

[2] 1st ed. reads : " added, after some centuries, two," etc.

[3] From " ENGLISH VISITOR " to " for yourself. ENGLISH VISITOR " added in 2nd ed. In 1st ed. the verses are read out by Landor himself.

APPENDIX

Cognate to thine—not higher, and not less fair—
And Magdalene and Isabella there
Shall say *without thee half our loves were lost*.

Here,[1] indeed, is little of the pathetic. You must rather have been thinking of the depravity of those who exerted their popularity to depress him, heedless that it precipitated him to the tomb.

"LANDOR.[2] If I bore malice toward any man I should wish him to write against me : but poor Keats, sinking under the blow, perceived not the incurable ignominy it inflicted by its recoil on the executioner.

"ENGLISH VISITOR. Such people as Gifford are to be acquitted : for how could they feel his poetry or estimate his virtues ? Gifford is the Harriet Wilson of our literary world ; the witherer of young names.[3] With the exception of Matthias he is the dullest, as Byron is the sharpest, of our satirists.

"LANDOR. I have no recollection of anything written by the couple you mentioned with Byron ; but of him and his sharpness we think alike. He has not exerted all his force, or he has not experienced all his felicity on me. Rather than the world should have been a loser in this part of his poetry I would have corrected and enlarged for him what he composed about me, and I would have furnished him with fresh materials. I only wish I could have

---

[1] 1st ed. reads (after the verses) : " ENGLISH VISITOR. Here," etc.

[2] From " LANDOR " to " executioner. ENGLISH VISITOR " added in 2nd ed.

[3] 1st ed. reads : " names. LANDOR. There however have been poets who ran, it appears, for refuge to this quarter. ENGLISH VISITOR. Doubtless it is a corner where many may stop a little, in case of need, but none would longer than the moment. As for refuge, it must be somebody at once pusillanimous and ignorant. LANDOR. Not remarkably so—nor indeed in other cases too prudent. He addresses Byron thus.

> " Why tar and sulphur hearts of oak,
> The honestest of English folk,
>   Singing upon them, O thou Nero,
> Byron ?—while yet unscorcht and free
> The devil take me but I 'll flee
>   To goodman Gifford, under zero.

" ENGLISH VISITOR. Whoever he is, I will give him my mind upon the subject, and in verse too.

> " 'Tis better at the stake than in the stall,
> And nobler is the axe than is the awl.

Byron is, I think, the wittiest of satirists. LANDOR. I think the same. Either he has not exerted all," etc.

diverted his pen from [1] Southey.   While he wrote or spoke against
me alone, I said nothing of him in print or conversation ; but the
taciturnity of pride gave way immediately to my zeal in defence of
my friend.   What I write is not written on slate ; and no finger, not
of Time himself, who dips it in the cloud of years, can efface it.
To condemn what is evil and to commend what is good is consistent.
To soften an asperity, to speak all the good we can after worse than
we wish, is *that*, and more.   If I must understand the meaning of
consistency as many do, I wish I may be inconsistent with all my
enemies.   There are many hearts which have risen higher and sunk
lower at his tales, and yet have been shocked and sorrowed at his
untimely death a great deal less than mine has been.   Honour and
glory to him for the extensive good he did ! peace and forgiveness
for the partial evil !

   " ENGLISH VISITOR.[2] Good resolutions, like good wine, are the
better the longer they are kept.   Byron was irritable and selfish,
restless and insincere : but what shall we say of his old enemies
across the Border, descending on Keats as he entered the field, and
bringing down the loyal militia and supplementary sharp-shooters
of the Edinburgh press until he had surrendered his pen and breathed
his last ? [3]

   " LANDOR. Let us say [4] that they have done, and hope they will
yet do, better things.   They might, like the beneficent deity of old
mythology, have fixed a new Delos, a Delos among the Cyclades of
poetry.   Fame often rests at first upon something accidental ; and

---

   [1] 1st ed. reads : " from a better man and better writer, Southey.   ENGLISH
VISITOR. I could imagine a part of that aspiration was for the assailant.   LANDOR.
There are many hearts," etc.
   [2] 1st ed. reads : " ENGLISH VISITOR. Come, I cannot talk of extensive good,
or indeed of one kind action, or (what might perhaps propitiate you) one fine
sentence, in the *goodman under zero* ; but while he is measuring your foot, tho'
with a clumsy and unclean hand, do not tread upon his fingers. LANDOR. I do
not always walk in the brushed path ; yet where I sit down quietly I will not dirty
my shoe wantonly.
> " Together we release the cloak,
>   A wretched wretched rag indeed ! *

" ENGLISH VISITOR. But what shall we say of higher men, descending," etc.
   [3] 1st ed. has a note : " ' I canna shake mysell loose o' the belief that there
has been some jookery-paukery of Satan's in a' this.' "—*Black Dwarf*.
   [4] 1st ed. reads : " think."

---

   * Wordsworth's *Alice Fell*.—W. S. L.

APPENDIX

often too is swept away or [1] for a time removed : but neither genius nor glory is conferred at once ; nor do they glimmer and fall like drops in a grotto, at a shout. Their foundations in the beginning may be scooped away by the slow machinery of malicious labour ; but after a season they increase with every surge that comes against them, and harden at every tempest to which they are exposed.[2]

" ENGLISH VISITOR. But certainly there are blemishes, which strike the most incurious and inobservant beholder.

" LANDOR. If so, why expose them ? why triumph over them ? In Keats, I acknowledge, there are many wild thoughts, and there are expressions which even outstrip them in extravagance : but in none of our poets, with the sole exception of Shakespeare, do we find so many phrases so happy in their boldness.

" ENGLISH VISITOR. There is a more vivid spirit, more genuine poetry, in him than in any of his contemporaries ; in whom it has rarely its full swing ; but the chords (excepting in Burns and Moore) are flattened, as it were, by leaves or feathers on them. The connexion has given you also some elbowings and shovings.

" LANDOR. And how much more reasonably than they were given to such gentle creatures as Keats ! He, like many other authors, young and aged, traversed in criticism both marsh and crag, to fill his bosom with every bitter and every thorny plant, that might pierce, blister, or unquiet it. I never look for them nor see them. The whole world might write against me, and leave me ignorant of it to the day of my death. A friend who announces to me such things, has performed the last act of his friendship. It is no more pardonable than to lift up the gnat-nets over my bed, on pretext of showing me there are gnats in the room.[3] If I owed a man a grudge,

[1] 1st ed. reads : " or removed at least, for a time. But," etc.

[2] 1st ed. reads : " exposed. ENGLISH VISITOR. The *Connexion* has given you also some elbowings and shovings. LANDOR. And how much," etc.

[3] 1st ed. reads : " room. Two numbers of the magazine edited by the *Connexion* were sent to me : the former contained (I hear) two entire conversations, and accused me of exaggerating when I said that Mina had surpassed all the generals of his age in extraordinary exploits. I might have added, that History has left us no example of such, performed by means apparently so inadequate. Bonaparte, when he rejected the guidance of others, failed in every important undertaking, with greater advantages than were ever possesst before. But few can think those great men who never trampled upon them. Greatness must have a fierce or a mysterious air, high titles, a swaggering gait, a swoln purse, a priest before, a lawyer at the side, and a hangman after her. Bonaparte with only the resources of Mina would have been lost and unheard of : Mina,

I would get him to write against me : but if any body owed me one, he would come and tell me of it.

" ENGLISH VISITOR. You appear more interested about this youth[1] than about Burns, whom I have known you extol to the skies.

" LANDOR. I do not recollect what I wrote on Burns, for I seldom keep a copy of anything, but I know that I wrote it many years after his decease, which was hardly less deplorable than Keats's.[2] One would imagine that those who, for the honour of our country, ought to have guarded and watched over this prodigy of genius, had considered only how they could soonest despatch him from the earth. They gave him a disreputable and sordid place, exactly of the kind in which he could indulge his only bad propensity.

" ENGLISH VISITOR. And now I remember[3] you allude to this propensity, not without an acknowledgment that you yourself would have joined him in its excess.

" LANDOR. How so ? If you can recollect it, the critics will thank you for it.

" ENGLISH VISITOR. These, I think, are the verses :

" Had we two met, blithe-hearted Burns,
    Tho' water is my daily drink,
    May God forgive me, but I think
We should have roared out toasts by turns.

" Inquisitive low-whispering cares
    Had found no room in either pate,[4]
    Until I asked thee, rather late,
Is there a hand-rail to the stairs ?

---

with half the resources of Bonaparte, would have liberated the world. The *Connexion*, as you denominate the Scotch magazinemen, after rifling me and thanking me, retracted the thanks (I am told) and retained the pilfer. If these clowns, instead of *making a leg* to personages who laugh both in public and in private at their awkwardness and servility, would look up and mind their market-cart, they would act much more wisely and becomingly : the jolt they have given to my new carriage has not hurt even the varnish. My four volumes (for a fourth there will be) contain more than seventy dialogues : let the sturdiest of the *Connexion* take the ten worst ; and if he equals them in ten years, I will give him a hot wheaten roll and a pint of *brown-stout* for breakfast—nay, under the rose, I will correct his English for him ever in future if he asks it *at* me. ENGLISH VISITOR. You appear more interested," etc.

[1] 1st ed., in a list of errata, bids us read : " these youths, Keats and Shelley."
[2] 1st ed. reads : " Keatsis."   [3] 1st ed. reads : " And I now remember."
[4] 1st ed. has a note : " *Pate*, as T. Warton sagely informs us, was not a ludicrous or illiberal word formerly. It occurs in our translation of the Psalms. ' His wickedness shall fall on his own *pate*.'—Ps. 7."

APPENDIX

" LANDOR. My Bacchus is, I protest, as Cowley's mistress : but, with a man like Burns, I do not know whether I should have cried out very anxiously

" Quò me, Bacche, rapis ?

" ENGLISH VISITOR.[1] The Scotch, never delicate or dextrous in ridicule, bantered in their coarse manner the poetry of Keats. It is their practice, and a practice not confined to them, to hinder popularity in its first ascent ; and when they cannot hinder it, to attend upon it obsequiously and overload it with incense. From their stiffness and awkwardness they do not appear, at first sight, an inconstant people ; yet none is less ashamed of committing the most open and scandalous inconsistency.

" A celebrated author, whose[2] name will survive many centuries, wrote in favour of the Princess of Wales while the old King was living, against her when she had lost her protector. He[3] flattered her husband, who had all the vices of all the Neros, without one virtue or semblance of virtue ; who abandoned two contemporary wives, every mistress, every relative, every friend, and every supporter.

" LANDOR. Can it be ? Excuse my question : you know my utter ignorance of parties in the literary circles, and how little I am disposed to believe what they assert[4] of one another.

" ENGLISH VISITOR. The truth of this is notorious. The same writer composed and sang a triumphal song on the death of a minister[5] whom, in his life-time, he had flattered,[6] and who was just in his coffin when the Minstrel sang *The Fox is run to earth ;* not among a few friends, but in the presence of many who neither loved nor esteemed, neither applauded nor countenanced him. Constable of Edinburgh heard him, and related the fact to Curran, who expressed

[1] 1st ed. reads : " ENGLISH VISITOR. His countrymen treated him, as is usual to men of genius, with more kindness after his death than while he was amongst them, and drawing away from those who had some pretentions, too large a portion, as they thought, of public notice. The Scotch do not appear to us, nor have they ever been considered, an inconstant people," etc.

[2] From " whose " to " centuries " added in 2nd ed.

[3] From " He " to " supporter " added in 2nd ed.

[4] 1st ed. reads : " assert one of another."

[5] When writing this, Landor apparently believed the absurd story that Sir Walter Scott had written *Tally ho to the Fox* while Fox was dying, and the hardly less absurd story that Scott was the author or instigator of the attack on Keats by *Blackwood.*

[6] 1st ed. reads : " flattered. He was just," etc.

his incredulity with great vehemence, and his abhorrence with greater than his incredulity.

" LANDOR. I believe there has rarely been [1] a less energetic or less consistent statesman than Mr. Fox: but he was friendly and affectionate; he was a gentleman and a scholar. When I heard of his decease, and how he had been abandoned at Chiswick by his colleagues in the ministry, one of whom he had raised to notice and distinction, I grieved that such indignity should have befallen him,[2] even in the midst of the recollection that honester men had experienced as unworthy and as ungrateful friends. I detested his abandonment of right principles in a coalition with a minister he had just before denounced; and I deplored his habit of gambling, a vice which brings after it more misery than any other, and perhaps than all united, and which misery falls on wives, mothers, and children, who never shared in the indulgence of that selfish passion. In a parliamentary leader it is more pernicious; because it alienates from him the more respectable and the most efficient supporters, and deprives a good cause of good men. For this reason, and indeed on this ground alone, I wrote a Latin epitaph, not in honour to him, but certainly not to gratify any resentment, which was very far from me; nor with any desire to be countenanced by the wealthier of the aristocracy, which was equally so; and least of all to ingratiate myself with the most profligate prince that ever was tolerated by the English people, a wretch as impure as Nero, and heartless as Caligula.

" Tyrants and usurpers, or those who would become so, are the only persons whose death should be the subject of rejoicing over wine; and it is braver and more generous to compass it than to sing it. Fox, too, had sung over wine; perhaps in that very room where he was lying in his shroud; but never did he exult in the death of an adversary, or look through his brimming glass at another's tears.[3] He was not always a patriotic or conscientious statesman, nor very strenuous at any time against corruptions and abuses: but many were then lamenting him; all who had ever known him personally. For in private life he was so amiable, that his political vices seemed to them but weaknesses, and oftentimes even as deep-

---

[1] 1st ed. reads: " been a weaker or a more profligate statesman," etc.

[2] 1st ed. reads: " him, and thought it almost too severe a chastisement, and certainly such as ought never to have been inflicted by those hands, for desertion from his standard, or almost any delinquency. Tyrants and usurpers," etc.

[3] 1st ed. reads: " tears. Many were then," etc.

APPENDIX

laid schemes for some beneficent system : and he spoke with such warmth and confidence, that there appeared to be in his character, in despite of the importunity [1] and pressure of numberless proofs against him, both energy and prudence.

" ENGLISH VISITOR. To [2] discover, or to recapitulate, or to report what is disadvantageous to man or author, is little praiseworthy : but to find merit in others is itself a merit ; unless it is found, as hares are found, only to be run down. To be assaulted [3] by satire or undermined by criticism, is deplorable to those chiefly to whom authorship is a profession, and whose families must waste away with the poison thrown into the fountain-head of their subsistence. I wish you yourself had never cracked the whip over Byron, differently as he was situated.

" LANDOR. I expressed the same wish the moment it was right and lawful.

" ENGLISH VISITOR. There was something in his mind not ungraceful [4] nor inelegant, although, from a deficiency of firmness, it wanted dignity. He issued forth against stronger and better men than himself, partly through wantonness and malignity, partly through ignorance of their powers and worth, and partly through impatience at their competition. He could comprehend nothing heroic, nothing disinterested. Shelley, at the gates of Pisa, threw himself between him and the dragoon, whose sword, in his indignation, was lifted and about to strike. Byron told a common friend some time afterward, that he could not conceive how any man living could act so. ' Do you know, he might have been killed ! and there was every appearance that he would be ! ' The answer was, ' Between you and Shelley there is but little similarity, and perhaps but little sympathy : yet what Shelley did then, he would do again, and always. There is not a human creature, even the most hostile, that he would hesitate to protect from injury at the imminent hazard of life. And yet life, which he would throw away so unguardedly, is somewhat more with him than with others : it is full of hopes and aspirations, it is teeming with warm feelings, it is rich and overrun with its own native simple enjoyments. In him every-

[1] 1st ed. reads : " importunity, crush, and pressure," etc.
[2] From " To " to " down " added in 2nd ed.
[3] 1st ed. reads : " assaulted or undermined by such an enemy as the Scot, is deplorable to those only to whom," etc.
[4] So in 1st and 2nd eds. Crump reads : " ungrateful."

thing that ever gave pleasure gives it still, with the same freshness, the same exuberance, the same earnestness to communicate and share it.'

" ' By God ! I cannot understand it ! ' cried Byron. ' A man to run upon a naked sword for another ! '

" LANDOR. He had drawn largely from his imagination, penuriously from his heart. He distrusted it : what wonder then if he had little faith in another's ! Had he lived among the best of the ancient Greeks, he would have satirized and reviled them : but their characters caught his eye softened by time and distance ; nothing in them of opposition, nothing of rivalry ; where they are, there they must stand ; they cannot come down nearer.[1] Of all great poets, for such I consider him, Byron has borrowed most from others, not excepting Ariosto, of whose description he reminds me—

> " Salta a cavallo e per *diversa strada*
> Va discorrendo, e *molti pone a sacco.*

Not only in the dresses which he puts on expressly for the ladies, not only in the oriental train and puffy turban, but also in the tragic pall, his perfumery has somewhat too large a proportion of musk in it ; which so hangs about those who are accustomed to spend many hours with him, that they seldom come forth again with satisfaction into what is fresher and purer. Yet Byron is, I think, the keenest and most imaginative of satirists.

" ENGLISH VISITOR. Those who spoke the most malignantly of him in his life-time have panegyrized him since his death, with so little truth, discretion and precision, that we may suppose it to have been done designedly ; and the rather, as the same insincerity hath been displayed toward others, both where there might be and where there could not be a jealousy of rivalship. After [2] his hot and

---

[1] 1st ed. reads : " nearer us. His hatred of tyranny, his disdain of tyrants, his ambition to excell in liberality the richer and the louder in our houses of parliament, urged him on ; and his name will therefor be redd among the first and most glorious in the tablets of the Parthenon. Two of these, I trust, will be inscribed to Eternity : one containing the defenders and benefactors of Greece ; the other those who became the hirelings of barbarians ; and foremost, the Parisian mamelukes of Napoleon Bonaparte. On reading the names, the friends of liberty will be consoled at its extinction in France ; among a people in which even a dream of it would be inauspicious, and round which, let us hope for the repose of the world, the Bourbon belly will coil daily closer and closer. ENGLISH VISITOR. In regard to Byron, those who spoke the most," etc.

[2] From " After " to " depreciated " added in 2nd ed.

stimulating spicery, we now are running to those sager poets who give us lemonade and ices ; just by the same direction as dogs recur to grass. We rush out of the sudatory of Byron to roll in the snow of Wordsworth.

" LANDOR. He suited the times. The rapid excitement and easy reading of novels, the only literature (if such it may be called) which interests the public, outrun the graver and measured steps of poetry. We have no longer decennial epics and labyrinthine tragedies. Our steeplechases are out of vogue : we canter up and down the narrow green lane with the ladies, and return with an appetite and small fatigue. Byron dealt chiefly in felt and furbelow, wavy Damascus daggers, and pocket-pistols studded with paste. He threw out frequent and brilliant sparks ; but his fire burnt to no purpose ; it blazed furiously when it caught muslin, and it hurried many a pretty wearer into an untimely blanket.

" ENGLISH VISITOR. They who were lately his most zealous admirers now disown him.

" LANDOR. Dress, medicine, poetry, are subject to fashion and variation. The same people have extolled and reviled both Wordsworth and Byron. Public taste must first be vitiated and then consulted. To praise immoderately the poet who before was immoderately depreciated, is [1] the easiest way to knock out a gilt nail-head from the coffin.

" ENGLISH VISITOR. An exploit not very glorious in itself, nor likely in the end to be very satisfactory, not even to the most inquisitive of minute collectors.

" LANDOR. In my opinion," etc.

The following passage is found only in the edition of 1828. In that edition, consequent on " In my opinion . . . despoil the dead," the reading is :

" Let me return to Shelley. Innocent and careless as a boy, he possessed all the delicate feelings of a gentleman, all the discrimination of a scholar, and united, in just degrees, the ardour of the poet with the patience and forbearance of the philosopher. His generosity and charity went far beyond those of any man (I believe) at present in existence. He was never known to speak evil of an enemy, unless that enemy had done some grievous injustice to

[1] 1st ed. reads (after " jealousy of rivalship," p. 126) : " This is the easiest."

another : and he divided his income of only one thousand pounds, with the fallen and the afflicted. This is the man against whom such clamours have been raised by the religious à la mode, and by those who live and lap under their tables : this is the man whom, from one false story about his former wife, I had refused to visit at Pisa. I blush in anguish at my prejudice and injustice, and ought hardly to feel it as a blessing or a consolation, that I regret him less than I should have done if I had known him personally. As to what remains of him now life is over, he occupies the third place among our poets of the present age—no humble station—for no other age since that of Sophocles has produced on the whole earth so many of such merit—and is incomparably the most elegant, graceful, and harmonious of the prose-writers.

" ENGLISH VISITOR. Ferdinand, I have observed in my travels, is the only prince in Italy who encourages the statuary or the painter ; and I was happy to see two rooms in Palazzo Pitti, now under the hands of two Florentine artists, which will rival in their frescos the best compositions of better times.

" FLORENTINE VISITOR. These are splendid works, and worthy of the princes that have succeeded to the Medici. At the same time I cannot but regrett, that so little care is taken, in our city, of labours not less magnificent, and more marvelous. The frescos of Andrea del Sarto, incomparably better than his oil-paintings, are unprotected and injured. Above all, I lament the decay, not from time but negligence, of that glorious last supper by Giotto, in the refectory of Santa Croce. Soil has been accumulated against the wall behind it several feet high. Draperies and attitudes not unworthy of Raphael and Frate Bartolomeo, will disappear shortly, and the restorer of painting in Italy will soon be known only as one of her best architects.

The following variant readings in ' King James I. and Isaac Casaubon,' in vol. iv. of the present edition, are to be noted, in the contexts indicated by footnotes in that volume :

P. 82. 1st ed. has a footnote : " Garnettus vester a Catesbeio consultus, essetne licitum sontes insontesque perdere, si alteri sine

APPENDIX

alteris extingui non possent, semel ita respondit in privatis suis
ædibus : ' Licere, si tantum ex ea re boni proventurum esset,
quantum aliquot insontium necem compensare potest.'—So that
murder may be committed even without advantage ! The Jesuit
requires only a balance of good, and reckons the murder itself as
merely an inoffensive means of obtaining it. ' Iterum in campis
suburbanis, quibus a palude nomen, in hanc sententiam—*et posse
et licere cum sontibus insontes exsufflari, magnique adeo meriti rem
fore, si id magno alicui bono catholicis caderet.*' A few factious
but learned men, deciding that such or such a thing is of great
advantage to catholics, may, not only justly but with glory, blow
up fifty or a hundred of their own *insontes* among two or three
hundred heretics."

P. 83. 1st ed. has a footnote to " indeed anyone may murder
you, let him only be persuaded by two or three factious but learned
men " : " The question was proposed and decided in the affirmative.
It was not an idle or a speculative one, but prepared the minds of
the Roman-catholics, and led the way to the murder of two kings,
Henry III. and Henry IV. of France. The name of the former was
inserted for *illustration.*—An liceat regem legitimum, *puta Henricum
III. Regem Galliarum Christianissimum, postquam a paucis seditiosis
sed doctis cœperit tyrannus appelari,* occidere ? It is lamentable
that the government of Europe should have permitted such questions
to be agitated by the clergy, to whom they least of all belong. It
became to imprison or punish capitally any pope who countenanced
these universal rebels. Let those who inveigh so violently, against
the *Illuminati,* the *Carbonarj,* the *Radicals,* read the following
language of the papal agents. The French regicide, Jacques
Clément, a supremæ auctoritatis judicibus de causâ suspecti parri-
cidii interrogatus, quum more patrio in reorum cellulâ sederet, non
per ambages aut ænigmata sed liquidò et disertè respondit, ideo
se quod fecerat fecisse, quia rex protestantibus Germaniæ princi-
pibus opem ferre parens in causâ Cliviensi Pontifici Maximo *rem
faceret ingratam, ac proinde dignus esset qui periret :* deum enim
se in terris Romanum Pontificem agnoscere, cujus voluntati qui sese
quovis pacto opponeret eum se habere exitio devotum. Ipsissima
feratis illius prodigii verba sunt, *Papa est deus et deus est Papa.*—
Happy that people, whose Gods were leeks ! religion could not

teach them that perfidy and murder were virtues. No treason of a priest against a king is criminal. Father Emanuel Sa, who has written *a guide to confessors*, says, Clerici rebellio in regem non est crimen læsae majestatis, *quia non est principi subjectus*—and again, —Tyrannice gubernans justum acquisitum dominum non potest spoliari sine *publico judicio* : latâ vero sententiâ *potest quisque fieri executor.*—Christ says, ' My kingdom is not of this world ' : the pope says, ' My kingdom is.' Pius V. excited to rebellion all the subjects of Elizabeth : Clement VIII. (it is ludicrous to hear the titles of these ruffians) ordered all the Roman-catholics ' quantum in ipsis esset, ut post Elizabethæ obitum rex *eligeretur*, omni sanguinis propinquitate spretâ ? ' For this purpose it was requisite that the consciences of men should be modified ; and hence arose *mental reservation,* to which all the abominations of all other religions, all even of popery itself, are trifles. Christ says, ' Let your discourse be yea, yea ; nay, nay ' : the Jesuit says, supported by the pope, ' The speech by equivocation being saved from a lie, the same speech may be without perjury confirmed by oath, or by any other way, though it were by receiving the sacrament, if just necessity so require.' Cannot a lie be circuitous ? Whatever is said in order to make a man believe an untruth, is a lie ; yet a Jesuit has no hesitation to swear it upon the sacrament ! and princes have no hesitation to let Jesuits be the instructors of youth ! Falsely, as my quotations prove, have they been called the supporters of thrones : they can never support them, but when they can govern from them, by means of deluded or affrighted princes. The papacy is the guardian of governments as a bawd is the guardian of girls ; for profit. Antonius Capellus, a Franciscan friar, says, ' Indignos esse reges qui ecclesiis suarum ditionum *ullo modo* praesint, quos Deus in Moyse sibi displicere apertè commonstravit.' Eudæmono-Johannes, a monk of Crete, a true Jesuit, extols the son of the Emperor Henry IV. for insulting the dead body of his father, who had been disobedient to the See of Rome. The opinions of these men are not private ; they are sanctioned *facultate superiorum*, by the doctors of theology, and by the chancery of the papal court. The spirit of their church has always been and always will be the same, whenever it can exercise its authority ; arrogant, intolerant, persecuting, unforgiving. Its poison has been sublimated, and its froth and fumes have been condensed, by the Jesuits, as may

APPENDIX

further be seen in Mariana and in Escobar, and in the demonstration of their fallacies by Arnaud and Pascal."

P. 85. 1st ed. reads : " united. The Council of Trent," etc. The passage "According to confessors," etc., is derived with slight change from what was a footnote in 1st ed. Portion of this footnote (" The question was proposed," etc.) was transferred to Casaubon's speech beginning : " If their conscience is not at their own disposal." The Latin (" An liceat regem," etc.) was then rendered into English.

P. 95. 1st ed. reads : " house again : Nicodemus asked," etc. ; and, above, " violence and injustice " for " levity and violence " ; " her affection and fidelity " for " her sweet temper, affection and fidelity." Below, 1st ed. reads : " cartful " for " cartload."

P. 97. In 1st ed. the passage from " Medals " is a footnote, reading : " Medals . . . massacre ! The following words are part," etc. (See footnote on p. 98.) From " His " to " applauded " not in 1st ed.

P. 98. Landor's footnote is in 1st ed. a continuation of his note to " Medals," etc., and reads slightly differently : " The only good " for " Almost the only good " ; " abolition of the Jesuits and of the inquisition " for " abolition of the Jesuits " ; " The catholic religion " for " Catholicism " ; " most ignoble " for " ignoble " ; " I am persuaded " for " we may be persuaded " ; and " world. In landscape . . . Titian were probably not excelled."

Vol. vi. p. 213. 1st ed. reads : " entertain of thyself. Great conversions have been brought about by trifling means. No longer ago than toward the close of Charles's reign, a young courtier of violent temper, a lecher and an infidel, knocked down his valet, for that, in dressing him (it being then the ungodly custom for one creature to dress another), he the valet had inadvertently put the breeches on the master the hinder part before. He might have corrected this, as many worse things have been corrected ; but in his wilfulness he sware a loud oath, that, to shame the fool⁻

(not meaning himself but his valet), he would wear the said breeches in the said position the whole day. Now, whether he had taken any food that, suddenly and abruptly, made this preposterous carriage of them inconvenient, or met any grave person whose reproof smote him sharply, or whether, as was reported, some worse object, affecting him very differently, crossed his path, so it was, that he returned to his lodgings quite discomfited, with many following, not of the household, nor called. He took shame to himself, and something of a fever supervened. Meanwhile the king died; and this death operated on his infirmity: hearing which, two chaplains of James accosted him kindly, and left many books with him, promising him the king's pardon and countenance if he would confess his sins to them. He confessed readily; and a pension was settled on him, which inclined him to frequent the royal chapel, in the hope, as he said, that no doubt whatever remain in his mind upon any doctrinal question. On the late accession of William, he was found in his place at chapel: and perhaps it pleased the Lord to place a Dutchman on the throne, for this reason among many in his inscrutable wisdom, namely, that he might rescue a stray soul, eager for the right path, from the captivity of Babylon.

" PETERBOROUGH. Nothing more likely. It seems an easier matter to turn his soul than his breeches.

" PENN. He hath become a presbyterian; one step nearer the truth. An effect, not indeed so great, but more sudden, and more beneficial to me, who am interested only in the same degree as thou art, by this conversion, was produced in my own family, thro means equally slight and, if there be any such, upon an equally fortuitous occasion. My good father," etc.

P. 263. 1st ed. has a footnote : " Lest I should be thought to have spoken here and in some other places, with too little reflexion and too little experience on our laws, let me add a line of elucidation to this sentence. It was decreed by Lord Ellenborough that I should live two years without rent, from a tenant who held a farm under me at about a thousand pounds yearly. After two years it was decreed by the same authority that every thing I claimed was due to me. My attorney forgot to demand it, but did not forget to bring in a heavy bill against me for forgetting it, which I dis-

APPENDIX

charged. This, on an encumbered and entailed estate, has deprived me of my country for thirteen years, and will deprive me of it for the remainder of my life. It obliged me to borrow three thousand pounds at fifteen per cent. ; to sell my furniture and pictures at a loss of some thousands more ; to suffer my house, recently built by me, to fall into ruin, and nearly a million of trees to be aban doned, to whoever chose to make an inroad for his cattle. An attempt to obtain redress would ruin my family, ' unto the third and fourth generation ': better stop at the second. This is only a part of what I have suffered from the iniquity or insufficiency of our judicature : and never in my life did I appeal to it without having first proposed a reference to private arbitration. Whoever does otherwise, in my opinion, deserves to lose the whole of his fortune."

SUPPRESSED DEDICATIONS

(For reasons stated by him in a letter to Forster, for which see *Wks.*, i. 443,
1876, Landor eventually suppressed the original Dedications of the
several volumes of the *Imaginary Conversations* : " Mina gave orders
to kill a woman ; Bolivar was a coxcomb and impostor," etc. But,
justified or not as compliments, they are 'too characteristic as prose
to be passed over. Those to Sir Robert Wilson and Lord Guilford
will appear among the miscellaneous prose hereafter.)

DEDICATION : VOL. I., 1824

TO

MAJOR-GENERAL STOPFORD,

ADJUTANT-GENERAL IN THE ARMY OF COLUMBIA

SIR,—There may be friends, I feel it, who have never seen each
other. In the moment of losing, and perhaps for many years, one
of my dearest relatives, I rejoice both in her marriage with you and
in the time of it, which presents me the opportunity of adding to
my congratulations the inscription of these dialogues.

There never was a period when public spirit was so feeble in
England, or political abilities so rare. Sordid selfishness and
frivolous amusement, I will not say, are become the characteristics
of our country, but, what is sufficiently calamitous and disgraceful,
place it upon a dead level with others. Rising far above and
passing far away from them, you have aided in establishing one of
those great republics which sprang into existence at the voice of
Bolivar, and enjoy for your exertions in the noblest cause the
highest distinction any mortal can enjoy, his esteem and confidence.

You will find in these Conversations a great variety of subjects
and of style. I have admitted a few little men, such as emperors
and ministers of modern cut, to shew better the just proportions
of the great ; as a painter would place a beggar under a triumphal

arch or a camel against a pyramid. The sentiments most often inculcated are those which in themselves are best ; which, even in times disastrous as our own, produced an Epaminondas, a Pelopidas, and a Phocion ; and in these, when genius lies flat and fruitless as the sea-sand, a Washington, a Kosciusko, and a Bolivar.

That government beyond a question is the most excellent, which has always been most esteemed by the best and wisest men, and which has produced them in the greatest number.

Exult in your glorious undertaking, and be assured that the work, and the satisfaction at completing it, will be durable.— Yours faithfully,   WALTER SAVAGE LANDOR.

FLORENCE, *October*, 1822.

DEDICATION : VOL. II., 1824

TO

GENERAL MINA

SIR,—I inscribe with your illustrious name the second volume of these dialogues, not because, of all the generals who have appeared in our age, you have displayed the greatest genius, the greatest constancy, and, what is equally rare, the greatest contempt of pleasure and titles and wealth and offices, but because your energies have been all exerted, under severe and unremitting adversity, in defence of law and civilization. Neither of these can exist in that country where anyone is above them, and can dictate through any organ, how far they shall go, when they shall speak, on whom they shall act feebly, on whom strongly. All the nations of Europe are in this condition, even those few the forms of whose government bear the image and superscription of Freedom. Turn your eyes upon the only republic (for such it is still called) now left in this quarter of the globe, and where will you find readier slaves to execute the mandates of Despotism ? All conquerors and oppressors have imposed an oligarchy, where it was possible, some under one name, some under another : such was imposed by Sparta on the Athenians, such upon the Swiss, as now upon the Spaniards, by France.

Switzerland, the asylum once of the persecuted, is hence become a mere porter's-lodge to the great prison-house, Europe. Law and Religion are the watch-words ! I am not in a temper for irony, nor could you bear it . . . but what is the reason, to speak gravely, why religion and law are in a worse condition now than they were seventeen centuries ago, while every other part of human knowledge has been so much improved ? It is because the two greatest classes of men, two entire professions, and governments, altogether, such as they are constituted, are interested in maintaining their abuses, and because the sceptre is rather the prop of weakness than the symbol of authority. Hence the cant to keep the child quiet, and the indulgence to let him grasp and beslaver and break in pieces what is not his. . . .

Every state, however small, contains more people than the wisest and most virtuous prince can render happy ; why then want more ? O ! but making them happy is quite another thing : subjects are to give happiness as a tribute, and to receive it as a gratuity. . . . If few subjects bring anxiety, many will bring more : if neither the fewer nor the numerous bring any, then the worth of them can be but small to the proprietor : his want therefor is childish, and should be corrected and coerced like other childish wants.

You Spaniards have committed two great errors : the first, in not removing to Cuba six or seven hundred known and proven traitors, condemning three or four of the most eminent to death ; the second, in not drawing closer the ties of affinity and commerce with Columbia, with a full acknowledgment of her independence. The former of these two duties can alone be questioned. Remove the case out of Spain into Rome, and ask yourself whether, if Lepidus had been crushed while he could be, Rome would not have been saved a hundred thousand of her best citizens at the expense of one among the most worthless. We should calculate for Humanity, and not leave the account in her hands, lest she drop it or lay it down.

The insolence of Despotism will urge her into schemes, if not subversive of her power, injurious to her quiet. The *Holy Allies* should in sound policy desire the establishment of republics in Greece, considering that country as a mere drain, whereby the ill humours of their subjects may be carried off. It should serve them as a galley of deportation, for those whose opinions are dangerous ; just as America is in regard to England : and there is also this

136

additional and paramount advantage, that, if they should publish their sentiments, neither the kings nor their subjects can read them : the former then cannot be offended, nor the latter led astray.

I know not, sir, whether you are a pious man, but if you are, you will see the finger of Providence in the midst of the calamities which distract your country.

Under it there springs forth in letters of fire a warning to the nations, of whatsoever race, language, or rites, throughout the new world, as (from the rapid vegetation, if I may say so, of its prosperity, and from the dissimilarity in every feature to this of ours) it may now indeed be called most emphatically—to form instantly a confederacy against external rule, against all dependence and usurpation, against institutions not founded upon that equable, sound, beneficent system, to which the best energies of Man, the sterner virtues, the milder charities, the comforts and satisfactions of life, its regulated and right affections, the useful arts, the ennobling sciences, with whatever is innocent in glory or exalted in pleasure, owe their origin, their protection, their progress, and their maturity. Columbia, without this invigorating shock, would have longer lain dormant or restless : Washington, to whom we principally are indebted for what little is left of freedom in the universe, would have set before her the bright example, and Bolivar would have followed it, in vain. She will receive into her bosom those whom circumstances armed against her, rather than jealousies or animosities or antipathies ; and she will number among her children, not only those who have stood forward to defend her, but those also who, confiding in her generosity, call upon her in their adversities for defence. Rising on the wreck of Spain, she will invite to her from Europe those whom wars have ruined, those whom commerce has deserted, those whom letters have cast into dungeons, those whom the ancient institutions of their country have blinded with unseasonable love, and the new ones have marked with reprobation. The veteran, still bleeding for the king who banished him, may rest his bones a little while on her fresh turf, forbidden to repose them in death under that which covers his father's.

Your unconquerable mind, sir, cannot be depressed ; mine is, and perhaps ought not to be.—God preserve you many years.

WALTER SAVAGE LANDOR.

FLORENCE, *November*, 1823.

IMAGINARY CONVERSATIONS

DEDICATION : VOL. III., 1828

TO

BOLIVAR

THE LIBERATOR

IF the volume I present to you, O Liberator, be in itself of a perishable nature, not even your name can support it; for dust drops off a golden image as readily as off an earthen one : and if the sentiments I profess are untrue, that illustrious name can but render them the more detestable. So be it !

Deign to accept, sir, I will not say the homage—such words ill suit both you and me—let me rather say the dutiful and pious offering, of one who from youth upward has laboured in the same cause with you, and whom nothing in life or death shall induce or force to desert it. I do not believe that these pages will, now or ever, lie inert on generous minds ; yet little is the effect I can hope from them, in comparison with what has been produced, and is still to be expected, from the iniquity of usurpers. Without it, even your own efforts would have been ineffectual. Freedom rises from tyranny, truth from falsehood, great men from great injuries. The moment is arrived when all despotic governments are ranged against all the constitutional, and (what is worse) when the more powerful of the latter shew an inclination to abandon the rest. Wherever there is any taint of monarchy, the government is disposed toward the despot of another state, rather than toward the people of it, or than toward those, whoever they may be, that resist him. For, the ministers, being the prince's, not the people's, cling to him on whom their authority and their salaries are dependent ; and his sympathies are with his kind. This great evil is avoided by the wiser institutions of America ; which continent will then only be secure, when no portion of it retains the vestiges of a court. Never can there be safety, or indeed peace, in the nations you have redeemed from bondage, while a neighbour is apprehensive of the principles you have laid down, and can hold out ecclesiastical wealth and aulic dignities, to unreflecting avarice and unenlightened ambition. The

138

SUPPRESSED DEDICATIONS

Anglo-Americans will equally see the necessity, that the several states of your continent shall enjoy the same rights and acknowledge the same interests ; and that, in the event of war with an European power, no American port be open to the enemy. Hardly then can we suppose that either you or they will permitt an arbitrary government, under whatever form, to be consolidated in your vicinity. Just reasons are not wanting for its subversion ; and not only what your policy and security, but what its own aggression and usurpation, have supplied. A puny, rickety, peevish despotism has displayed already its fatuous family-lineaments, and has grasped and defaced and dismembered what lies nearest. Such being the fact, no free people will oppose your claims of restitution and indemnity, or deny your right of making war for the indignity and injury done to your allie.

It cannot be imagined that the empire of Brazil will make the person who occupies it happier than the kingdom of Portugal would do ; the country of his birth, of his family, of his education, of his affections. In fact, the possession of power was never, on the whole, the happiness of any one : the entrance into the possession is alone attended by enjoyment. Splendour gratifies pride, novelty gratifies weakness, and dominion all the infirmities of the human mind, where it has nothing else in it but infirmities.

He has had this, such as it is. Let him consider, if he can consider any thing rationally, whether he would not bring more content, to himself, his father, and his country, by returning to Portugal. He might remove from the people of his native land the apprehension of a bigoted and cruel tyrant ; he might render its crown secure ; he might retrieve its embarrassments ; he might annihilate its parties ; he might extend its commerce ; he might (by only giving it a free constitution) draw under his sceptre the whole Peninsula. Gladly would the Brazilians pay millions for perfect independence, which nothing but a republican form of government can ensure to them. Until they possess it, they and the Portuguese, from mutual distrust, will be compelled to maintain such a military and naval force as would be else unnecessary ; and both nations will be invidious and hateful to their neighbours. If the title of Emperor is amusing to the last in the list of emperors, he must enjoy it in common with the sovrans of Muscovy, of Morocco, and of Austria ; in common with that wild and witless adventurer

139

whom the shouts of aggregated nations shook from his sanguinary throne. These men, or their predecessors, have given it to themselves. Is it better to call one's self a wise man, a brave man, a good man, or to be it ? is it better to rule, or to be acknowledged worthy of ruling ? If the latter, if the voices, and hearts of men are anything, should he not rather bend his brow over your footsteps, and, without your labours and anxieties, be *in his way* a liberator ? To obtain the title, he has nothing more to do than to perform again that feat, which he has already performed with much applause ; to step aboard a frigate and traverse the Atlantic. Whatever may be his decision, and the wisest is not the most to be expected, so long as he remains on your continent, he, and his accomplices of all countries, must be watched with an unintermitted vigilance and a lofty jealousy. So long as he remains, I say it plainly, he will double or triple the expenditure of every state in your confederation. He must either then be bought out or driven out : I would recommend the milder scheme, as the more frugal, and in no respect injurious to your mercantile or political relations.

Let something be now effected by wisdom : the good that hath arisen latterly, originated in folly, and was exposed to chance. Napoleon and Ferdinand, the worst princes and worst politicians in Europe, equally void of faith, reflexion, and humanity ; equally false and fickle, equally rapacious and ungrateful, equally cool, complacent, collected, in cruelty, equally rash in prosperity, equally indecisive, blind, locomotionless, torpid, in adversity, were the causes of that liberty which they both abhorred. Massacres, perjuries, parricides, national shame, defeat, subjection, degradation, should be traced and recorded, O Bolivar ! but History has other pages for your attention. Timoleon in ancient days, Washington in later, have left the most glorious name among mortals, by the union of military and civic virtues, and the effect of them on society. What they did, you have done more largely : their difficulties were great, yours were greater : they delivered many, you more : they hazarded their fortunes, you ceded yours : they established freedom, you freedom and civilization : they found men to act with, you created them. Rarely hath it happened that Humanity hath not wept at last over those who best served her : but these lived honoured and beloved among the people they had delivered, and descended to the grave (if by years be the computation) not immaturely.

May Providence assign to you, O Liberator! the same destiny!   WALTER SAVAGE LANDOR.

June 3, 1825.

P.S.—God grant that the accusations brought lately against Bolivar, of injustice, of cruelty, of apostasy, of usurpation, be founded on error, and even on malignity, rather than on truth. For the greatest crimes of many millions are of less importance than a single one in him. I cannot give credit to these evil reports : if however they should be true and unexaggerated still I do not regret, and never shall, that I praised him in his unfallen state, the *Liberator*, the *Protector*. Nothing keeps bad men bad so much as praise ; nothing so much as praise keeps good men good. Whenever I have another motive for mine, let me be exposed as the vilest and most pernicious sycophant ! Our safety as eulogists lies among our commendations of the dead.

July 1, 1827.

THE PENTAMERON

THE PENTAMERON[1]

(*Pentameron and Pentalogia*, 1837 ; *Wks.*, ii., 1846 ; *Wks.*, iii., 1876.)

THE EDITOR'S INTRODUCTION

WANTING a bell for my church at San Vivaldo, and hearing that our holy religion is rapidly gaining ground in England, to the unspeakable comfort and refreshment of the Faithful, I bethought myself that I might peradventure obtain such effectual aid, from the piety and liberality of the converts, as well-nigh to accomplish the purchase of one. Desirous moreover of visiting that famous nation, of whose spiritual prosperity we all entertain such animated hopes, now that the clouds of ignorance begin to break and vanish, I resolved that nothing on my part should be wanting to so blessed a consummation. Therefore, while I am executing my mission in regard to the bell, I omit no opportunity of demonstrating how much happier and peacefuller are we who live in unity, than those who, abandoning the household of Faith, clothe themselves with shreds and warm themselves with shavings.

Subsidiary to the aid I solicit, I brought with me, and here lay before the public, translated by the best hand I could afford to engage, " *Certain Interviews of Messer Francesco Petrarca and Messer Giovanni Boccaccio*, etc.," which, the booksellers tell me, should be entitled " *The Pentameron*," unless I would return with nothing in my pocket. I am ignorant what gave them this idea of my intent, unless it be my deficiency in the language, for certainly I had come to no such resolution. Assurances are made to me by the intelligent and experienced in such merchandise, that the manuscript is honestly worth from twenty-five to thirty francesconi, or

---

[1] 1st ed. reads : " The Pentameron or interviews of Messer Giovanni Boccaccio and Messer Fr. Petrarcha, when said Messer Giovanni lay infirm at his viletta hard by Certaldo : after which they saw not each other on one side of Paradise, shewing how they discoursed upon that famous theologian Messer Dante Alighieri, and sundry other matters. Edited by Pievana D. Grigi.

dollars. To such a pitch hath England risen up again, within these few years, after all the expenditure of her protracted war.

Is there any true Italian, above all is there any worthy native of Certaldo or San Vivaldo, who revolveth not in his mind what a surprise and delight it will be to Giovanni in Paradise, the first time he hears, instead of that cracked and jarring tumbril (which must have grated in his ear most grievously ever since its accident, and have often tried his patience), just such another as he was wont to hear when he rode over to join our townspeople at their *festa?* It will do his heart good, and make him think of old times ; and perhaps he may drop a couple of prayers to the Madonna for whoso had a hand in it.

Lest it should be bruited in England or elsewhere, that being in my seventieth year, I have unadvisedly quitted my parish, "*fond of change*," to use the blessed words of Saint Paul, I am ready to show the certificate of Monsignore, my diocesan, approving of my voyage. Monsignore was pleased to think me capable of undertaking it, telling me that I looked hale, spoke without quavering, and, by the blessing of our lady, had nigh upon half my teeth in their sockets, while, pointing to his own and shaking his head, he repeated the celebrated lines of Horatius Flaccus, who lived in the reign of Augustus, a short time before the Incarnation :—

> Non ebur, sed horridùm
> Buccâ dehiscit [1] in meâ lacuna !

Then, turning the discourse from so melancholy a topic, he was pleased to relate from the inexhaustible stores of his archæological requirements, that no new bell whatever had been consecrated in his diocese of Samminiato since the year of our Lord 1611 : in which year, on the first Sunday of August, a thunderbolt fell into the belfry of the Duomo, by the negligence of Canonico Malatesta, who, according to history, in his hurry to dine with Conte Geronimo Bardi, at our San Vivaldo, omitted a word in the mass. While he was playing at bowls after dinner on that Sunday, or, as some will have it, while he was beating Ser Matteo Filicaia at backgammon, and the younger men and ladies of those two noble families were bird-catching with the *civetta*, it began to thunder : and, within

---

[1] 1st ed. reads : " renidet."

the evening, intelligence of the thunderbolt was brought to the Canonico. On his return the day following it was remarked, says the chronicler, that the people took off their caps at the distance of only two or three paces, instead of fifteen or twenty, and few stopped who met him : for the rumour had already gone abroad of his omission. He often rode, as usual, to Conte Geronimo's, gammoned Ser Matteo, hooded the *civetta*, lined a twig or two, stood behind the spinette, hummed the next note, turned over the pages of the music-book for the *contessine*, beating time on the chair-back, and showing them what he could do now and then on the *viola di gamba*. Only eight years had elapsed when, in the flower of his age (for he had scarcely seen sixty), he was found dead in his bed, after as hearty and convivial a supper as ever Canonico ate. No warning, no *olio santo*, no viaticum, poor man ! Candles he had ; and it was as much as he had, poor sinner ! And this also happened in the month of August ! Monsignore, in his great liberality, laid no heavy stress on the coincidence ; but merely said,

" Well, Pievano ! a mass or two can do him no harm ; let us hope he stands in need of few more ; but when you happen to have leisure, and nobody else to think about, prythee clap a wet clout on the fire there below in behalf of Canonico Malatesta."

I have done it gratis, and I trust he finds the benefit of it. In the same spirit and by the same authority I gird myself for this greater enterprise. Unable to form a satisfactory opinion on the manuscript, I must again refer to my superior. It is the opinion then of Monsignore, that our five dialogues were written down by neither of the interlocutors, but rather by some intimate, who loved them equally. " For," said Monsignore, " it was the practice of Boccaccio to stand up among his personages, and to take part himself in their discourses. Petrarca, who was fonder of sheer dialogue and had much practice in it, never acquired any dexterity in this species of composition, it being all question and answer, short, snappish, quibbling, and uncomfortable. I speak only of his *Remedies of Adversity and Prosperity*, which indeed leave his wisdom all its wholesomeness, but render it somewhat apt to cleave to the roof of the mouth. The better parts of Homer are in dialogue : and downward from him to Galileo the noblest works of human genius have assumed this form : among the rest I am sorry to find no few heretics and scoffers. At the present day the fashion is over : every man pushes every other man behind him, and will let none speak out but himself.

The *Interviews* took place not within the walls of Certaldo, although within the parish, at Boccaccio's villa. It should be notified to the curious, that about this ancient town, small, deserted, dilapidated as it is, there are several towers and turrets yet standing, one of which belongs to the mansion inhabited in its day by Ser Giovanni. His tomb and effigy are in the church. Nobody has opened the grave to throw light upon his relics ; nobody has painted the marble ; nobody has broken off a foot or a finger to do him honour ; not even an English name is engraven on the face ; although the English hold confessedly the highest rank in this department of literature. In Italy, and particularly in Tuscany, the remains of the illustrious are inviolable ; and, among the illustrious, men of genius hold the highest rank. The arts are more potent than curiosity, more authoritative than churchwardens : what Englishman will believe it ? Well ! let it pass, courteous strangers ! ye shall find me in future less addicted to the marvellous. At present I have only to lay before you an ancient and (doubt it not) an authentic account of what passed between my countrymen, Giovanni and Francesco, before they parted for ever. It seemed probable, at this meeting, that Giovanni would have been called away first ; for heavy and of long continuance had been his infirmity : but he outlived it three whole years. He could not outlive his friend so many months, but followed him to the tomb before he had worn the glossiness off the cloak Francesco in his will bequeathed to him.

We struggle with Death while we have friends around to cheer us ; the moment we miss them we lose all heart for the contest. Pardon my reflection ! I ought to have remembered I am not in my stone pulpit, nor at home.

PRETE DOMENICO GRIGI,

Pievano of San Vivaldo.

LONDON, *October* 1, 1836.

FIRST DAY'S INTERVIEW

BOCCACCIO. Who is he that entered, and now steps so silently and softly, yet with a foot so heavy it shakes my curtains?

Frate Biagio! can it possibly be you?

No more physic for me, nor masses neither, at present.

Assunta! Assuntina! who is it?

ASSUNTA.[1] I can not say, Signor Padrone! he puts his finger in the dimple of his chin, and smiles to make me hold my tongue.

BOCCACCIO. Fra Biagio! are you come from Samminiato for this! You need not put your finger there. We want no secrets. The girl knows her duty and does her business. I have slept well, and wake better. *[Raising himself up a little.*

Why? who are you? It makes my eyes ache to look aslant over the sheets; and I can not get to sit quite upright so conveniently; and I must not have the window-shutters opened, they tell me.

PETRARCA. Dear Giovanni! have you then been very unwell?

BOCCACCIO. O that sweet voice! and this fat friendly hand of thine, Francesco!

---

[1] 1st ed. has the following note: " I am inclined to believe it must have been Assunta Nardi, who was probably at this time the only servant of Ser Giovanni; for we find in the register at Certaldo the marriage of Fiamminga Nardi, daughter of Simplizio Nardi and of Assunta his wife; and, on her tombstone that ' she was erewhile nurse and governess in the house of Ser Giovanni Boccaccio of this Parish.' What her name was before marriage is uncertain. She left behind several sons and daughters: one son, the second, was a plumber; and our account-book informs us that on the 14th of March, 1388, six *lire* and three *soldi* were disbursed to him ' for an entirely new tongue, and red pigments thereunto applied, in the dragon at the market-place; likewise for iron bars; likewise for solder round the perforation for keeping the saint (viz. George) upon his horse.' His daughter Lisa married Agapeto Camarelli of Colli; which Agapeto rose to be sacristan in that burg; and his great nephew Claudio Neri was sub-librarian in the library of the Duomo at Samminiato. His son-in-law, Simone Mazzuoli, became a most distinguished carpenter, and erected the canopy, still extant, over the episcopal throne in said Duomo. His descendant, in the third degree, was nothing less than page to the Cardinal Uberto degli Albizzi. We may augur from the prosperity of Assunta's descendants, that her life was discreet and irreproachable.—D. G."

THE PENTAMERON

Thou hast distilled all the pleasantest flowers, and all the whole-
somest herbs of spring, into my breast already.

What showers we have had this April, ay! How could you
come along such roads? If the devil were my labourer, I would
make him work upon these of Certaldo. He would have little
time and little itch for mischief ere he had finished them, but
would gladly fan himself with an Agnus-castus, and go to sleep all
through the carnival.

PETRARCA. Let us cease to talk both of the labour and the
labourer. You have then been dangerously ill?

BOCCACCIO. I do not know: they told me I was: and truly a
man might be unwell enough, who has twenty masses said for him,
and fain sigh when he thinks what he has paid for them. As I
hope to be saved, they cost me a *lira* each. Assunta is a good
market-girl in eggs, and mutton, and cow-heel; but I would not
allow her to argue and haggle about the masses. Indeed she knows
best whether they were not fairly worth all that was asked for them,
although I could have bought a winter cloak for less money. However, we do not want both at the same time. I did not want the
cloak: I wanted *them* it seems. And yet I begin to think God
would have had mercy on me, if I had begged it of him myself in
my own house. What think you?

PETRARCA. I think he might.

BOCCACCIO. Particularly if I offered him the sacrifice on which
I wrote to you.

PETRARCA. That letter has brought me hither.

BOCCACCIO. You do then insist on my fulfilling my promise, the
moment I can leave my bed. I am ready and willing.

PETRARCA. Promise! none was made. You only told me that,
if it pleased God to restore you to your health again, you are ready
to acknowledge his mercy by the holocaust of your *Decameron*.
What proof have you that God would exact it? If you could
destroy the *Inferno* of Dante, would you?

BOCCACCIO. Not I, upon my life! I would not promise to burn
a copy of it on the condition of a recovery for twenty years.

PETRARCA. You are the only author who would not rather
demolish another's work than his own; especially if he thought it
better: a thought which seldom goes beyond suspicion.

BOCCACCIO. I am not jealous of anyone: I think admiration

150

pleasanter. Moreover, Dante and I did not come forward at the same time, nor take the same walks. His flames are too fierce for you and me : we had trouble enough with milder. I never felt any high gratification in hearing of people being damned ; and much less would I toss them into the fire myself. I might indeed have put a nettle under the nose of the learned judge in Florence, when he banished you and your family ; but I hardly think I could have voted for more than a scourging to the foulest and fiercest of the party.

PETRARCA. Be as compassionate, be as amiably irresolute, toward your own *Novelle*, which have injured no friend of yours, and deserve more affection.

BOCCACCIO. Francesco ! no character I ever knew, ever heard of, or ever feigned, deserves the same affection as you do ; the tenderest lover, the truest friend, the firmest patriot, and, rarest of glories ! the poet who cherishes another's fame as dearly as his own.

PETRARCA. If aught of this is true, let it be recorded of me that my exhortations and intreaties have been successful, in preserving the works of the most imaginative and creative genius that our Italy, or indeed our world, hath in any age beheld.

BOCCACCIO. I would not destroy his poems, as I told you, or think I told you. Even the worst of the Florentines, who in general keep only one of God's commandments, keep it rigidly in regard to Dante—

Love them who curse you.

He called them all scoundrels, with somewhat less courtesy than cordiality, and less afraid of censure for veracity than adulation : he sent their fathers to hell, with no inclination to separate the child and parent : and now they are hugging him for it in his shroud ! Would you ever have suspected them of being such lovers of justice ?

You must have mistaken my meaning ; the thought never entered my head : the idea of destroying a single copy of Dante ! And what effect would that produce ! There must be fifty, or near it, in various parts of Italy.

PETRARCA. I spoke of you.

BOCCACCIO. Of me ! My poetry is vile ; I have already thrown into the fire all of it within my reach.

PETRARCA. Poetry was not the question. We neither of us are

such poets as we thought ourselves when we were younger, and as younger men think us still. I meant your *Decameron*; in which there is more character, more nature, more invention, than either modern or ancient Italy, or than Greece, from whom she derived her whole inheritance, ever claimed or ever knew. Would you consume a beautiful meadow because there are reptiles in it; or because a few grubs hereafter may be generated by the succulence of the grass?

BOCCACCIO. You amaze me : you utterly confound me.

PETRARCA. If you would eradicate twelve or thirteen of the *Novelle*, and insert the same number of better, which you could easily do within as many weeks, I should be heartily glad to see it done. Little more than a tenth of the *Decameron* is bad : less than a twentieth of the *Divina Commedia* is good.

BOCCACCIO. So little ?

PETRARCA. Let me never seem irreverent to our master.

BOCCACCIO. Speak plainly and fearlessly, Francesco ! Malice and detraction are strangers to you.

PETRARCA. Well then : at least sixteen parts in twenty of the *Inferno* and *Purgatorio* are detestable, both in poetry and principle : the higher parts are excellent indeed.

BOCCACCIO. I have been reading the *Paradiso* more recently. Here it is, under the pillow. It brings me happier dreams than the others, and takes no more time in bringing them. Preparation for my lectures made me remember a great deal of the poem. I did not request my auditors to admire the beauty of the metrical version :

> Osanna sanctus deus Sabbaoth,
> Super-illustrans charitate tuâ
> Felices ignes horum Malahoth,[1]

nor these, with a slip of Italian between two pales of Latin :

> Modicum,* et non videbitis me,
> Et iterum, sorelle mie dilette,
> Modicum, et vos videbitis me.[2]

---

[1] *Paradiso*, vii. 1.

* It may puzzle an Englishman to read the lines beginning with *Modicum*, so as to give the metre. The secret is, to draw out *et* into a dissyllable, et-te, as the Italians do, who pronounce Latin verse, if possible, worse than we, adding a syllable to such as end with a consonant.—W. S. L.

[2] *Purgatorio*, xxxiii. 10. For all these references I am indebted to Mr. Stephen Wheeler.

THE PENTAMERON

I dare not repeat all I recollect of

Pape Setan, Pape Setan, aleppe,[1]

as there is no holy-water-sprinkler in the room : and you are aware
that other dangers awaited me, had I been so imprudent as to show
the Florentines the allusion of our poet. His *gergo* is perpetually
in play, and sometimes plays very roughly.

PETRARCA. We will talk again of him presently. I must now
rejoice with you over the recovery and safety of your prodigal son,
the *Decameron*.

BOCCACCIO. So then, you would preserve at any rate my favourite
volume from the threatened conflagration.

PETRARCA. Had I lived at the time of Dante, I would have
given him the same advice in the same circumstances. Yet how
different is the tendency of the two productions ! Yours is somewhat too licentious ; and young men, in whose nature, or rather
in whose education and habits, there is usually this failing, will
read you with more pleasure than is commendable or innocent.
Yet the very time they occupy with you, would perhaps be spent
in the midst of those excesses or irregularities, to which the moralist,
in his utmost severity, will argue that your pen directs them. Now
there are many who are fond of standing on the brink of precipices,
and who nevertheless are as cautious as any of falling in. And
there are minds desirous of being warmed by description, which
without this warmth, might seek excitement among the things
described.

I would not tell you in health what I tell you in convalescence,
nor urge you to compose what I dissuade you from cancelling.
After this avowal, I do declare to you, Giovanni, that in my opinion,
the very idlest of your tales will do the world as much good as evil ;
not reckoning the pleasure of reading, nor the exercise and recreation of the mind, which in themselves are good. What I reprove
you for, is the indecorous and uncleanly ; and these, I trust, you
will abolish. Even these, however, may repel from vice the ingenuous and graceful spirit, and can never lead any such toward
them. Never have you taken an inhuman pleasure in blunting
and fusing the affections at the furnace of the passions ; never,
in hardening by sour sagacity and ungenial strictures, that delicacy

[1] *Inferno*, vii. 7.

153

which is more productive of innocence and happiness, more estranged
from every track and tendency of their opposites, than what in
cold, crude systems hath holden the place and dignity of the highest
virtue.   May you live, O my friend, in the enjoyment of health,
to substitute the facetious for the licentious, the simple for the
extravagant, the true and characteristic for the indefinite and
diffuse.

BOCCACCIO. I dare not defend myself under the bad example of
any : and the bad example of a great man is the worst defence of
all.   Since, however, you have mentioned Messer Dante Alighieri,
to whose genius I never thought of approaching, I may perhaps
have been formerly the less cautious of offending by my levity,
after seeing him display as much or more of it in hell itself.

PETRARCA. The best apology for Dante, in his poetical character,
is presented by the indulgence of criticism, in considering the
Inferno and *Purgatorio* as a string of *Satires*, part in narrative and
part in action ; which renders the title of *Commedia* more applicable.
The filthiness of some passages would disgrace the drunkenest
horse-dealer ; and the names of such criminals are recorded by the
poet as would be forgotten by the hangman in six months.   I wish
I could expatiate rather on his injudiciousness than on his ferocity,
in devising punishments for various crimes ; or rather, than on his
malignity in composing catalogues of criminals to inflict them on.
Among the rest we find a gang of coiners.   He calls by name all
the rogues and vagabonds of every city in Tuscany, and curses
every city for not sending him more of them.   You would fancy
that Pisa might have contented him ; no such thing.   He hoots,

" Ah Pisa !   scandal to the people in whose fine country *si*
means *yes*, why are thy neighbours slack to punish thee ?   May
Capraia and Gorgona stop up the mouth of the Arno, and drown
every soul within thee ! " [1]

BOCCACCIO. None but a prophet is privileged to swear and curse
at this rate, and several of those got broken heads for it.

PETRARCA. It did not happen to Dante, though he once was
very near it, in the expedition of the exiles to recover the city.
Scarcely had he taken breath after this imprecation against the
Pisans, than he asks the Genoese why such a parcel of knaves as
themselves were not scattered over the face of the earth.

[1] *Inferno*, xxxiii. 79.

154

THE PENTAMERON

BOCCACCIO. Here he is equitable. I wonder he did not incline to one or other of these rival republics.

PETRARCA. In fact, the Genoese fare a trifle better under him than his neighbours the Pisans do.

BOCCACCIO. Because they have no Gorgona and Capraia to block them up. He can not do all he wishes, but he does all he can, considering the means at his disposal. In like manner Messer Gregorio Peruzzi, when he was tormented by the quarrels and conflicts of Messer Gino Ubaldini's trufle-dog at the next door, and Messer Guidone Fantecchi's shop-dog, whose title and quality are in abeyance, swore bitterly, and called the Virgin and St. Catherine to witness that he would cut off their tails if ever he caught them. His cook, Niccolo Buonaccorsi, hoping to gratify his master, set baits for them, and captured them both in the kitchen. But unwilling to cast hands prematurely on the delinquents, he, after rating them for their animosities and their ravages, bethought himself in what manner he might best conduct his enterprise to a successful issue. He was the rather inclined to due deliberation in these counsels, as they, laying aside their private causes of contention in front of their common enemy, and turning the principal stream of their ill-blood into another channel, agreed in demonstrations which augured no little indocility. Messer Gregorio hath many servants, and moreover all the conveniences which so plenteous a house requires. Among the rest is a long hempen cloth suspended by a roller. Niccolo, in the most favourable juncture, was minded to slip this hempen cloth over the two culprits, whose consciences had made them slink toward the door against which it was fastened. The smell of it was not unsatisfactory to them, and an influx of courage had nearly borne away the worst suspicions. At this instant, while shrewd inquisitiveness and incipient hunger were regaining the ascendancy, Niccolo Buonaccorsi, with all the sagacity and courage, all the promptitude and timeliness of his profession, covered both conspirators in the inextricable folds of the fatal winding-sheet, from which their heads alone emerged. Struggles, and barkings, and exhibitions of teeth, and plunges forward, were equally ineffectual. He continued to twist it about them, until the notes of resentment partook of remonstrance and pain : but he told them plainly he would never remit a jot, unless they became more domesticated and reasonable.

In this state of exhaustion and contrition he brought them into the presence of Ser Gregorio, who immediately turned round toward the wall, crossed himself, and whispered an *ave*. At ease and happy as he was at the accomplishment of a desire so long cherished, no sooner had he expressed his piety at so gracious a dispensation, than, reverting to the captor and the captured, he was seized with unspeakable consternation. He discovered at once that he had made as rash a vow as Jeptha's. Alas! one of the children of captivity, the trufle-dog, had no tail! Fortunately for Messer Gregorio, he found a friend among the White Friars, Frate Geppone Pallorco, who told him that when we can not do a thing promised by vow, whether we fail by moral inability or by physical, we must do the thing nearest it ; " which," said Fra Geppone, " hath always been my practice. And now," added this cool, considerate white friar, " a dog may have no tail, and yet be a dog to all intents and purposes, and enable a good Christian to perform anything reasonable he promised in his behalf. Whereupon I would advise you, Messer Gregorio, out of the loving zeal I bear toward the whole family of the Peruzzi, to amerce him of that which, if not tail, is next to tail. Such function, I doubt not, will satisfactorily show the blessed Virgin, and Saint Catherine, your readiness and solicitude to perform the vow solemnly made before these two adorable ladies, your protectresses and witnesses." Ser Gregorio bent his knee at first hearing their names, again at the mention of them in this relationship toward him, called for the kitchen knife, and, in absolving his promise, had lighter things to deal with than Gorgona and Capraia.

PETRARCA. Giovanni! this will do instead of one among the worst of the hundred : but with little expenditure of labour you may afford us a better.

Our great fellow-citizen, if indeed we may denominate him a citizen who would have left no city standing in Italy, and less willingly his native one, places in the mouth of the devil, together with Judas Iscariot, the defenders of their country, and the best men in it, Brutus and Cassius.[1] Certainly his feeling of patriotism was different from theirs.

I should be sorry to imagine that it subjected him to any harder mouth or worse company than his own, although in a spirit so

[1] *Inferno*, xxxiv. 65.

contrary to that of the two Romans, he threatened us Florentines with the sword of Germans. The two Romans, now in the mouth of the devil, chose rather to lose their lives than to see their country, not under the government of invaders, but of magistrates from their own city placed irregularly over them ; and the laws, not subverted, but administered unconstitutionally. That Frenchmen and Austrians should argue and think in this manner, is no wonder, no inconsistency : that a Florentine, the wisest and greatest of Florentines, should have done it, is portentous.

How merciful is the Almighty, O Giovanni ! What an argument is here ! how much stronger and more convincing than philosophers could devise or than poets could utter, unless from inspiration, against the placing of power in the hands of one man only, when the highest genius at that time in the world, or perhaps at any time, betrays a disposition to employ it with such a licentiousness of inhumanity.

BOCCACCIO. He treats Nero with greater civility : yet Brutus and Cassius, at worst, but slew an atheist, while the other rogue flamed forth like the pestilential dog-star, and burnt up the first crop of Christians to light the ruins of Rome. And the artist of these ruins thought no more of his operation than a scene-painter would have done at the theatre.

PETRARCA. Historians have related that Rome was consumed by Nero for the purpose of suppressing the rising sect, by laying all the blame on it. Do you think he cared what sect fell or what sect rose ? Was he a zealot in religion of any kind ? I am sorry to see a lying spirit the most prevalent one, in some among the earliest and firmest holders of that religion which is founded on truth and singleness of intention. There are pious men who believe they are rendering a service to God by bearing false witness in his favour, and who call on the father of lies to hold up his light before the Sun of Righteousness.

We may mistake the exact day when the conflagration began : certain it is, however, that it was in summer : * and it is presumable that the commencement of the persecution was in winter, since Juvenal represents the persecuted as serving for lamps in the streets. Now, as the Romans did not frequent the theatres, nor other places

* Des Vignolles has calculated that the conflagration began on the 19th of July, in the year 64, and the persecution on the 15th of November.—W. S. L.

of public entertainment, by night, such conveniences were uncalled
for in summer, a season when the people retired to rest betimes,
from the same motive as at present, the insalubrity of the evening
air in the hot weather. Nero must have been very forbearing if
he waited those many months before he punished a gang of incendiaries. Such clemency is unexampled in milder princes.

BOCCACCIO. But the Christians were not incendiaries, and he
knew they were not.

PETRARCA. It may be apprehended that, among the many
virtuous of the new believers, a few seditious were also to be found,
forming separate and secret associations, choosing generals or
superiors to whom they swore implicit obedience, and under whose
guidance or impulse they were ready to resist, and occasionally to
attack, the magistrates, and even the prince ; men aspiring to rule
the state by carrying the sword of assassination under the garb
of holiness. Such persons are equally odious to the unenlightened
and the enlightened, to the arbitrary and the free. In the regular
course of justice, their crimes would have been resisted by almost
as much severity, as they appear to have undergone from despotic
power and popular indignation.

BOCCACCIO. We will talk no longer about these people. But
since the devil has really and *bonâ fide* Brutus and Cassius in his
mouth, I would advise him to make the most of them, for he will
never find two more such morsels on the same platter. Kings,
emperors and popes would be happy to partake with him of so
delicate and choice a repast : but I hope he has fitter fare for
them.

Messer Dante Alighieri does not indeed make the most gentle
use of the company he has about him in hell and purgatory. Since,
however, he hath such a selection of them, I wish he could have
been contented, and could have left our fair Florentines to their
own fancies in their dressing-rooms.

" The time," he cries, " is not far distant, when there will be
an indictment on parchment, forbidding the impudent young
Florentines to show their breasts and nipples." [1]

Now, Francesco, I have been subject all my life to a strange
distemper in the eyes, which no oculist can cure, and which, while
it allows me to peruse the smallest character in the very worst

---

[1] *Purgatorio*, xxiii. 98.

female hand, would never let me read an indictment on parchment where female names are implicated, although the letters were a finger in length. I do believe the same distemper was very prevalent in the time of Messer Dante ; and those Florentine maids and matrons who were not afflicted by it, were too modest to look at letters and signatures stuck against the walls.

He goes on, " Was there ever girl among the Moors or Saracens, on whom it was requisite to inflict spiritual or *other* discipline to make her go covered ? "

Some of the *other* discipline, which the spiritual guides were, and are still, in the habit of administering, have [1] exactly the contrary effect to make them go covered, whatsoever may be urged by the confessor.

" If the shameless creatures," he continued, " were aware of the speedy chastisement which Heaven is preparing for them, they would at this instant have their mouths wide open to roar withal."

PETRARCA. This is not very exquisite satire, nor much better manners.

BOCCACCIO. Whenever I saw a pretty Florentine in such a condition, I lowered my eyes.

PETRARCA. I am glad to hear it.

BOCCACCIO. Those whom I could venture to cover, I covered with all my heart.

PETRARCA. Humanely done. You might likewise have added some gentle admonition.

BOCCACCIO. They would have taken anything at my hands rather than that. Truly they thought themselves as wise as they thought me : and who knows but they were, at bottom ?

PETRARCA. I believe it may, in general, be best to leave them as we find them.

BOCCACCIO. I would not say that, neither. Much may be in vain, but something sticks.

PETRARCA. They are more amused than nettled [2] by anything we can advance against them, and are apt to make light of the gravest. It is only the hour of reflection that is at last the hour of sedateness and improvement.

BOCCACCIO. Where is the bell that strikes it ?

[1] Thus in 1st ed.
[2] 1st and all subsequent eds., including Crump's, read : " settled."

THE PENTAMERON

PETRARCA. Fie! fie! Giovanni! This is worse than the indictment on parchment.

BOCCACCIO. Women like us none the less for joking with them about their foibles. In fact, they take it ill when we cease to do so, unless it is age that compels us. We may give our courser the rein to any extent, while he runs in the common field and does not paw against privacy, nor open his nostrils on individuality. I mean the individuality of the person we converse with, for another's is pure zest.

PETRARCA. Surely you can not draw this hideous picture from your own observation ; has any graver man noted it ?

BOCCACCIO. Who would believe your graver men upon such matters ? Gout and gravel, bile and sciatica, are the upholsterers that stuff their moral sentences. Crooked and cramp are truths written with chalkstones. When people like me talk as I have been talking, they may be credited. We have no ill-will, no ill-humour, to gratify ; and vanity has no trial here at issue. He was certainly born on an unlucky day for his friends, who never uttered any truths but unquestionable ones. Give me food that exercises my teeth and tongue, and ideas that exercise my imagination and discernment.

PETRARCA. When you are at leisure, and in perfect health, weed out carefully the few places of your *Decameron* which are deficient in these qualities.

BOCCACCIO. God willing ; I wish I had undertaken it when my heart was lighter. Is there anything else you can suggest for its improvement, in particular or in general ?

PETRARCA. Already we have mentioned the inconsiderate and indecorous. In what you may substitute hereafter, I would say to you, as I have said to myself, do not be on all occasions too ceremonious in the structure of your sentences.

BOCCACCIO. You would surely wish me to be round and polished. Why do you smile ?

PETRARCA. I am afraid these qualities are often of as little advantage in composition as they are corporeally. When action and strength are chiefly the requisites, we may perhaps be better with little of them. The modulations of voice and language are infinite. Cicero has practised many of them ; but Cicero has his favourite swells, his favourite flourishes and cadences. Our Italian language is in the enjoyment of an ampler scope and compass ; and we are liberated from the horrible sounds of *us, am, um, ant, int, unt,* so predominant in the finals of Latin nouns and verbs. We may be told that they give strength to the dialect : we might as well be told that bristles give strength to the boar. In our Italian we possess the privilege of striking off the final vowel from the greater part of masculine nouns, and from the greater part of tenses in the verbs, when we believe they impede our activity and vigour.

Boccaccio. We are as wealthy in words as is good for us ; and she who gave us these, would give us more if needful. In another age it is probable that curtailments will rather be made than additions ; for it was so with the Latin and Greek. Barbaric luxury sinks down into civic neatness, and chaster ornaments fill rooms of smaller dimensions.

Petrarca. Cicero came into possession of the stores collected by Plautus, which he always held very justly in the highest estimation ; and Sallust is reported to have misapplied a part of them. At his death they were scattered and lost.

Boccaccio. I am wiser than I was when I studied the noble orator, and wiser by his means chiefly. In return for his benefits, if we could speak on equal terms together, the novelist with the philosopher, the citizen of Certaldo with the Roman consul, I would fain whisper in his ear, " Escape from rhetoric by all manner of means : and if you must cleave (as indeed you must) to that old shrew, Logic, be no fonder of exhibiting her than you would be of a plain, economical wife. Let her be always busy, never intrusive ; and readier to keep the chambers clean and orderly than to expatiate on their proportions or to display their furniture."

Petrarca. The citizen of Certaldo is fifty-fold more richly endowed with genius than the Roman consul, and might properly——

Boccaccio. Stay ! stay ! Francesco ! or they will shave all the rest of thy crown for thee, and physic thee worse than me.

Petrarca. Middling men, favoured in their lifetime by circumstances, often appear of higher stature than belongs to them ; great men always of lower. Time, the sovran, invests with befitting raiment and distinguishes with proper ensigns the familiars he has received into his eternal habitations : in these alone are they deposited : you must wait for them.

No advice is less necessary to you, than the advice to express your meaning as clearly as you can. Where the purpose of glass is to be seen through, we do not want it tinted nor wavy. In certain kinds of poetry the case may be slightly different; such, for instance, as are intended to display the powers of association and combination in the writer, and to invite and exercise the compass and comprehension of the intelligent. Pindar and the Attic tragedians wrote in this manner, and rendered the minds of their audience more alert and ready and capacious. They found some fit for them, and made others. Great painters have always the same task to perform. What is excellent in their art can not be thought excellent by many, even of those who reason well on ordinary matters, and see clearly beauties elsewhere. All correct perceptions are the effect of careful practice. We little doubt that a mirror would direct us in the most familiar of our features, and that our hand would follow its guidance, until we try to cut a lock of our hair. We have no such criterion to demonstrate our liability to error in judging of poetry; a quality so rare that perhaps no five contemporaries ever were masters of it.

BOCCACCIO. We admire by tradition; we censure by caprice; and there is nothing in which we are more ingenious and inventive. A wrong step in politics sprains a foot in poetry; eloquence is never so unwelcome as when it issues from a familiar voice; and praise hath no echo but from a certain distance. Our critics, who know little about them, would gaze with wonder at anything similar, in our days, to Pindar and Sophocles, and would cast it aside, as quite impracticable. They are in the right: for sonnet and canzonet charm greater numbers. There are others, or may be hereafter, to whom far other things will afford far higher gratification.

PETRARCA. But our business at present is with prose and Cicero; and our question now is, what is Ciceronian? He changed his style according to his matter and his hearers. His speeches to the people vary from his speeches to the senate. Toward the one he was impetuous and exacting; toward the other he was usually but earnest and anxious, and sometimes but submissive and imploring, yet equally unwilling, on both occasions, to conceal the labour he had taken to captivate their attention and obtain success. At the tribunal of Cæsar, the dictator, he laid aside his costly armour, contracted the folds of his capacious robe, and became calm, insinuating, and adulative, showing his spirit not utterly extinguished, his dignity not utterly fallen, his consular year not utterly abolished from his memory, but Rome, and even himself, lowered in the presence of his judge.

BOCCACCIO. And after all this, can you bear to think what I am ?

PETRARCA. Complacently and joyfully ; venturing, nevertheless, to offer you a friend's advice.

Enter into the mind and heart of your own creatures : think of them long, entirely, solely : never of style, never of self, never of critics, cracked or sound. Like the miles of an open country, and of an ignorant population, when they are correctly measured they become smaller. In the loftiest rooms and richest entablatures are suspended the most spider-webs ; and the quarry out of which palaces are erected is the nursery of nettle and bramble.

BOCCACCIO. It is better to keep always in view such writers as Cicero, than to run after those idlers who throw stones that can never reach us.

PETRARCA. If you copied him to perfection, and on no occasion lost sight of him, you would be an indifferent, not to say a bad writer.

BOCCACCIO. I begin to think you are in the right. Well then, retrenching some of my licentious tales, I must endeavour to fill up the vacancy with some serious and some pathetic.

PETRARCA. I am heartily glad to hear of this decision ; for, admirable as you are in the jocose, you descend from your natural position when you come to the convivial and the festive. You were placed among the Affections, to move and master them, and gifted with the rod that sweetens the fount of tears. My nature leads me also to the pathetic ; in which, however, an imbecile writer may obtain celebrity. Even the hard-hearted are fond of such reading, when they are fond of any ; and nothing is easier in the world than to find and accumulate its sufferings. Yet this very profusion and luxuriance of misery is the reason why few have excelled in describing it. The eye wanders over the mass without noticing the peculiarities. To mark them distinctly is the work of genius ; a work so rarely performed, that, if time and space may be compared, specimens of it stand at wider distances than the trophies of Sesostris. Here we return again to the *Inferno* of Dante, who overcame the difficulty. In this vast desert are its greater and its less oasis ; Ugolino and Francesca di Rimini. The peopled region is peopled chiefly with monsters and moschitoes : the rest for the most part is sand and suffocation.

BOCCACCIO. Ah ! had Dante remained through life the pure solitary lover of Bice, his soul had been gentler, tranquiller, and more generous. He scarcely hath described half the curses he went through, nor the roads he took on the journey : theology, politics, and that barbican of the *Inferno*, marriage, surrounded with its

> Selva selvaggia ed aspra e forte.[1]

Admirable is indeed the description of Ugolino, to whoever can endure the sight of an old soldier gnawing at the scalp of an old archbishop.

PETRARCA. The thirty lines from

> Ed io sentj,[2]

are unequalled by any other continuous thirty in the whole dominions of poetry.

BOCCACCIO. Give me rather the six on Francesca : for if in the former I find the simple, vigorous, clear narration, I find also what I would not wish, the features of Ugolino reflected full in Dante. The two characters are similar in themselves ; hard, cruel, inflexible, malignant, but, whenever moved, moved powerfully. In Francesca, with the faculty of divine spirits, he leaves his own nature (not indeed the exact representative of theirs) and converts all his strength into tenderness. The great poet, like the original man of the Platonists, is double, possessing the further advantage of being able to drop one half at his option, and to resume it. Some of the tenderest on paper have no sympathies beyond ; and some of the austerest in their intercourse with their fellow-creatures, have deluged the world with tears. It is not from the rose that the bee gathers her honey, but often from the most acrid and the most bitter leaves and petals.

> Quando legemmo il disiato riso
>> Esser baciato da cotanto amante,
> Questi, che mai da me non fia diviso !
>> La bocca mi baciò tutto tremante :
> *Galeotto* fù il libro, e chi lo scrisse :
>> Quel giorno più non vi leggemmo avante.[3]

---

[1] *Inferno*, i. 5. [2] *Inferno*, xxxiii. 46. [3] *Inferno*, v. 133 ; corrected.

THE PENTAMERON

In the midst of her punishment, Francesca, when she comes to the tenderest part of her story, tells it with complacency and delight; and, instead of naming Paolo, which indeed she never has done from the beginning, she now designates him as

Questi che mai da me non fia diviso![1]

Are we not impelled to join in her prayer, wishing them happier in their union?

PETRARCA. If there be no sin in it.

BOCCACCIO. Ay, and even if there be—God help us!

What a sweet aspiration in each cesura of the verse! three love-sighs fixed and incorporate! Then, when she hath said

La bocca mi baciò, tutto tremante,

she stops: she would avert the eyes of Dante from her: he looks for the sequel: she thinks he looks severely: she says,

" *Galeotto* is the name of the book,"

fancying by this timorous little flight she has drawn him far enough from the nest of her young loves. No, the eagle beak of Dante and his piercing eyes are yet over her.

" *Galeotto* is the name of the book."

" What matters that? "

" And of the writer."

" Or that either? "

At last she disarms him: but how?

" *That* day we read no more."

Such a depth of intuitive judgment, such a delicacy of perception, exists not in any other work of human genius; and from an author who, on almost all occasions, in this part of the work, betrays a deplorable want of it.

PETRARCA. Perfection of poetry! The greater is my wonder at discovering nothing else of the same order or cast in this whole section of the poem. He who fainted at the recital of Francesca,

And he who fell as a dead body falls,[2]

would exterminate all the inhabitants of every town in Italy! What execrations against Florence, Pistoia, Siena, Pisa, Genoa!

[1] *Inferno*, v. 135.   [2] *Inferno*, v. 142.

what hatred against the whole human race ! what exultation and merriment at eternal and immitigable sufferings ! Seeing this, I can not but consider the *Inferno* as the most immoral and impious book that ever was written. Yet, hopeless that our country shall ever see again such poetry, and certain that without it our future poets would be more feebly urged forward to excellence, I would have dissuaded Dante from cancelling it, if this had been his intention. Much however as I admire his vigour and severity of style in the description of Ugolino, I acknowledge with you that I do not discover so much imagination, so much creative power, as in the Francesca. I find indeed a minute detail of probable events : but this is not all I want in a poet : it is not even all I want most in a scene of horror. Tribunals of justice, dens of murderers, wards of hospitals, schools of anatomy, will afford us nearly the same sensations, if we hear them from an accurate observer, a clear reporter, a skilful surgeon, or an attentive nurse. There is nothing of sublimity in the horrific of Dante, which there always is in Æschylus and Homer. If you, Giovanni, had described so nakedly the reception of Guiscardo's heart by Gismonda, or Lorenzo's head by Lisabetta, we could hardly have endured it.

BOCCACCIO. Prythee, dear Francesco, do not place me over Dante : I stagger at the idea of approaching him.

PETRARCA. Never think I am placing you blindly or indiscriminately. I have faults to find with you, and even here. Lisabetta should by no means have been represented cutting off the head of her lover, " *as well as she could* " with a clasp-knife. This is shocking and improbable. She might have found it already cut off by her brothers, in order to bury the corpse more commodiously and expeditiously. Nor indeed is it likely that she should have intrusted it to her waiting-maid, who carried home in her bosom a treasure so dear to her, and found so unexpectedly and so lately.

BOCCACCIO. That is true : I will correct the oversight. Why do we never hear of our faults until everybody knows them, and until they stand in record against us ?

PETRARCA. Because our ears are closed to truth and friendship for some time after the triumphal course of composition. We are too sensitive for the gentlest touch ; and when we really have the most infirmity, we are angry to be told that we have any.

BOCCACCIO. Ah Francesco ! thou art poet from scalp to heel :

but what other would open his breast as thou hast done ! They
show ostentatiously far worse weaknesses ; but the most honest of
the tribe would forswear himself on this. Again, I acknowledge it,
you have reason to complain of Lisabetta and Gismonda.

PETRARCA. They keep the soul from sinking in such dreadful
circumstances by the buoyancy of imagination. The sunshine of
poetry makes the colour of blood less horrible, and draws up a
shadowy and a softening haziness where the scene would otherwise
be too distinct. Poems, like rivers, convey to their destination
what must without their appliances be left unhandled : these to
ports and arsenals, this to the human heart.

BOCCACCIO. So it is ; and what is terror in poetry is horror in
prose. We may be brought too close to an object to leave any
room for pleasure. Ugolino affects us like a skeleton, by dry
bony verity.

PETRARCA. We can not be too distinct in our images ; but
although distinctness, on this and most other occasions, is desirable
in the imitative arts, yet sometimes in painting, and sometimes in
poetry, an object should not be quite precise. In your novel of
Andrevola and Gabriotto, you afford me an illustration.

> Le pareva dal corpo di lui uscire una
> cosa oscura e terribile.

This is like a dream : this *is* a dream. Afterward, you present
to us such palpable forms and pleasing colours as may relieve and
soothe us.

> Ed avendo molte rose, bianche e vermi-
> glie, colte, perciocche la stagione era.

BOCCACCIO. Surely you now are mocking me. The roses, I
perceive, would not have been there, had it not been the season.

PETRARCA. A poet often does more and better than he is aware
at the time, and seems at last to know as little about it as a silkworm
knows about the fineness of her thread.

The uncertain dream that still hangs over us in the novel, is
intercepted and hindered from hurting us by the spell of the roses,
of the white and the red ; a word the less would have rendered it
incomplete. The very warmth and geniality of the season shed
their kindly influence on us ; and we are renovated and ourselves

again by virtue of the clear fountain where we rest. Nothing of this poetical providence comes to our relief in Dante, though we want it oftener. It would be difficult to form an idea of a poem, into which so many personages are introduced, containing so few delineations of character, so few touches that excite our sympathy, so few elementary signs for our instruction, so few topics for our delight, so few excursions for our recreation. Nevertheless, his powers of language are prodigious; and, in the solitary places where he exerts his force rightly, the stroke is irresistible. But how greatly to be pitied must he be, who can find nothing in paradise better than sterile theology! and what an object of sadness and of consternation, he who rises up from hell like a giant refreshed!

Boccaccio. Strange perversion! A pillar of smoke by day and of fire by night; to guide no one. Paradise had fewer wants for him to satisfy than hell had; all of which he fed to repletion. But let us rather look to his poetry than his temper.

Petrarca. We will then.

A good poem is not divided into little panes like a cathedral window; which little panes themselves are broken and blurred, with a saint's coat on a dragon's tail, a doctor's head on the bosom of a virgin martyr, and having about them more lead than glass, and more gloom than colouring. A good satire or good comedy, if it does not always smile, rarely and briefly intermits it, and never rages. A good epic shows us more and more distinctly, at every book of it we open, the features and properties of heroic character, and terminates with accomplishing some momentous action. A good tragedy shows us that greater men than ourselves have suffered more severely and more unjustly; that the highest human power hath suddenly fallen helpless and extinct; or, what is better to contemplate and usefuller to know, that uncontrolled by law, unaccompanied by virtue, unfollowed by contentment, its possession is undesirable and unsafe. Sometimes we go away in triumph with Affliction proved and purified, and leave her under the smiles of heaven. In all these consummations the object is excellent; and here is the highest point to which poetry can attain. Tragedy has no bye-paths, no resting-places; there is everywhere action and passion. What do we find of this nature, or what of the epic, in the Orpheus and Judith, the Charon and Can della Scala, the Sinon and Maestro Adamo?

168

THE PENTAMERON

BOCCACCIO. Personages strangely confounded ! In this cate-
gory it required a strong hand to make Pluto and Pepe Satan keep
the peace, both having the same pretensions, and neither the
sweetest temper.

PETRARCA. Then the description of Mahomet is indecent and
filthy. Yet Dante is scarcely more disgusting in this place, than
he is insipid and spiritless in his allegory of the marriages, between
Saint Francesco and Poverty, Saint Dominico and Faith. I speak
freely and plainly to you, Giovanni, and the rather, as you have
informed me that I have been thought invidious to the reputation
of our great poet ; for such he is transcendently, in the midst of
his imperfections. Such likewise were Ennius and Lucilius in the
same period of Roman literature. They were equalled, and perhaps
excelled : will Dante ever be, in his native tongue ? The past
generations of his countrymen, the glories of old Rome, fade before
him the instant he springs upward, but they impart a more constant
and a more genial delight.

BOCCACCIO. They have less hair-cloth about them, and smell less
cloisterly ; yet they are only choristers.

The generous man, such as you, praises and censures with equal
freedom, not with equal pleasure : the freedom and the pleasure
of the ungenerous are both contracted, and lie only on the left
hand.

PETRARCA. When we point out to our friends an object in the
country, do we wish to diminish it ? do we wish to show it overcast ?
Why then should we in those nobler works of creation, God's only
representatives, who have cleared our intellectual sight for us, and
have displayed before us things more magnificent than Nature
would without them have revealed ?

We poets are heated by proximity. Those who are gone warm
us by the breath they leave behind them in their course, and *only*
warm us : those who are standing near, and just before, fever us.
Solitude has kept me uninfected ; unless you may hint perhaps
that pride was my preservative against the malignity of a worse
disease.

BOCCACCIO. It might well be, though it were not ; you having
been crowned in the capital of the Christian world.

PETRARCA. That indeed would have been something, if I had
been crowned for my Christianity, of which I suspect there are

better judges in Rome than there are of poetry. I would rather be preferred to my rivals by the two best critics of the age than by all the others ; who, if they think differently from the two wisest in these matters, must necessarily think wrong.

BOCCACCIO. You know that not only the two first, but many more, prefer you ; and that neither they, nor any who are acquainted with your character, can believe that your strictures on Dante are invidious or uncandid.

PETRARCA. I am borne toward him by many strong impulses. Our families were banished by the same faction : he himself and my father left Florence on the same day, and both left it for ever. This recollection would rather make me cling to him than cast him down. Ill fortune has many and tenacious ties : good fortune has few and fragile ones. I saw our illustrious fellow-citizen once only, and when I was a child. Even the sight of such a poet, in early days, is dear to him who aspires to become one, and the memory is always in his favour. The worst I can recollect to have said against his poem to others, is, that the architectural fabric of the *Inferno* is unintelligible without a long study, and only to be under-stood after distracting our attention from its inhabitants. Its locality and dimensions are at last uninteresting, and would better have been left in their obscurity. The zealots of Dante compare it, for invention, with the infernal regions of Homer and Virgil. I am ignorant how much the Grecian poet invented, how much existed in the religion, how much in the songs and traditions of the people. But surely our Alighieri has taken the same idea, and even made his descent in the same part of Italy, as Æneas had done before. In the *Odyssea* the mind is perpetually relieved by variety of scene and character. There are vices enough in it, but rising from lofty or from powerful passions, and under the veil of mystery and poetry : there are virtues too enough, and human and definite and practic-able. We have man, although a shade, in his own features, in his own dimensions : he appears before us neither cramped by systems nor jaundiced by schools ; no savage, no cit, no cannibal, no doctor. Vigorous and elastic, he is such as poetry saw him first ; he is such as poetry would ever see him. In Dante, the greater part of those who are not degraded, are debilitated and distorted. No heart swells here, either for overpowered valour or for unrequited love. In the shades alone, but in the shades of Homer, does Ajax rise to

THE PENTAMERON

his full loftiness: in the shades alone, but in the shades of Virgil, is Dido the arbitress of our tears.

BOCCACCIO. I must confess there are nowhere two whole cantos in Dante which will bear a sustained and close comparison with the very worst book of the *Odyssea* or the *Æneid;* that there is nothing of the same continued and unabated excellence, as Ovid's in the contention for the armour of Achilles ; the most heroic of heroic poetry, and only censurable, if censurable at all, because the eloquence of the braver man is more animated and more persuasive than his successful rival's. I do not think Ovid the best poet that ever lived, but I think he wrote the most of good poetry, and, in proportion to its quantity, the least of bad or indifferent. The *Inferno*, the *Purgatorio*, the *Paradiso*, are pictures from the walls of our churches and chapels and monasteries, some painted by Giotto and Cimabue, some earlier. In several of these we detect not only the cruelty, but likewise the satire and indecency of Dante. Sometimes there is also his vigour and simplicity, but oftener his harshness and meagreness and disproportion. I am afraid the good Alighieri, like his friends the painters, was inclined to think the angels were created only to flagellate and burn us ; and Paradise only for us to be driven out of it. And in truth, as we have seen it exhibited, there is but little hardship in the case.

The opening of the third canto of the *Inferno* has always been much admired. There is indeed a great solemnity in the words of the inscription on the portal of hell : nevertheless, I do not see the necessity for three verses out of six. After

> Per me si va nell' eterno dolore,[1]

it surely is superfluous to subjoin

> Per me si va tra la perduta gente ;

for, beside the *perduta gente*, who else can suffer the eternal woe ? And when the portal has told us that " *Justice moved the high Maker to make it*," surely it might have omitted the notification that his " *divine power* " did it.

> Fecemi la divina potestate ;

---

[1] *Inferno*, iii. 2.

THE PENTAMERON

The next piece of information I wish had been conveyed even in darker characters, so that they never could have been deciphered. The following line is,

La somma Sapienza e 'l primo Amore.

If God's first love was hell-making, we might almost wish his affections were as mutable as ours are : that is, if holy church would countenance us therein.

PETRARCA. Systems of poetry, of philosophy, of government, form and model us to their own proportions. As our systems want the grandeur, the light, and the symmetry of the ancient, we can not hope for poets, philosophers, or statesmen, of equal dignity. Very justly do you remark that our churches and chapels and monasteries, and even our shrines and tabernacles on the roadside, contain in painting the same punishments as Alighieri had registered in his poem : and several of these were painted before his birth. Nor surely can you have forgotten that his master, Brunetto Latini, composed one on the same plan.

The Virtues and Vices, and persons under their influence, appear to him likewise in a wood, wherein he, like Dante, is bewildered. Old walls are the tablets both copy : the arrangement is the device of Brunetto. Our religion is too simple in its verities, and too penurious in its decorations, for poetry of high value. We can not hope or desire that a pious Italian will ever have the audacity to restore to Satan a portion of his majesty, or to remind the faithful that he is a fallen angel.

BOCCACCIO. No, no, Francesco ; let us keep as much of him down as we can, and as long.

PETRARCA. It might not be amiss to remember that even human power is complacent in security, and that Omnipotence is ever omnipotent, without threats and fulminations.

BOCCACCIO. These, however, are the main springs of sacred poetry, of which I think we already have enough.

PETRARCA. But good enough ?

BOCCACCIO. Even much better would produce less effect than that which has occupied our ears from childhood, and comes sounding and swelling with a mysterious voice from the deep and dark recesses of antiquity.

PETRARCA. I see no reason why we should not revert, at times,

172

to the first intentions of poetry. Hymns to the Creator were its earliest efforts.

BOCCACCIO. I do not believe a word of it, unless He himself was graciously pleased to inspire the singer ; of which we have received no account. I rather think it originated in pleasurable song, perhaps of drunkenness, and resembled the dithyrambic. Strong excitement alone could force and hurry men among words displaced and exaggerated ideas.

Believing that man fell, first into disobedience, next into ferocity and fratricide, we may reasonably believe that war-songs were among the earliest of his intellectual exertions. When he rested from battle he had leisure to think of love ; and the skies and the fountains and the flowers reminded him of her, the coy and beautiful, who fled to a mother from the ardour of his pursuit. In after years he lost a son, his companion in the croft and in the forest : images too grew up there, and rested on the grave. A daughter, who had wondered at his strength and wisdom, looked to him in vain for succour at the approach of death. Inarticulate grief gave way to passionate and wailing words, and Elegy was awakened. We have tears in this world before we have smiles, Francesco ! we have struggles before we have composure ; we have strife and complaints before we have submission and gratitude. I am suspicious that if we could collect the " winged words " of the earliest hymns, we should find that they called upon the Deity for vengeance. Priests and rulers were far from insensible to private wrongs. Chryses in the *Iliad* is willing that his king and country should be enslaved, so that his daughter be sent back to him. David in the *Psalms* is no unimportunate or lukewarm applicant for the discomfiture and extermination of his adversaries : and, among the visions of felicity, none brighter is promised a fortunate warrior, than to dash the infants of his enemy against the stones. The Holy Scriptures teach us that the human race was created on the banks of the Euphrates, and where the river hath several branches. Here the climate is extremely hot ; and men, like birds, in hot climates, never sing well. I doubt whether there was ever a good poet in the whole city and whole plain of Babylon. Egypt had none but such as she imported. Mountainous countries bear them as they bear the more fragrant plants and savoury game. Judæa had hers : Attica reared them among her thyme and hives ; and Tuscany may lift her laurels not a span below.   Never have the accents of poetry been heard on the fertile banks of the Vistula ; and Ovid [1] taught the borderers of the Danube an indigenous* song in vain.

PETRARCA. Orpheus, we hear, sang on the banks of the Hebrus.

BOCCACCIO. The banks of the Hebrus may be level or rocky, for what I know about them : but the river is represented by the poets as rapid and abounding in whirlpools ; hence, I presume, it runs among rocks and inequalities.   Be this as it may : do you imagine that Thrace in those early days produced a philosophical poet ?

PETRARCA. We have the authority of history for it.

BOCCACCIO. Bad authority, too, unless we sift and cross-examine it.   Undoubtedly there were narrow paths of commerce, in very ancient times, from the Euxine to the Caspian, and from the Caspian to the kingdoms of the remoter East.   Merchants in those days were not only the most adventurous, but the most intelligent men : and there were ardent minds, uninfluenced by a spirit of lucre, which were impelled by the ardour of imagination into untravelled regions.   Scythia was a land of fable, not only to the Greeks, but equally to the Romans.   Thrace was a land of fable, we may well believe, to the nearest towns of northern India.   I imagine that Orpheus, whoever he was, brought his knowledge from that quarter. We are too apt to fancy that Greece owed everything to the Phœnicians and Egyptians.   The elasticity of her mind threw off, or the warmth of her imagination transmuted, the greater part of her earlier acquisitions.   She was indebted to Phœnicia for nothing but her alphabet ; and even these signs she modified, and endowed them with a portion of her flexibility and grace.

PETRARCA. There are those who tell us that Homer lived before the age of letters in Greece.

BOCCACCIO. I wish they knew the use of them as well as he did. Will they not also tell us that the commerce of the two nations was carried on without the numerals (and such were letters) by which traders cast up accounts ?   The Phœnicians traded largely with every coast of the Ægean sea ; and among their earliest correspondents were the inhabitants of the Greek maritime cities, insular

---

[1] Ovid, *Epist.* iv. 13, 19.
 * Aptaque sunt nostris barbara verba modis.
What are all the other losses of literature in comparison with this ?—W. S. L

and continental. Is it credible that Cyprus, that Crete, that Attica, should be ignorant of the most obvious means by which commerce was maintained ? or that such means should be restricted to commerce, among a people so peculiarly fitted for social intercourse, so inquisitive, so imaginative, as the Greeks ?

PETRARCA. Certainly it is not.

BOCCACCIO. The Greeks were the most creative, the Romans the least creative, of mankind. No Roman ever invented anything. Whence then are derived the only two works of imagination we find among them ; the story of the *Ephesian* Matron*, and the story of *Psyche ?* Doubtless from some country farther eastward than Phœnicia and Egypt. The authors in which we find these insertions are of little intrinsic worth.

When the Thracians became better known to the Greeks they turned their backs upon them as worn-out wonders, and looked toward the inexhaustible Hyperboreans. Among these too she [1] placed wisdom and the arts, and mounted instruments through which a greater magnitude was given to the stars.

PETRARCA. I will remain no longer with you among the Thracians or the Hyperboreans. But in regard to low and level countries, as unproductive of poetry, I entreat you not to be too fanciful nor too exclusive. Virgil was born on the Mincio, and has rendered the city of his birth too celebrated to be mistaken.

BOCCACCIO. He was born in the territory of Mantua, not in the city. He sang his first child's song on the shoulders of the Apennines ; his first man's under the shadow of Vesuvius.

I would not assert that a great poet must necessarily be born on a high mountain : no indeed, no such absurdity : but where the climate is hot, the plains have never shown themselves friendly to the imaginative faculties. We surely have more buoyant spirits on the mountain than below, but it is not requisite for this effect that our cradles should have been placed on it.

PETRARCA. What will you say about Pindar ?

BOCCACCIO. I think it more probable that he was reared in the vicinity of Thebes than within the walls. For Bœotia, like our

* One similar, and better conceived, is given by Du Halde from the Chinese. If the fiction of Psyche had reached Greece so early as the time of Plato, it would have caught his attention, and he would have delivered it down to us, however altered.—W. S. L.

[1] Query : " they."

Tuscany, has one large plain, but has also many eminences, and is bounded on two sides by hills.

Look at the vale of Capua ! Scarcely so much as a sonnet was ever heard from one end of it to the other ; perhaps the most spirited thing was some Carthaginian glee, from a soldier in the camp of Hannibal. Nature seems to contain in her breast the same milk for all, but feeding one for one aptitude, another for another ; and, as if she would teach him a lesson as soon as he could look about him, she has placed the poet where the air is unladen with the exhalations of luxuriance.

PETRARCA. In my delight to listen to you after so long an absence, I have been too unwary ; and you have been speaking too much for one infirm. Greatly am I to blame, not to have moderated my pleasure and your vivacity. You must rest now : to-morrow we will renew our conversation.

BOCCACCIO. God bless thee, Francesco ! I shall be talking with thee all night in my slumbers. Never have I seen thee with such pleasure as to-day, excepting when I was deemed worthy by our fellow-citizens of bearing to thee, and of placing within this dear hand of thine, the sentence of recall from banishment, and when my tears streamed over the ordinance as I read it, whereby thy paternal lands were redeemed from the public treasury.

Again God bless thee ! Those tears were not quite exhausted : take the last of them.

SECOND DAY'S INTERVIEW

PETRARCA. How have you slept, Giovanni ?

BOCCACCIO. Pleasantly, soundly, and quite long enough. You too methinks have enjoyed the benefit of riding ; for you either slept well or began late. Do you rise in general three hours after the sun ?

PETRARCA. No indeed.

BOCCACCIO. As for me, since you would not indulge me with your company an hour ago, I could do nothing more delightful than to look over some of your old letters.

PETRARCA. Ours are commemorative of no reproaches, and laden with no regrets. Far from us

> With drooping wing the spell-bound spirit moves
> O'er flickering friendships and extinguisht loves.

BOCCACCIO. Ay, but as I want no record of your kindness now you are with me, I have been looking over those to other persons, on past occasions. In the Latin one to the tribune, whom the people at Rome usually call Rienzi, I find you address him by the denomination of Nicolaus Laurentii. Is this the right one ?

PETRARCA. As we Florentines are fond of omitting the first syllable in proper names, calling Luigi *Gigi*, Giovanni *Nanni*, Francesco *Cecco*, in like manner at Rome they say *Renzi* for Lorenzi, and by another corruption it has been pronounced and written Rienzi. Believe me, I should never have ventured to address the personage who held and supported the highest dignity on earth, until I had ascertained his appellation : for nobody ever quite forgave, unless in the low and ignorant, a wrong pronunciation of his name ; the humblest being of opinion that they have one of their own, and one both worth having and worth knowing. Even dogs, they observe, are not miscalled. It would have been as Latin in sound, if not in structure, to write Rientius as Laurentius : but it would certainly have been offensive to a dignitary of his station, as being founded on a sportive and somewhat childish familiarity.

THE PENTAMERON

BOCCACCIO. Ah Francesco ! we were a good deal younger in those days ; and hopes sprang up before us like mushrooms : the sun produced them, the shade produced them, every hill, every valley, every busy and every idle hour.

PETRARCA. The season of hope precedes but little the season of disappointment. Where the ground is unprepared, what harvest can be expected ? Men bear wrongs more easily than irritations ; and the Romans, who had sunk under worse degradation than any other people on record, rose up against the deliverer who ceased to consult their ignorance. I speak advisedly and without rhetoric on the foul depths of their debasement. The Jews, led captive into Egypt and into Babylon, were left as little corrupted as they were found ; and perhaps some of their vices were corrected by the labours that were imposed on them. But the subjugation of the Romans was effected by the depravation [1] of their morals, which the priesthood took away, giving them ceremonies and promises instead. God had indulged them in the exercise of power : first the kings abused it, then the consuls, then the tribunes. One only magistrate was remaining who never had violated it, farther than in petty frauds and fallacies suited to the occasion, not having at present more within his reach. It was now his turn to exercise his functions, and no less grievously and despotically than the preceding had done. For this purpose the Pontifex Maximus needed some slight alterations in the popular belief ; and he collected them from that Pantheon which Roman policy had enlarged at every conquest. The priests of Isis had acquired the highest influence in the city : those of Jupiter were jealous that foreign Gods should become more than supplementary and subordinate : but as the women in general leaned toward Isis, it was in vain to contest the point, and prudent to adopt a little at a time from the discipline of the shaven brother-hood. The names and titles of the ancient Gods had received many additions, and they were often asked which they liked best. Different ones were now given them ; and gradually, here and there, the older dropped into desuetude. Then arose the star in the east ; and all was manifested.

BOCCACCIO. Ay, ay, but the second company of shepherds sang to a different tune from the first, and put them out. Trumpeters ran in among them, horses neighed, tents waved their pennons,

[1] 1st ed. reads : " deviation."

178

and commanders of armies sought to raise themselves to supreme authority, some by leading the faction of the ancient faith, and some by supporting the recenter. At last the priesthood succeeded to the power of the pretorian guard, and elected, or procured the election of, an emperor. Every man who loved peace and quiet took refuge in a sanctuary, now so efficient to protect him ; and nearly all who had attained a preponderance in wisdom and erudition, brought them to bear against the worn-out and tottering institutions, and finally to raise up the coping-stone of an edifice which overtopped them all.

PETRARCA. At present we fly to princes as we fly to caves and arches, and other things of the mere earth, for shelter and protection.

BOCCACCIO. And when they afford it at all, they afford it with as little care and knowledge. Like Egyptian embalmers, they cast aside the brains as useless or worse, but carefully swathe up all that is viler and heavier, and place it in their painted catacombs.

PETRARCA. What Dante saw in his day, we see in ours. The danger is, lest first the wiser, and soon afterward the unwiser, in abhorrence at the presumption and iniquity of the priesthood, should abandon religion altogether, when it is forbidden to approach her without such company.

BOCCACCIO. Philosophy is but the calix of that plant of paradise, religion. Detach it, and it dies away ; meanwhile the plant itself, supported by its proper nutriment, retains its vigour.

PETRARCA. The good citizen and the calm reasoner come at once to the same conclusion : that philosophy can never hold many men together ; that religion can ; and those who [1] are without it would not let philosophy, nor law, nor humanity exist. Therefore it is our duty and interest to remove all obstruction from it ; to give it air, light, space, and freedom ; carrying in our hands a scourge for fallacy, a chain for cruelty, and an irrevocable ostracism for riches that riot in the house of God.

BOCCACCIO. Moderate wealth is quite enough to teach with.

PETRARCA. The luxury and rapacity of the church, together with the insolence of the barons, excited that discontent which emboldened Nicola de Rienzi to assume the station of tribune. Singular was the prudence, and opportune the boldness, he manifested at first. His modesty, his piety, his calm severity, his un-

[1] All eds., including Crump's, read : " who without it."

biassed justice, won to him the affections of every good citizen, and struck horror into the fastnesses of every castellated felon. He might by degrees have restored the republic of Rome, had he preserved his moderation : he might have become the master of Italy, had he continued the master of himself : but he allowed the weakest of the passions to run away with him : he fancied he could not inebriate himself soon enough with the intemperance of power. He called for seven crowns, and placed them successively on his head. He cited Lewis of Bavaria and Charles of Bohemia to appear and plead their causes before him ; and lastly, not content with exasperating and concentrating the hostility of barbarians, he set at defiance the best and highest feelings of his more instructed countrymen, and displayed his mockery of religion and decency by bathing in the porphyry font of the Lateran. How my soul grieved for his defection ! How bitterly burst forth my complaints, when he ordered the imprisonment of Stefano Colonna in his ninetieth year ! For these atrocities you know with what reproaches I assailed him, traitor as he was to the noblest cause that ever strung the energies of mankind. For this cause, under his auspices, I had abandoned all hope of favour and protection from the pontiff : I had cast into peril, almost into perdition, the friendship, familiarity, and love of the Colonnas. Even you, Giovanni, thought me more rash than you would say you thought me, and wondered at seeing me whirled along with the tempestuous triumphs that seemed mounting toward the Capitol. It is only in politics that an actor [1] appears greater by the magnitude of the theatre ; and we readily and enthusiastically give way to the deception. Indeed, whenever a man capable of performing great and glorious actions is emerging from obscurity, it is our duty to remove, if we can, all obstruction from before him ; to increase his scope and his powers, to extol and amplify his virtues. This is always requisite, and often insufficient, to counteract the workings of malignity round about him. But finding him afterward false and cruel, and, instead of devoting himself to the commonwealth, exhausting it by his violence and sacrificing it to his vanity, then it behoves us to stamp the foot, and to call in the people to cast down the idol. For nothing is so immoral or pernicious as to keep up the illusion of greatness in wicked men. Their crimes, because they have fallen into the gulf of them, we call misfortunes ;

[1] 1st ed. reads : " action."

and, amid ten thousand mourners, grieve only for him who made them so. Is this reason ? is this humanity ?

BOCCACCIO. Alas ! it is man.

PETRARCA. Can we wonder then that such wretches have turned him to such purposes ? The calmness, the sagacity, the sanctitude of Rienzi, in the ascent to his elevation, rendered him only the more detestable for his abuse of power.

BOCCACCIO. Surely the man grew mad.

PETRARCA. Men often give the hand to the madness that seizes them. He yielded to pride and luxury : behind them came jealousy and distrust : fear followed these, and cruelty followed fear. Then the intellects sought the subterfuge that bewildered them ; and an ignoble flight was precluded by an ignominious death.

BOCCACCIO. No mortal is less to be pitied, or more to be detested, than he into whose hands are thrown the fortunes of a nation, and who squanders them away in the idle gratification of his pride and his ambition. Are not these already gratified to the full by the confidence and deference of his countrymen ? Can silks, and the skins of animals, can hammered metals and sparkling stones, enhance the value of legitimate dominion over the human heart ? Can a wise man be desirous of having a less wise successor ? And, of all the world, would he exhibit this inferiority in a son ? Irrational as are all who aim at despotism, this is surely the most irrational of their speculations. Vulgar men are more anxious for title and decoration than for power ; and notice, in their estimate, is preferable to regard. We ought as little to mind the extinction of such existences as the dying down of a favourable wind in the prosecution of a voyage. They are fitter for the calendar than for history, and it is well when we find them in last year's.

PETRARCA. What a year was Rienzi's last to me ! What an extinction of all that had not been yet extinguished ! Visionary as was the flash of his glory, there was another more truly so, which this, my second great loss and sorrow, opened again before me.[1]

---

[1] 1st ed. reads : " me.

> Nor youth nor age nor virtue can avoid
> Miseries that fly in darkness through the world
> Striking at random irremissibly,
> Until our sun sinks through the waves, until
> The golden brim melts from its brightest cloud,
> And all that we have seen hath disappeared.

Verona," etc.

THE PENTAMERON

Verona ! loveliest of cities, but saddest to my memory ! while
the birds were singing in thy cypresses the earliest notes of spring,
the blithest of hope, the tenderest of desire, she, my own Laura,
fresh as the dawn around her, stood before me. It was her transit ;
I knew it ere she spake.*

O Giovanni ! the heart that has once been bathed in love's
pure fountain, retains the pulse of youth for ever. Death can only
take away the sorrowful from our affections : the flower expands ;
the colourless film that enveloped it falls off and perishes.

BOCCACCIO. We may well believe it : and, believing it, let us
cease to be disquieted for their absence who have but retired into
another chamber. We are like those who have overslept the hour :
when we rejoin our friends, there is only the more joyance and
congratulation. Would we break a precious vase, because it is
as capable of containing the bitter as the sweet ? No : the very
things which touch us the most sensibly are those which we should
be the most reluctant to forget. The noble mansion is most distinguished by the beautiful images it retains of beings past away ;
and so is the noble mind.

The damps of autumn sink into the leaves and prepare them for
the necessity of their fall : and thus insensibly are we, as years
close round us, detached from our tenacity of life by the gentle
pressure of recorded sorrows. When the graceful dance and its
animating music are over, and the clapping of hands (so lately
linked) hath ceased ; when youth and comeliness and pleasantry
are departed,

> Who would desire to spend the following day
> Among the extinguisht lamps, the faded wreaths,
> The dust and desolation left behind ?

But whether we desire it or not, we must submit. He who
hath appointed our days hath placed their contents within them,
and our efforts can neither cast them out nor change their quality.
In our present mood we will not dwell too long on this subject, but
rather walk forth into the world, and look back again on the bustle
of life. Neither of us may hope to exert in future any extraordinary
influence on the political movements of our country, by our presence

* This event is related by Petrarca as occurring on the sixth of April, the day
of her decease.—W. S. L.

or intervention : yet surely it is something to have set at defiance the mercenaries who assailed us, and to have stood aloof from the distribution of the public spoils. I have at all times taken less interest than you have taken in the affairs of Rome ; for the people of that city neither are, nor were of old, my favourites.

It appears to me that there are spots accursed, spots doomed to eternal sterility ; and Rome is one of them. No gospel announces the glad tidings of resurrection to a fallen nation. Once down, and down for ever. The Babylonians, the Macedonians, the Romans, prove it. Babylon is a desert, Macedon a den of thieves, Rome (what is written as an invitation on the walls of her streets) one vast *immondezzaio*, morally and substantially.

PETRARCA. The argument does not hold good throughout. Persia was conquered : yet Persia long afterward sprang up again with renovated strength and courage, and Sapor mounted his war-horse from the crouching neck of Valentinian. In nearly all the campaigns with the Romans she came off victorious : none of her kings or generals were ever led in triumph to the Capitol ; but several Roman emperors lay prostrate on their purple in the fields of Parthia. Formidable at home, victorious over friends and relatives, their legions had seized and subdivided the arable lands of Campania and the exuberant pastures of the Po ; but the glebe that bordered the Araxes was unbroken by them. Persia, since those times, has passed through many vicissitudes, of defeat and victory, of obscurity and glory : and why may not our country ? Let us take hopes where we can find them, and raise them where we find none.

BOCCACCIO. In some places we may ; in others, the fabric of hopes is too arduous an undertaking. When I was in Rome nothing there reminded me of her former state, until I saw a goose in the grass under the Capitoline hill. This perhaps was the only one of her inhabitants that had not degenerated. Even the dogs looked sleepy, mangy, suspicious, perfidious, and thievish. The goose meanwhile was making his choice of herbage about triumphal arches and monumental columns, and picking up worms ; the surest descendants, the truest representatives, and enjoying the inalienable succession, of the Cæsars. This is all that goose or man can do at Rome. She, I think, will be the last city to rise from the dead.

PETRARCA. There is a trumpet, and on earth, that shall awaken even her.

THE PENTAMERON

BOCCACCIO. I should like to live and be present.

PETRARCA. This can not be expected. But you may live many years, and see many things to make you happy. For you will not close the doors too early in the evening of existence against the visits of renovating and cheerful thoughts, which keep our lives long up, and help them to sink at last without pain or pressure.

BOCCACCIO. Another year or two perhaps, with God's permission. Fra Biagio felt my pulse on Wednesday, and cried, " Courage ! Ser Giovanni ! there is no danger of Paradise yet : the Lord forbid ! "

" Faith ! " said I, " Fra Biagio ! I hope there is not. What with prayers and masses, I have planted a foot against my old homestead, and will tug hard to remain where I am."

" A true soldier of the faith ! " quoth Fra Biagio, and drank a couple of flasks to my health. Nothing else, he swore to Assunta, would have induced him to venture beyond one ; he hating all excesses, they give the adversary such advantage over us ; although God is merciful and makes allowances.

PETRARCA. Impossible as it is to look far and with pleasure into the future, what a privilege is it, how incomparably greater than any other that genius can confer, to be able to direct the backward flight of fancy and imagination to the recesses they most delighted in ; to be able, as the shadows lengthen in our path, to call up before us the youth of our sympathies in all their tenderness [1] and purity !

BOCCACCIO. Mine must have been very pure, I suspect, for I am sure they were very tender. But I need not call them up ; they come readily enough of their own accord ; and I find it perplexing at times to get entirely rid of them. Sighs are very troublesome when none meet them half-way. The worst of mine now are while I am walking uphill. Even to walk upstairs, which used occasionally to be as pleasant an exercise as any, grows sadly too much for me. For which reason I lie here below ; and it is handier too for Assunta.

PETRARCA. Very judicious and considerate. In high situations, like Certaldo and this villetta, there is no danger from fogs or damps of any kind. The skylark yonder seems to have made it her first station in the air.

BOCCACCIO. To welcome thee, Francesco !

[1] 1st ed. reads : " kindness."

184

THE PENTAMERON

PETRARCA. Rather say, to remind us both of our Dante. All the verses that ever were written on the nightingale are scarcely worth the beautiful triad of this divine poet on the lark.

> Qual lodoletta che 'n aere si spazia,
> Prima cantando, e poi tace contenta
> Dell' ultima dolcezza che la sazia.[1]

In the first of them do not you see the twinkling of her wings against the sky ? As often as I repeat them my ear is satisfied, my heart (like hers) contented.

BOCCACCIO. I agree with you in the perfect and unrivalled beauty of the first ; but in the third there is a redundance. Is not *contenta* quite enough, without *che la sazia ?* The picture is before us, the sentiment within us, and behold ! we kick when we are full of manna.

PETRARCA. I acknowledge the correctness and propriety of your remark ; and yet beauties in poetry must be examined as carefully as blemishes, and even more ; for we are more easily led away by them, although we do not dwell on them so long. We two should never be accused, in these days, of malevolence to Dante, if the whole world heard us. Being here alone, we may hazard our opinions even less guardedly, and set each other right as we see occasion.

BOCCACCIO. Come on then ; I will venture. I will go back to find fault ; I will seek it even in Francesca.

To hesitate, and waver, and turn away from the subject, was proper and befitting in her. The verse, however, in no respect satisfies me. Anyone would imagine from it that *Galeotto* was really both the title of the book and the name of the author ; neither of which is true. Galeotto, in the *Tavola Rotonda*, is the person who interchanges the correspondence between Lancilotto and Ginevra. The appellation is now become the generic of all men whose business it is to promote the success of others in illicit love. Dante was stimulated in his satirical vein, when he attributed to Francesca a ludicrous expression, which she was very unlikely in her own nature, and greatly more so in her state of suffering, to employ or think of, whirled round as she was incessantly with her lover. Neither was it requisite to say, " the book was a Galeotto, and so was the author," when she had said already that a passage

---

[1] *Paradiso*, xx. 73.

in it had seduced her. Omitting this unnecessary and ungraceful line, her confusion and her delicacy are the more evident, and the following comes forth with fresh beauty. In the commencement of her speech I wish these had likewise been omitted,

" E ciò sa 'l tuo dottore ; " [1]

since he knew no more about it than anybody else. As we proceed, there are passages in which I can not find my way, and where I suspect the poet could not show it me. For instance, is it not strange that Briareus should be punished in the same way as Nimrod, when Nimrod sinned against the living God, and when Briareus attempted to overthrow one of the living God's worst antagonists, Jupiter ? an action which our blessed Lord, and the doctors of the holy church, not only attempted, but (to their glory and praise for evermore) accomplished.

PETRARCA. Equally strange that Brutus and Cassius (a remark which escaped us in our mention of them yesterday) should be placed in the hottest pit of hell for slaying Cæsar, and that Cato, who would have done the same thing with less compunction, should be appointed sole guardian and governor of purgatory.

BOCCACCIO. What interest could he have made to be promoted to so valuable a post, in preference to doctors, popes, confessors, and fathers ? Wonderful indeed ! and they never seemed to take it much amiss.

PETRARCA. Alighieri not only throws together the most opposite and distant characters, but even makes Jupiter and our Saviour the same person.

> E se lecito m' è, o sommo *Giove !*
> Che fosti 'n terra per noi *crucifisso*.[2]

BOCCACCIO. Jesus Christ ought no more to be called Jupiter than Jupiter ought to be called Jesus Christ.

PETRARCA. In the whole of the *Inferno* I find only the descriptions of Francesca and of Ugolino at all admirable. Vigorous expressions there are many, but lost in their application to base objects ; and insulated thoughts in high relief, but with everything crumbling round them. Proportionally to the extent, there is a scantiness of poetry, if delight is the purpose or indication of it.

---

[1] *Inferno,* v. 123.　　　　　　　　　　[2] *Purgatorio,* vi. 118.

THE PENTAMERON

Intensity shows everywhere the powerful master : and yet intensity is not invitation. A great poet may do everything but repel us. Established laws are pliant before him : nevertheless his office hath both its duties and its limits.

BOCCACCIO. The simile in the third canto, the satire at the close of the fourth, and the description at the commencement of the eighth, if not highly admirable, are what no ordinary poet could have produced.

PETRARCA. They are streaks of light in a thunder-cloud. You might have added the beginning of the twenty-seventh, in which the poetry of itself is good, although not excellent, and the subject of it assuages the weariness left on us, after passing through so many holes and furnaces, and undergoing the dialogue between Sinon [1] and Master Adam.

BOCCACCIO. I am sorry to be reminded of this. It is like the brawl of the two fellows in Horace's *Journey to Brundusium.* They are the straightest parallels of bad wit and bad poetry that ancient and modern times exhibit. Ought I to speak so sharply of poets who elsewhere have given me so great delight ?

PETRARCA. Surely you ought. No criticism is less beneficial to an author or his reader than one tagged with favour and tricked with courtesy. The gratification of our humours is not the intent and scope of criticism, and those who indulge in it on such occasions are neither wise nor honest.

BOCCACCIO. I never could see why we should designedly and prepensely give to one writer more than his due, to another less. If we offer an honest man ten crowns when we owe him only five, he is apt to be offended. The perfumer and druggist weigh out the commodity before them to a single grain. If they do it with odours and powders, should not we attempt it likewise, in what is either the nutriment or the medicine of the mind ? I do not wonder that Criticism has never yet been clear-sighted and expert among us : I do, that she has never been dispassionate and unprejudiced. There are critics who, lying under no fear of a future state in literature, and all whose hope is for the present day, commit injustice without compunction. Every one of these people has some favourite object for the embraces of his hatred, and a figure of straw will never serve the purpose. He must throw his stone at what stands out ;

[1] All eds. read, nonsensically : " Simon."

187

he must twitch the skirt of him who is ascending. Do you imagine that the worst writers of any age were treated with as much asperity as you and I ? No, Francesco ![1] give the good folks their due : they are humaner to their fellow-creatures.

PETRARCA. Disregarding the ignorant and presumptuous, we have strengthened our language by dipping it afresh in its purer and higher source, and have called the Graces back to it. We never have heeded how Jupiter would have spoken, but only how the wisest men would, and how words follow the movements of the mind. There [2] are rich and copious veins of mineral in regions far remote from commerce and habitations : these veins are useless : so are those writings of which the style is uninviting and inaccessible, through its ruggedness, its chasms, its points, its perplexities, its obscurity. There are scarcely three authors, beside yourself, who appear to heed whether any guest will enter the gate, quite satisfied with the consciousness that they have stores within. Such wealth, in another generation, may be curious, but cannot be current. When a language grows up all into stalk, and its flowers begin to lose somewhat of their character, we must go forth into the open fields, through the dingles, and among the mountains, for fresh seed. Our ancestors did this, no very long time ago. Foremost in zeal, in vigour and authority, Alighieri took on himself the same patronage and guardianship of our adolescent dialect, as Homer of the Greek : and my Giovanni hath since endowed it so handsomely, that additional bequests, we may apprehend, will only corrupt its principles, and render it lax and lavish.

BOCCACCIO. Beware of violating those canons of criticism you have just laid down. We have no right to gratify one by misleading another, nor, when we undertake to show the road, to bandage the eyes of him who trusts us for his conductor. In regard to censure, those only speak ill who speak untruly, unless a truth be barbed by malice and aimed by passion. To be useful to as many as possible is the especial duty of a critic, and his utility can only be attained by rectitude and precision. He walks in a garden which is not his own ; and he neither must gather the blossoms to embellish his discourse, nor break the branches to display his strength. Rather

[1] 1st ed. reads : " Giovanni."
[2] A very similar passage, spoken by Barrow, will be found in the Conversation of Barrow and Newton, vol. iv. of this edition.

let him point to what is out of order, and help to raise what is lying on the ground.

PETRARCA. Auditors, and readers in general, come to hear or read, not your opinion delivered, but their own repeated. Fresh notions are as disagreeable to some as fresh air to others ; and this inability to bear them is equally a symptom of disease. Impatience and intolerance are sure to be excited at any check to admiration in the narratives of Ugolino and of Francesca : nothing is to be abated : they are not only to be admirable, but entirely faultless.

BOCCACCIO. You have proved to me that, in blaming our betters, we ourselves may sometimes be unblamed. When authors are removed by death beyond the reach of irritation at the touch of an infirmity, we best consult their glory by handling their works comprehensively and unsparingly. Vague and indefinite criticism suits only slight merit, and presupposes it. Lineaments irregular and profound as Dante's are worthy of being traced with patience and fidelity. In the charts of our globe we find distinctly marked the promontories and indentations, and oftentimes the direction of unprofitable marshes and impassable sands and wildernesses : level surfaces are unnoted. I would not detract one atom from the worth of Dante ; which can not be done by summing it up exactly, but may be by negligence in the computation.

PETRARCA. Your business, in the lectures, is not to show his merits, but his meaning ; and to give only so much information as may be given without offence to the factious. Whatever you do beyond, is for yourself, your friends, and futurity.

BOCCACCIO. I may write more lectures, but never shall deliver them in person as the first. Probably, so near as I am to Florence, and so dear as Florence hath always been to me, I shall see that city no more. The last time I saw it, I only passed through. Four years ago, you remember, I lost my friend Acciaioli. Early in the summer of the preceding, his kindness had induced him to invite me again to Naples, and I undertook a journey to the place where my life had been too happy. There are many who pay dearly for sunshine early in the season : many, for pleasure in the prime of life. After one day lost in idleness at Naples, if intense and incessant thoughts (however fruitless) may be called so, I proceeded by water to Sorento, and thence over the mountains to Amalfi. Here, amid whatever is most beautiful and most wonderful in scenery,

THE PENTAMERON

I found the Seniscalco. His palace, his gardens, his terraces, his woods, abstracted his mind entirely from the solicitudes of state ; and I was gratified at finding in the absolute ruler of a kingdom, the absolute master of his time. Rare felicity ; and he enjoyed it the more after the toils of business and the intricacies of policy. His reception of me was most cordial. He showed me his long avenues of oranges and citrons : he helped me to mount the banks of slippery short herbage, whence we could look down on their dark masses, and their broad irregular belts, gemmed with golden fruit and sparkling flowers. We stood high above them, but not above their fragrance, and sometimes we wished the breeze to bring us it, and sometimes to carry a part of it away : and the breeze came and went as if obedient to our volition. Another day he conducted me farther from the palace, and showed me, with greater pride than I had ever seen in him before, the pale-green olives, on little smooth plants, the first year of their bearing. " I will teach my people here," said he, " to make as delicate oil as any of our Tuscans." We had feasts among the caverns : we had dances by day under the shade of the mulberries, by night under the lamps of the arcade : we had music on the shore and on the water.

When next I stood before him, it was afar from these. Torches flamed through the pine-forest of the Certosa : priests and monks led the procession : the sound of the brook alone filled up the intervals of the dirge : and other plumes than the dancers' waved round what was Acciaioli.

PETRARCA. Since in his family there was nobody who, from education or pursuits or consanguinity, could greatly interest him ; nobody to whom so large an accumulation of riches would not rather be injurious than beneficial, and place rather in the way of scoffs and carpings than exalt to respectability ; I regret that he omitted to provide for the comforts of your advancing years.

BOCCACCIO. The friend would not spoil the philosopher. Our judgment grows the stronger by the dying-down of our affections.

PETRARCA. With a careful politician and diplomatist all things find their places but men : and yet he thinks he has niched it nicely, when, as the gardener is left in the garden, the tailor on his board at the casement, he leaves the author at his desk : to remove him would put the world in confusion.

BOCCACCIO. Acciaioli knew me too well to suppose we could

190

serve each other : and his own capacity was amply sufficient for all the exigencies of the state. Generous,* kind, constant soul ! the emblazoned window throws now its rich mantle over him, moved gently by the vernal air of Marignole, or, as the great chapel-door is opened to some visitor of distinction, by the fresh eastern breeze from the valley of the Elsa. We too (mayhap) shall be visited in the same condition ; but in a homelier edifice, but in a humbler sepulchre, but by other and far different guests. While they are discussing and sorting out our merits, which are usually first discovered among the nettles in the churchyard, we will carry this volume with us, and show Dante what we have been doing.

PETRARCA. We [1] have each of us had our warnings : indeed all men have them : and not only at our time of life, but almost every day of their existence. They come to us even in youth ; although, like the lightnings that are said to play incessantly, in the noon and in the morning and throughout the year, we seldom see and never look for them. Come, as you proposed, let us now continue with our Dante.

Ugolino relates to him his terrible dream,[2] in which he fancied that he had seen Gualando, Sismondi, and Lanfranco, killing his children : and he says that, when he awakened, he heard them moan in their sleep. In such circumstances, his awakening ought rather to have removed the impression he laboured under ; since it showed him the vanity of the dream, and afforded him the consolation that the children were alive. Yet he adds immediately, what, if he were to speak it at all, he should have deferred.

" You are very cruel if you do not begin to grieve, considering what my heart presaged to me ; and, if you do not weep at it, what is it you are wont to weep at ? "

BOCCACCIO. Certainly this is ill-timed ; and the conference would indeed be better without it anywhere.

PETRARCA. Farther on, in whatever way we interpret

Poscia più che 'l dolor potè 'l digiuno,[3]

the poet falls sadly from his sublimity.

---

* This sentiment must be attributed to the gratitude of Boccaccio, not to the merits of Acciaioli, who treated him unworthily.—W. S. L. [Note added in second ed.]

[1] 1st ed. reads : " PETRARCA. Come let us proceed with him. Ugolino relates," etc.

[2] *Inferno*, xxxiii. 32. [3] *Inferno*, xxxiii. 75.

THE PENTAMERON

BOCCACCIO. If the fact were as he mentions, he should have suppressed it, since we had already seen the most pathetic in the features, and the most horrible in the stride, of Famine. Gnawing, not in hunger, but in rage and revenge, the archbishop's skull, is, in the opinion of many, rather ludicrous than tremendous.

PETRARCA. In mine, rather disgusting than ludicrous : but Dante (we must whisper it) is the great master of the disgusting. When the ancients wrote indecently and loosely, they presented what either had something alluring or something laughable about it, and, if they disgusted, it was involuntarily. Indecency is the most shocking in deformity. We call indecent, while we do not think it, the nakedness of the Graces and the Loves.

BOCCACCIO. When we are less barbarous we shall become more familiar with them, more tolerant of sliding beauty, more hospitable to erring passion, and perhaps as indulgent to frailty as we are now to ferocity. I wish I could find in some epitaph, " he loved so many " : it is better than, " he killed so many." Yet the world hangs in admiration over this ; you and I should be found alone before the other.

PETRARCA. Of what value are all the honours we can expect from the wisest of our species, when even the wisest hold us lighter in estimation than those who labour to destroy what God delighted to create, came on earth to ransom, and suffered on the cross to save ! Glory then, glory can it be, to devise with long study, and to execute with vast exertions, what the fang of a reptile or the leaf of a weed accomplishes in an hour ? Shall anyone tell me, that the numbers sent to death or to wretchedness make the difference, and constitute the great ? Away then from the face of nature as we see her daily ! away from the interminable varieties of animated creatures ! away from what is fixed to the earth and lives by the sun and dew ! Brute inert matter does it : behold it in the pestilence, in the earthquake, in the conflagration, in the deluge !

BOCCACCIO. Perhaps we shall not be liked the better for what we ourselves have written : yet I do believe we shall be thanked for having brought to light, and for having sent into circulation, the writings of other men. We deserve as much, were it only that it gives people an opportunity of running over us, as ants over the images of gods in orchards, and of reaching by our means the less crude fruits of less ungenial days. Be this as it may, we have spent our time well in doing it, and enjoy (what idlers never can) as pleasant a view in looking back as forward.

Now do tell me, before we say more of the *Paradiso*, what can I offer in defence of the Latin scraps from litanies and lauds, to the number of fifty or thereabout ?

PETRARCA. Say nothing at all, unless you can obtain some Indulgences for repeating them.

BOCCACCIO. And then such verses as these, and several score of no better :

> Io credo ch' ei credette ch' io credesse.[1]
> O Jacopo, dicea, da sant' Andrea,
> Come Livio scrive, che non erra.
> Nel quale un cinquecento diece e cinque.
> Mille ducento con sessanta sei.
> Pape Satan, Pape Satan aleppè.
> Raffael mai *amec, zabi, almi.*
> Non avria pur dall' orlo fatto *cricchi.*

PETRARCA. There is no occasion to look into and investigate a puddle ; we perceive at first sight its impurity ; but it is useful to analyse, if we can, a limpid and sparkling water, in which the common observer finds nothing but transparency and freshness : for in this, however the idle and ignorant ridicule our process, we may exhibit what is unsuspected, and separate what is insalubrious. We must do then for our poet that which other men do for themselves ; we must defend him by advancing the best authority for something as bad or worse ; and although it puzzle our ingenuity, yet we may almost make out in quantity, and quite in quality, our spicilege from Virgil himself. If younger men were present, I would admonish and exhort them to abate no more of their reverence for the Roman poet on the demonstration of his imperfections, than of their love for a parent or guardian who had walked with them far into the country, and had shown them its many beauties and blessings, on his lassitude or his debility. Never will such men receive too much homage. He who can best discover their blemishes, will best appreciate their merit, and most zealously guard their honour. The flippancy with which genius is often treated by mediocrity, is the surest sign of a prostrate mind's incontinence and impotence.

[1] *Inferno*, xiii. 25, xiii. 133, xxviii. 12 ; *Purgatorio*, xxxiii. 43 ; *Inferno*, vii. 1, xxxi. 67, xxxii. 30.

THE PENTAMERON

It will gratify the national pride of our Florentines, if you show them how greatly the nobler parts of their fellow-citizen excel the loftiest of his Mantuan guide.

BOCCACCIO. Of Virgil?

PETRARCA. Even so.

BOCCACCIO. He had no suspicion of his equality with this prince of Roman poets, whose footsteps he follows with reverential and submissive obsequiousness.

PETRARCA. Have you never observed that persons of high rank universally treat their equals with deference ; and that ill-bred ones are often smart and captious ? Even their words are uttered with a brisk and rapid air, a tone higher than the natural, to sustain the factitious consequence and vapouring independence they assume. Small critics and small poets take all this courage when they licentiously shut out the master ; but Dante really felt the veneration he would impress. Suspicion of his superiority he had none whatever, nor perhaps have you yourself much more.

BOCCACCIO. I take all proper interest in my author ; I am sensible to the duties of a commentator ; but in truth I dare hardly entertain that exalted notion. I should have the whole world against me.

PETRARCA. You must expect it for *any* exalted notion ; for anything that so startles a prejudice as to arouse a suspicion that it may be dispelled. You must expect it if you throw open the windows of infection. Truth is only unpleasant in its novelty. He who first utters it, says to his hearer, " You are less wise than I am." Now who likes this ?

BOCCACCIO. But surely if there are some very high places in our Alighieri, the inequalities are perpetual and vast ; whereas the regularity, the continuity, the purity of Virgil, are proverbial.

PETRARCA. It is only in literature that what is proverbial is suspicious ; and mostly in poetry. Do we find in Dante, do we find in Ovid, such tautologies and flatnesses as these ?

> Quam si dura silex—*aut stet Marpessia cautes.*[1]
> Majus adorta nefas—*majoremque orsa furorem.*
> Arma *amens* capio—nec *sat rationis* in armis.

---

[1] *Æn.*, vi. 471, vii. 386, ii. 314.

THE PENTAMERON

Superatne—*et vescitur aura* [1]
Ætheria—neque adhuc crudelibus occubat umbris?
Omnes—cœlicolas—omnes supera alta tenentes.
Scuta *latentia condunt.*
Has inter voces—*media inter talia verba.*
Finem dedit—*ore loquendi.*
Insonuere cavæ—*sonitumque dedere cavernæ.*
Ferro accisam—crebrisque *bipennibus.*
Nec nostri generis puerum—*nec sanguinis.*

BOCCACCIO. These things look very ill in Latin; and yet they had quite escaped my observation. We often find, in the *Psalms of David,* one section of a sentence placed as it were in symmetry with another, and not at all supporting it by presenting the same idea. It is a species of piety to drop the nether lip in admiration; but in reality it is not only the modern taste that is vitiated; the ancient is little less so, although differently. To say over again what we have just ceased to say, with nothing added, nothing improved, is equally bad in all languages and all times.[2]

PETRARCA. But in these repetitions we may imagine one part of the chorus to be answering another part opposite.

BOCCACCIO. Likely enough. However, you have ransacked poor Virgil to the skin, and have stripped him clean.

PETRARCA. Of all who have ever dealt with *Winter,* he is the most frost-bitten. Hesiod's description of the snowy season is more poetical and more formidable. What do you think of these icicles?—

Œraque dissiliunt vulgo; *vestesque rigescunt!* [3]

BOCCACCIO. Wretched falling-off.

PETRARCA. He comes close enough presently.

Stiriaque hirsutis dependent horrida barbis.[4]

---

[1] *Æn.,* i. 546, vi. 787, iii. 237, xii. 318, vi. 76, ii. 53, ii. 627; *Ec.,* viii. 45. But *Æn.,* ii. 53, and *Ec.* misquoted.

[2] 1st ed. reads: "times. Surely you have ransacked," etc.

[3] 1st ed. has the following note: "These verses are noticed in the treatise 'De usu Latini Sermonis.' Remarks on the characters of Proteus, Mezentius, etc., may be found in the Imaginary Conversation of Tooke and Johnson. Some who read this volume may never read those." The reference is to Tooke's severe condemnation of this line (*Georg.,* iii. 360) as "an instance of the art of sinking."

[4] *Georg.,* iii. 363.

THE PENTAMERON

We will withdraw from the Alps into the city.   And now are you not smitten with reverence at seeing

> Romanos rerum dominos ; *gentemque togatam ?* [1]

> The masters of the world—and *long-tailed coats !*

Come to Carthage.   What a recommendation to a beautiful queen does Æneas offer, in himself and his associates !

> *Lupi ceu*
> *Raptores ;* atrâ in nebulâ, quos *improba ventris*
> Exegit cæcos rabies ! [2]

Ovid is censured for his

> *Consiliis* non *curribus* utere nostris. [3]

Virgil never for

> *Inceptoque* et *sedibus* hæret in iisdem. [4]

The same in its quality, but more forced. [5]

The affectation of Ovid was light and playful ; Virgil's was wilful, perverse, and grammatistical.   Are we therefore to suppose that every hand able to elaborate a sonnet may be raised up against the majesty of Virgil ?   Is ingratitude so rare and precious, that we should prefer the exposure of his faults to the enjoyment of his harmony ?   He first delivered it to his countrymen in unbroken links under the form of poetry, and consoled them for the eloquent tongue that had withered on the Rostra.   It would be no difficult matter to point out at least twenty bad passages in the *Æneid*, and a proportionate number of worse in the *Georgics*.   In your comparison of poet with poet, the defects as well as the merits of each ought to be placed side by side.   This is the rather to be expected, as Dante professes to be Virgil's disciple.   You may easily show that his humility no more became him than his fierceness.

BOCCACCIO.   You have praised the harmony of the Roman poet. Now in single verses I think our poetry is sometimes more harmonious

---

[1] *Æn.*, i. 282.   [2] *Æn.* ii. 355.
[3] *Met.*, ii. 146.   [4] *Æn.*, ii. 654.
[5] 1st ed. reads : " forced.   Of all faults, however, the *hypallage* is incomparably the worst and seems Virgil's favourite.   Such is

> Odor attulit auras

The affectation," etc.   See the Conversation of Tooke and Johnson.

196

than the Latin, but never in whole sentences. Advantage could perhaps be taken of our metre if we broke through the stanza. Our language is capable, I think, of all the vigour and expression of the Latin ; and, in regard to the pauses in our versification, in which chiefly the harmony of metre consists, we have greatly the advantage. What, for instance, is more beautiful than your

> Solo—e pensoso—i più deserti campi
> Vo—misurando—a passi tardi—e lenti.

PETRARCA. My critics have found fault with the *lenti,* calling it an expletive, and ignorant that equally in Italian and Latin the word signifies both *slow* and *languid,* while *tardi* signifies *slow* only.

BOCCACCIO. Good poetry, like good music, pleases most people, but the ignorant and inexpert lose half its pleasures, the invidious lose them all. What a paradise lost is here !

PETRARCA. If we deduct the inexpert, the ignorant, and the invidious, can we correctly say it pleases most people ? But either my worst compositions are the most admired, or the insincere and malignant bring them most forward for admiration, keeping the others in the background ! Sonnetteers, in consequence, have started up from all quarters.

BOCCACCIO. The sonnet seems peculiarly adapted to the languor of a melancholy and despondent love, the rhymes returning and replying to every plaint and every pulsation. Our poetasters are now converting it into the penfold and pound of stray thoughts and vagrant fancies. No sooner have they collected in their excursions as much matter as they conveniently can manage, than they seat themselves down and set busily to work, punching it neatly out with a clever cubic stamp of fourteen lines in diameter.

PETRARCA. A pretty sonnet may be written on a lambkin or a parsnep, there being room enough for truth and tenderness on the edge of a leaf or the tip of an ear ; but a great poet must clasp the higher passions breast high, and compel them in an authoritative tone to answer his interrogatories.

We will now return again to Virgil, and consider in what relation he stands to Dante. Our Tuscan and Homer are never inflated.

BOCCACCIO. Pardon my interruption ; but do you find that Virgil is ? Surely he has always borne the character of the most chaste, the most temperate, the most judicious among the poets.

THE PENTAMERON

PETRARCA. And will not soon lose it. Yet never had there swelled, in the higher or the lower regions of poetry, such a gust as here, in the exordium of the *Georgics* :

> Tuque adeo, quem mox quæ sint habitura deorum
> Concilia incertum est, urbisne invisere, Cæsar,
> Terrarumque velis curam, et te maximus orbis
> Auctorem frugum ? [1]——

BOCCACCIO. Already forestalled !
PETRARCA.

> . . . tempestatumque potentem.

BOCCACCIO. Very strange coincidence of opposite qualifications.
PETRARCA.

> Accipiat, cingens maternâ tempora myrto :
> An deus immensi venias maris.

BOCCACCIO. Surely he would not put down Neptune ?
PETRARCA.

> ——ac tua nautæ
> Numina sola colant : *tibi serviat ultima Thule.*

BOCCACCIO. Catch him up ! catch him up ! uncoil the whole of the vessel's rope ! never did man fall overboard so unluckily, or sink so deep on a sudden.
PETRARCA.

> Teque sibi generum Tethys *emat omnibus undis?*

BOCCACCIO. Nobody in his senses would bid against her : what indiscretion ! and at her time of life too !

> Tethys then really, most gallant Cæsar !
> If you would only condescend to please her,
> With all her waves would you good graces buy,
> And you should govern all the Isle of Skie.

PETRARCA.

> Anne novum *tardis* sidus te mensibus addas ?

BOCCACCIO. For what purpose ? If the months were *slow*, he was not likely to mend their speed by mounting another passenger. But the vacant place is such an inviting one !

[1] *Georg.,* i. 24, and later the passage from 27 to 35.

THE PENTAMERON

PETRARCA.

> Qua locus Erigonen inter Chelasque sequentes
> Panditur.

BOCCACCIO. Plenty of room, sir !

PETRARCA.

> . . . ipse tibi jam brachia contrahit ardens,
> Scorpius. . . .

BOCCACCIO. I would not incommode him ; I would beg him to be quite at his ease.

PETRARCA.

> . . . et cœli justâ plus parte reliquit.
> Quicquid eris (nam te nec sperent Tartara regem
> Nec tibi regnandi veniet tam dira cupido,
> Quamvis Elysios miretur Græcia campos,
> Nec repetita sequi curet Proserpina matrem).

BOCCACCIO. Was it not enough to have taken all Varro's invocation, much enlarged, without adding these verses to the other twenty-three ?

PETRARCA. Vainly will you pass through the later poets of the empire, and look for the like extravagance and bombast. Tell me candidly your opinion, not of the quantity but of the quality.

BOCCACCIO. I had scarcely formed one upon them before. Honestly and truly, it is just such a rumbling rotundity as might have been blown, with much ado, if Lucan and Nero had joined their pipes and puffed together into the same bladder. I never have admired, since I was a schoolboy, the commencement or the conclusion of the *Georgics ;* an unwholesome and consuming fungus at the foot of the tree, a withered and loose branch at the summit.

BOCCACCIO. Virgil and Dante are altogether so different, that, unless you will lend me your whole store of ingenuity, I shall never bring them to bear one upon the other.

PETRARCA. Frequently the points of comparison are salient in proportion as the angles of similitude recede : and the absence of a quality in one man usually makes us recollect its presence in another ; hence the comparison is at the same time natural and involuntary. Few poets are so different as Homer and Virgil, yet no comparison has been made oftener. Ovid, although unlike

199

Homer, is greatly more like him than Virgil is ; for there is the same facility, and apparently the same negligence, in both. The great fault in the *Metamorphoses* is in the plan, as proposed in the argument,

> primaque ab origine mundi
> In mea *perpetuum* deducere tempora carmen.[1]

Had he divided the more interesting of the tales, and omitted all the transformations, he would have written a greater number of exquisite poems than any author of Italy or Greece. He wants on many occasions the gravity of Virgil ; he wants on all the variety of cadence ; but it is a very mistaken notion that he either has heavier faults or more numerous. His natural air of levity, his unequalled and unfailing ease, have always made the contrary opinion prevalent. Errors and faults are readily supposed, in literature as in life, where there is much gaiety : and the appearance of ease, among those who never could acquire or understand it, excites a suspicion of negligence and faultiness. Of all the ancient Romans, Ovid had the finest imagination ; he likewise had the truest tact in judging the poetry of his contemporaries and predecessors. Compare his estimate with Quintilian's of the same writers, and this will strike you forcibly. He was the only one of his countrymen who could justly appreciate the labours of Lucretius.

> Carmina sublimis tunc sunt peritura Lucretî,
> Exitio terras quum dabit una dies.[2]

And the kindness with which he rests on all the others, shows a benignity of disposition which is often lamentably deficient in authors who write tenderly upon imaginary occasions.

I begin to be inclined to your opinion in regard to the advantages of our Italian versification. It surely has a greater variety, in its usual measure, than the Latin, in dactyls, and spondees. We admit several feet into ours : the Latin, if we believe the grammarians, admits only two into the heroic ; and at least seven verses in every ten conclude with a dissyllabic word.

BOCCACCIO. We are taught indeed that the final foot of an hexameter is always a spondee : but our ears deny the assertion, and prove to us that it never is, any more than it is in the Italian. In both the one and the other the last foot is uniformly a trochee

---

[1] *Met.*, i. 3.   [2] *Amor.*, i. 15, 23.

in pronunciation. There is only one species of Latin verse which ends with a true inflexible spondee, and this is the *scazon*. Its name of the *limper* is but little prepossessing, yet the two most beautiful and most perfect poems of the language are composed in it—the *Miser Catulle* and the *Sirmio*.

PETRARCA. This is likewise my opinion of those two little golden images, which however are insufficient to raise Catullus on an equality with Virgil : nor would twenty such. Amplitude of dimensions is requisite to constitute the greatness of a poet, besides his symmetry of form and his richness of decoration. We have conversed more than once together on the defects and oversights of the correct and elaborate Mantuan, but never without the expression of our gratitude for the exquisite delight he has afforded us. We may forgive him his Proteus and his Pollio ; but we can not well forbear to ask him, how Æneas came to know that Acragas was *formerly* the sire of high-mettled steeds, even if such had been the fact ? But such was only the fact a thousand years afterwards, in the reign of Gelon.

BOCCACCIO. Was it *then ?* Were the horses of Gelon and Theron and Hiero, of Agrigentine or Sicilian breed ? The country was never celebrated for a race adapted to chariots ; such horses were mostly brought from Thessaly, and probably some from Africa. I do not believe there was ever a fine one in Italy before the invasion of Pyrrhus. No doubt, Hannibal introduced many. Greece herself, I suspect, was greatly indebted to the studs of Xerxes for the noblest of her prizes on the Olympic plain. In the kingdom of Naples I have observed more horses of high blood than in any other quarter of Italy. It is there that Pyrrhus and Hannibal were stationary : and, long after these, the most warlike of men, the Normans, took possession of the country. And the Normans would have horses worthy of their valour, had they unyoked them from the chariot of the sun. Subduers of France, of Sicily, of Cyprus, they made England herself accept their laws.

Virgil, I remember, in the *Georgics*, has given some directions in the choice of horses. He speaks unfavourably of the white : yet painters have been fond of representing the leaders of armies mounted on them. And the reason is quite as good as the reason of a writer on husbandry, Cato or Columella, for choosing a house-dog of a contrary colour : it being desirable that a general should be as conspicuous as possible, and a dog, guarding against thieves, as invisible.

I love beyond measure in Virgil his kindness toward dumb creatures. Although he represents his Mezentius as a hater of the Gods, and so inhuman as to fasten dead bodies to the living, and violates in him the unity of character more than character was ever violated before, we treat as impossible all he has been telling us of his atrocities, when we hear his allocution to Rhœbus.

PETRARCA. The dying hero, for hero he is transcendently above all the others in the *Æneid*, is not only the kindest father, not only the most passionate in his grief for Lausus, but likewise gives way to manly sorrows for the mute companion of his warfare.

> Rhœbe diu, res si qua diu mortalibus usquam,
> Viximus.[1]

Here the philosophical reflection addressed to the worthy quadruped, on the brief duration of human and equine life, is ill applied. It is not the thought for the occasion ; it is not the thought for the man. He could no more have uttered it than Rhœbus could have appreciated it. This is not however quite so great an absurdity as the tender apostrophe of the monster Proteus to the dead Eurydice. Beside, the youth of Lausus, and the activity and strength of Mezentius, as exerted in many actions just before his fall, do not allow us to suppose that he who says to his horse,

> Diu viximus,

had passed the meridian of existence.

BOCCACCIO. Francesco ! it is a pity you had no opportunity of looking into the mouth of the good horse Rhœbus : perhaps his teeth had not lost all their marks.

PETRARCA. They would have been lost upon me, though horses' mouths to the intelligent are more trustworthy than many others.

BOCCACCIO. I [2] have always been of opinion that Virgil is inferior to Homer, not only in genius, but in judgment, and to an equal degree at the very least. I shall never dare to employ half your suggestions in our irritable city, for fear of raising up two new factions, the Virgilians and the Dantists.

---

[1] *Æn.*, x. 861.   [2] 1st ed. reads : " BOCCACCIO. I shall never dare," etc.

THE PENTAMERON

PETRARCA. I wish in good truth and seriousness you could raise them, or anything like zeal for genius, with whomsoever it might abide.

BOCCACCIO. You really have almost put me out of conceit with Virgil.

PETRARCA. I have done a great wrong then both to him and you. Admiration is not the pursuivant to all the steps even of an admirable poet; but respect is stationary. Attend him where the ploughman is unyoking the sorrowful ox from his companion dead at the furrow; follow him up the arduous ascent where he springs beyond the strides of Lucretius; and close the procession of his glory with the coursers and cars of Elis.

THIRD DAY'S INTERVIEW

It being now the Lord's day, Messer Francesco thought it meet that he should rise early in the morning and bestir himself, to hear mass in the parish church at Certaldo. Whereupon he went on tiptoe, if so weighty a man could indeed go in such a fashion, and lifted softly the latch of Ser Giovanni's chamber-door, that he might salute him ere he departed, and occasion no wonder at the step he was about to take. He found Ser Giovanni fast asleep, with the missal wide open across his nose, and a pleasant smile on his genial joyous mouth. Ser Francesco leaned over the couch, closed his hands together, and, looking with even more than his usual benignity, said in a low voice,

" God bless thee, gentle soul ! the mother of purity and innocence protect thee ! "

He then went into the kitchen, where he found the girl Assunta, and mentioned his resolution. She informed him that the horse had eaten his two beans,* and was as strong as a lion and as ready as a lover. Ser Francesco patted her on the cheek, and called her *semplicetta !* She was overjoyed at this honour from so great a man, the bosom-friend of her good master, whom she had always thought the greatest man in the world, not excepting Monsignore, until he told her he was only a dog confronted with Ser Francesco. She tripped alertly across the paved court into the stable, and took down the saddle and bridle from the farther end of the rack. But Ser Francesco, with his natural politeness, would not allow her to equip his palfrey.

" This is not the work for maidens," said he ; " return to the house, good girl ! "

She lingered a moment, then went away ; but, mistrusting the dexterity of Ser Francesco, she stopped and turned back again, and peeped through the half-closed door, and heard sundry sobs and wheezes round about the girth. Ser Francesco's wind ill seconded

* Literally, *due fave*, the expression on such occasions to signify a small quantity.—W. S. L.

his intention ; and, although he had thrown the saddle valiantly and stoutly in its station, yet the girths brought him into extremity. She entered again, and dissembling the reason, asked him whether he would not take a small beaker of the sweet white wine before he set out, and offered to girdle the horse while his Reverence bitted and bridled him. Before any answer could be returned, she had begun. And having now satisfactorily executed her undertaking, she felt irrepressible delight and glee at being able to do what Ser Francesco had failed in. He was scarcely more successful with his allotment of the labour ; found unlooked-for intricacies and complications in the machinery, wondered that human wit could not simplify it, and declared that the animal had never exhibited such restiveness before. In fact, he never had experienced the same grooming. At this conjuncture, a green cap made its appearance, bound with straw-coloured ribbon, and surmounted with two bushy sprigs of hawthorn, of which the globular buds were swelling, and some bursting, but fewer yet open. It was young Simplizio Nardi, who sometimes came on the Sunday morning to sweep the courtyard for Assunta.

" O ! this time you are come just when you were wanted," said the girl.

" Bridle, directly, Ser Francesco's horse, and then go away about your business."

The youth blushed, and kissed Ser Francesco's hand, begging his permission. It was soon done. He then held the stirrup ; and Ser Francesco, with scarcely three efforts, was seated and erect on the saddle. The horse, however, had somewhat more inclination for the stable than for the expedition ; and, as Assunta was handing to the rider his long ebony staff, bearing an ivory caduceus, the quadruped turned suddenly round. Simplizio called him *bestiaccia !* and then, softening it, *poco garbato !* and proposed to Ser Francesco that he should leave the bastone behind, and take the crab-switch he presented to him, giving at the same time a sample of its efficacy, which covered the long grizzle hair of the worthy quadruped with a profusion of pink blossoms, like embroidery. The offer was declined ; but Assunta told Simplizio to carry it himself, and to walk by the side of Ser Canonico quite up to the church-porch, having seen what a sad, dangerous beast his reverence had under him.

205

THE PENTAMERON

With perfect good will, partly in the pride of obedience to Assunta, and partly to enjoy the renown of accompanying a canon of holy church, Simplizio did as she enjoined.

And now the sound of village bells, in many hamlets and convents and churches out of sight, was indistinctly heard, and lost again ; and at last the five of Certaldo seemed to crow over the faintness of them all. The freshness of the morning was enough of itself to excite the spirits of youth ; a portion of which never fails to descend on years that are far removed from it, if the mind has partaken in innocent mirth while it was its season and its duty to enjoy it. Parties of young and old passed the canonico and his attendant with mute respect, bowing and bare-headed ; for that ebony staff threw its spell over the tongue, which the frank and hearty salutation of the bearer was inadequate to break. Simplizio, once or twice, attempted to call back an intimate of the same age with himself ; but the utmost he could obtain was a *riveritissimo !* and a genuflexion to the rider. It is reported that a heart-burning rose up from it in the breast of a cousin, some days after, too distinctly apparent in the long-drawn appellation of *Gnor** Simplizio.

Ser Francesco moved gradually forward, his steed picking his way along the lane, and looking fixedly on the stones with all the sobriety of a mineralogist. He himself was well satisfied with the pace, and told Simplizio to be sparing of the switch, unless in case of a hornet or a gadfly. Simplizio smiled, toward the hedge, and wondered at the condescension of so great a theologian and astrologer, in joking with him about the gadflies and hornets in the beginning of April. " Ah ! there are men in the world who can make wit out of anything ! " said he to himself.

As they approached the walls of the town, the whole country was pervaded by a stirring and diversified [1] air of gladness. Laughter and songs and flutes and viols, inviting voices and complying responses, mingled with merry bells and with processional hymns, along the woodland paths and along the yellow meadows. It was really the *Lord's Day*, for he made his creatures happy in it, and their hearts were thankful. Even the cruel had ceased from cruelty ; and the rich man alone exacted from the animal his daily labour. Ser Francesco made this remark, and told his youthful guide that

* Contraction of *signor*, customary in Tuscany.—W. S. L.
[1] 1st ed. reads : " diversifying."

THE PENTAMERON

he had never been before where he could not walk to church on a Sunday ; and that nothing should persuade him to urge the speed of his beast, on the seventh day, beyond his natural and willing foot's-pace. He reached the gates of Certaldo more than half an hour before the time of service, and he found laurels suspended over them, and being suspended ; and many pleasant and beautiful faces were protruded between the ranks of gentry and clergy who awaited him. Little did he expect such an attendance ; but Fra Biagio of San Vivaldo, who himself had offered no obsequiousness or respect, had scattered the secret of his visit throughout the whole country. A young poet, the most celebrated in the town, approached the canonico with a long scroll of verses, which fell below the knee, beginning,

How shall we welcome our illustrious guest ?

To which Ser Francesco immediately replied, " Take your favourite maiden, lead the dance with her, and bid all your friends follow ; you have a good half-hour for it."

Universal applauses succeeded, the music struck up, couples were instantly formed. The gentry on this occasion led out the cittadinanza, as they usually do in the villeggiatura, rarely in the carnival, and never at other times. The elder of the priests stood round in their sacred vestments, and looked with cordiality and approbation on the youths, whose hands and arms could indeed do much, and did it, but whose active eyes could rarely move upward the modester of their partners.

While the elder of the clergy were thus gathering the fruits of their liberal cares and paternal exhortations, some of the younger looked on with a tenderer sentiment, not unmingled with regret. Suddenly the bells ceased ; the figure of the dance was broken ; all hastened into the church ; and many hands that joined on the green, met together at the font, and touched the brow reciprocally with its lustral waters, in soul-devotion.

After the service, and after a sermon a good church-hour in length to gratify him, enriched with compliments from all authors, Christian and Pagan, informing him at the conclusion that, although he had been crowned in the Capitol, he must die, being born mortal, Ser Francesco rode homeward. The sermon seemed to have sunk deeply into him, and even into the horse under him, for both of them nodded, both snorted, and one stumbled. Simplizio was twice fain to cry.

" Ser Canonico ! Riverenza ! in this country if we sleep before dinner it does us harm. There are stones in the road, Ser Canonico, loose as eggs in a nest, and pretty nigh as thick together, huge as mountains."

" Good lad ! " [1] said Ser Francesco, rubbing his eyes, " toss the biggest of them out of the way, and never mind the rest."

The horse, although he walked, shuffled almost into an amble as he approached the stable, and his master looked up at it with nearly the same contentment. Assunta had been ordered to wait for his return, and cried,

" O Ser Francesco ! you are looking at our long apricot, that runs the whole length of the stable and barn, covered with blossoms as the old white hen is with feathers. You must come in the summer, and eat this fine fruit with Signor Padrone. You cannot think how ruddy and golden and sweet and mellow it is. There are peaches in all the fields, and plums, and pears, and apples, but there is not another apricot for miles and miles. Ser Giovanni brought the stone from Naples before I was born : a lady gave it to him when she had eaten only half the fruit off it : but perhaps you may have seen her, for you have ridden as far as Rome, or beyond. Padrone looks often at the fruit, and eats it willingly ; and I have seen him turn over the stones in his plate, and choose one out from the rest, and put it into his pocket, but never plant it."

" Where is the youth ? " inquired Ser Francesco.

" Gone away," answered the maiden.

" I wanted to thank him," said the Canonico.

" May I tell him so ? " asked she.

" And give him," continued he, holding a piece of silver . . .

" I will give him something of my own, if he goes on and behaves well," said she : " but Signor Padrone would drive him away for ever, I am sure, if he were tempted in an evil hour to accept a quattrino, for any service he could render the friends of the house."

Ser Francesco was delighted with the graceful animation of this ingenuous girl, and asked her, with a little curiosity, how she could afford to make him a present.

" I do not intend to make him a present," she replied : " but

---

[1] 1st ed. reads : " Good God ! "

it is better he should be rewarded by me," she blushed and hesitated, " or by Signor Padrone," she added, " than by your reverence. He has not done half his duty yet ; not half. I will teach him : he is quite a child ; four months younger than me."

Ser Francesco went into the house, saying to himself at the doorway,

" Truth, innocence, and gentle manners, have not yet left the earth. There are sermons that never make the ears weary. I have heard but few of them, and come from church for this."

Whether Simplizio had obeyed some private signal from Assunta, or whether his own delicacy had prompted him to disappear, he was now again in the stable, and the manger was replenished with hay. A bucket was soon after heard ascending from the well ; and then two words, " Thanks, Simplizio."

When Petrarca entered the chamber, he found Boccaccio with his breviary in his hand, not looking into it indeed, but repeating a thanksgiving in an audible and impassioned tone of voice. Seeing Ser Francesco, he laid the book down beside him, and welcomed him.

" I hope you have an appetite after your ride," said he, " for you have sent home a good dinner before you."

Ser Francesco did not comprehend him, and expressed it not in words but in looks.

" I am afraid you will dine sadly late to-day : noon has struck this half-hour, and you must wait another, I doubt. However, by good luck, I had a couple of citrons in the house, intended to assuage my thirst if the fever had continued. This being over, by God's mercy, I will try (please God !) whether we two greyhounds cannot be a match for a leveret."

" How is this ? " said Ser Francesco.

" Young Marc-Antonio Grilli, the cleverest lad in the parish at noosing any wild animal, is our patron of the feast. He has wanted for many a day to say something in the ear of Matilda Vercelli. Bringing up the leveret to my bedside, and opening the lips, and cracking the knuckles, and turning the foot round to show the quality and quantity of the hair upon it, and to prove that it really and truly was a leveret, and might be eaten without offence to my teeth, he informed me that he had left his mother in the yard, ready to dress it for me ; she having been cook to the prior. He protested he owed the *crowned martyr* a forest of leverets, boars, deers, and everything else within them, for having commanded the most backward girls to dance directly. Whereupon he darted forth at Matilda, saying, ' The *crowned martyr* orders it,' seizing both her hands, and swinging her round before she knew what she was about. He soon had an opportunity of applying a word, no doubt as dexterously as hand or foot ; and she said submissively, but seriously, and almost sadly, ' Marc-Antonio, now all the people have seen it, they will think it.'

" And, after a pause,

" ' I am quite ashamed : and so should you be : are not you now ? '

" The others had run into the church. Matilda, who scarcely had noticed it, cried suddenly,

" ' O Santissima ! we are quite alone.'

" ' Will you be mine ? ' cried he, enthusiastically.

" ' O ! they will hear you in the church,' replied she.

" ' They shall, they shall,' cried he again, as loudly.

" ' If you will only go away.'

" ' And then ? '

" ' Yes, yes, indeed.'

" ' The Virgin hears you : fifty saints are witnesses.'

" ' Ah ! they know you made me : they will look kindly on us.'

" He released her hand : she ran into the church, doubling her veil (I will answer for her) at the door, and kneeling as near it as she could find a place.

" ' By St. Peter,' said Marc-Antonio, ' if there is a leveret in the wood, the *crowned martyr* shall dine upon it this blessed day.' And he bounded off, and set about his occupation. I inquired what induced him to designate you by such a title. He answered, that everybody knew you had received the crown of martyrdom at Rome, between the pope and antipope, and had performed many miracles, for which they had canonised you, and that you wanted only to die to become a saint."

The leveret was now served up, cut into small pieces, and covered with a rich tenacious sauce, composed of sugar, citron, and various spices. The appetite of Ser Francesco was contagious. Never was dinner more enjoyed by two companions, and never so much by a greater number. One glass of a fragrant wine, the colour of honey, and unmixed with water, crowned the repast. Ser Francesco then went into his own chamber, and found, on his ample mattress, a cool, refreshing sleep, quite sufficient to remove all the fatigues of the morning ; and Ser Giovanni lowered the pillow against which he had seated himself, and fell into his usual repose. Their separation was not of long continuance : and, the religious duties of the Sabbath having been performed, a few reflections on literature were no longer interdicted.

BOCCACCIO. How happens it, O Francesco ! that nearly at the close of our lives, after all our efforts and exhortations, we are standing quite alone in the extensive fields of literature ? We are only like to *scoria* struck from the anvil of the gigantic Dante. We carry our fire along with us in our parabola, and, behold ! it falls extinguished on the earth.

PETRARCA. Courage ! courage ! we have hardly yet lighted the lamp and shown the way.

BOCCACCIO. You are a poet ; I am only a commentator, and must soothe my own failures in the success of my master.

I can not but think again and again, how fruitlessly the bravest have striven to perpetuate the ascendency or to establish the basis of empire, when Alighieri hath fixed a language for thousands of years, and for myriads of men ; a language far richer and more beautiful than our glorious Italy ever knew before, in any of her regions, since the Attic and the Dorian contended for the prize of eloquence on her southern shores. Eternal honour, eternal veneration, to him who raised up our country from the barbarism that surrounded her ! Remember how short a time before him, his master Brunetto Latini wrote in French ; prose indeed ; but whatever has enough in it for poetry, has enough for prose out of its shreds and selvages.

PETRARCA. Brunetto ! Brunetto ! it was not well done in thee. An Italian, a poet, write in French ! What human ear can tolerate its nasty nasalities ? what homely intellect be satisfied with its barebone poverty ? By good fortune we have nothing to do with it in the course of our examination. Several things in Dante himself you will find more easy to explain than to excuse. You have already given me a specimen of them, which I need not assist you in rendering more copious.

BOCCACCIO. There are certainly some that require no little

circumspection.   Difficult as they are to excuse, the difficulty lies more on the side of the clergy than the laity.

PETRARCA. I understand you.   The *gergo* of your author has always a reference to the court of the Vatican.   Here he speaks in the dark : against his private enemies he always is clear and explicit.

Unless you are irresistibly pressed into it, give no more than two, or at most three lectures, on the verse which, I predict, will appear to our Florentines the cleverest in the poem.

Chi nel viso degli uomini legge O M O.

BOCCACCIO. We were very near a new civil war about the interpretation of it.

PETRARCA. Foolisher questions have excited general ones. What, I wonder, rendered you all thus reasonable at last ?

BOCCACCIO. The majority, which on few occasions is so much in the right, agreed with me that the two eyes are signified by the two vowels, the nose by the centre of the consonant, and the temples by its exterior lines.

PETRARCA. In proceeding to explore the Paradise more minutely, I must caution you against remarking to your audience, that, although the nose is between the eyes, the temples are not, exactly. An observation which, if well established, might be resented as somewhat injurious to the Divinity of the *Commedia*.

BOCCACCIO. With all its flatnesses and swamps, many have preferred the *Paradiso* to the other two sections of the poem.

PETRARCA. There is as little in it of very bad poetry, or we may rather say, as little of what is no poetry at all, as in either, which are uninviting from an absolute lack of interest and allusion, from the confusedness of the ground-work, the indistinctness of the scene, and [1] the paltriness (in great measure) of the agents.   If we are amazed at the number of Latin verses in the *Inferno* and *Purgatorio*, what must we be at their fertility in the *Paradiso*, where they drop on us in ripe clusters through every glen and avenue ! We reach the conclusion of the sixteenth canto before we come in sight of poetry, or more than a glade with a gleam upon it.   Here we find a description of Florence in her age of innocence : but the scourge of satire sounds in our ears before we fix the attention.

BOCCACCIO. I like the old Ghibelline best in the seventeenth,

[1] 1st ed. reads : " for."

where he dismisses the doctors, corks up the Latin, ceases from psalmody, looses the arms of Calfucci and Arigucci, sets down Caponsacco in the market, and gives us a stave of six verses which repays us amply for our heaviest toils and sufferings.

Tu lascerai ogni cosa diletta, etc.[1]

But he soon grows weary of tenderness and sick of sorrow, and returns to his habitual exercise of throwing stones and calling names.

Again we are refreshed in the twentieth. Here we come to the simile : here we look up and see his lark, and are happy and lively as herself. Too soon the hard fingers of the master are round our wrists again : we are dragged into the school, and are obliged to attend the divinity-examination, which the poet undergoes from Saint Simon-Peter. He acquits himself pretty well, and receives a handsome compliment from the questioner, who, " *inflamed with love*," acknowledges he has given " *a good account of the coinage, both in regard to weight and alloy.*"

" Tell me," continues he, " have you any of it in your pocket ? "

" Yea," replies the scholar, " and so shining and round that I doubt not what mint it comes from."

Saint Simon-Peter does not take him at his word for it, but tries to puzzle and pose him with several hard queries. He answers both warily and wittily, and grows so contented with his examining master, that, instead of calling him, " *a sergeant of infantry*," as he did before, he now entitles him, " *the baron.*"

I must consult our bishop ere I venture to comment on these two verses :

Credo una essenza, sì una e sì trina
Che sofferà congiunto *sunt et este*,[2]

as whatever may peradventure lie within them, they are hardly worth the ceremony of being burnt alive for, although it should be at the expense of the Church.

PETRARCA. I recommend to you the straightforward course ; but I believe I must halt a little, and advise you to look about you. If you let people see that there are so many faults in your author, they will reward you, not according to your merits, but according to its defects. On celebrated writers, when we speak in public, it is safer

---

[1] *Paradiso,* xvii. 55. [2] *Paradiso,* xxiv. 140.

to speak magnificently than correctly. Therefore be not too cautious in leading your disciples, and in telling them, here you may step securely, here you must mind your footing : for a florin will drop out of your pocket at every such crevice you stop to cross.

BOCCACCIO. The room is hardly light enough to let me see whether you are smiling : but, being the most ingenuous soul alive, and by no means the least jocose one, I suspect it. My office is, to explain what is difficult, rather than to expatiate on what is beautiful or to investigate what is amiss. If those who invite me to read the lectures, mark out the topics for me, nothing is easier than to keep within them. Yet with how true and entire a pleasure shall I point out to my fellow-citizens such a glorious tract of splendour as there is in the single line,

> Ciò ch'io vedevo mi sembrava un riso
> Dell' universo ! [1]

With what exultation shall I toss up my gauntlet into the balcony of proud Antiquity, and cry, *Descend! Contend!*

I have frequently heard your admiration of this passage, and therefore I dwell on it the more delighted. Beside, we seldom find anything in our progress that is not apter to excite a very different sensation. School-divinity can never be made attractive to the Muses ; nor will Virgil and Thomas Aquinas ever cordially shake hands. The unrelenting rancour against the popes is more tedious than unmerited : in a poem I doubt whether we would not rather find it unmerited than tedious. For, of all the sins against the spirit of poetry, this is the most unpardonable. Something of our indignation, and a proportion of our scorn, may fairly be detached from the popes, and thrown on the pusillanimous and perfidious who suffered such excrescences to shoot up, exhausting and poisoning the soil they sprang from.

PETRARCA. I do not wonder they make Saint Peter " redden," as we hear they do, but I regret that they make him stammer,

> Quegli ch' usurpa in terra il luogo mio,
> Il luogo mio, il luogo mio, etc. [2]

Alighieri was not the first catholic who taught us that the papacy is usurpation, nor will he be (let us earnestly hope) the last to inculcate so evident a doctrine.

---

[1] *Paradiso*, xxvii. 4. [2] *Paradiso*, xxvii. 22.

BOCCACCIO. Canonico of Parma ! Canonico of Parma ! you make my hair stand on end. But since nobody sees it beside yourself, prythee tell me how it happens that an infallible pope should denounce as damnable the decision of another infallible pope, his immediate predecessor ? Giovanni the twenty-second, whom you knew intimately, taught us that the souls of the just could not enjoy the sight of God until after the day of universal judgment. But the doctors of theology at Paris, and those learned and competent clerks, the kings of France and Naples, would not allow him to die before he had swallowed the choke-pear they could not chew. The succeeding pope, who called himself an ass, in which infallibility was less wounded, and neither king nor doctor carped at it (for not only was he one, but as truth-telling a beast as Balaam's), condemned this error, as indeed well he might, after two kings had set their faces against it. But on the whole, the thing is ugly and perplexing. That they were both infallible we know ; and yet they differed ! Nay, the former differed from himself, and was pope all the while ; of course infallible ! Well, since we may not solve the riddle, let us suppose it is only a mystery the more, and be thankful for it.

PETRARCA. That is best.

BOCCACCIO. I never was one of those who wish for ice to slide upon in summer. Being no theologian, I neither am nor desire to be sharp-sighted in articles of heresy : but it is reported that there are among Christians some who hesitate to worship the Virgin.

PETRARCA. Few, let us hope.

BOCCACCIO. Hard hearts ! Imagine her, in her fifteenth year, fondling the lovely babe whom she was destined to outlive ! destined to see shedding his blood, and bowing his head in agony. Can we ever pass her by and not say from our hearts :

" O thou whose purity had only the stain of compassionate tears upon it ! blessings, blessings on thee ! "

I never saw her image but it suspended my steps on the highway of the world, discoursed with me, softened and chastened me, showing me too clearly my unworthiness by the light of a reproving smile.

PETRARCA. Woe betide those who cut off from us any source of tenderness, and shut out from any of our senses the access to devotion !

Beatrice, in the place before us, changes colour too, as deeply as ever she did on earth ; for Saint Peter,[1] in his passion, picks up and flourishes some very filthy words. He does not recover the use of his reason on a sudden ; but, after a long and bitter complaint that faith and innocence are only to be found in little children ; and that the child moreover who loves and listens to its mother while it lisps, wishes to see her buried when it can speak plainly ; he informs us that this corruption ought to excite no wonder, since the human race must of necessity go astray, not having any one upon earth to govern it.

BOCCACCIO. Is not this strange though ; from the mouth of one inspired ? We are taught that there never shall be wanting a head to govern the church ; could Saint Peter [2] say that it *was* wanting ? I feel my catholicism here touched to the quick. However, I am resolved not to doubt : the more difficulties I find, the fewer questions I raise : the saints must settle it, as well as they can, among themselves.

PETRARCA. They are nearer the fountain of truth than we are ; and I am confident Saint Paul was in the right.

BOCCACCIO. I do verily believe he may have been, although at Rome we might be in jeopardy for saying it. Well is it for me that my engagement is to comment on Alighieri's *Divina Commedia* instead of his treatise *De Monarchiâ*. He says bold things there, and sets apostles and popes together by the ears. That is not the worst. He would destroy what is and should be, and would establish what never can nor ought to be.

PETRARCA. If a universal monarch could make children good universally, and keep them as innocent when they grow up as when they were in the cradle, we might wish him upon his throne tomorrow. But Alighieri, and those others who have conceived such a prodigy, seem to be unaware that what they would establish for the sake of unity, is the very thing by which this unity must be demolished. For, since universal power does not confer on its possessor universal intelligence, and since a greater number of the cunning could and would assemble round him, he must (if we suppose him like the majority and nearly the totality of his class) appoint a greater proportion of such subjects to the management and control of his dominions. Many of them would become the rulers of cities and of provinces in which they have no connexions or affinities, and

---

[1] 1st ed. reads : " Paul."   [2] 1st ed. reads : " Paul."

in which the preservation of character is less desirable to them than the possession of power. The operations of injustice, and the opportunities of improvement, would be alike concealed from the monarch in the remoter parts of his territories ; and every man of high station would exercise more authority than he.

BOCCACCIO. Casting aside the impracticable scheme of universal monarchy, if kings and princes there must be, even in the midst of civility and letters, why can not they return to European customs, renouncing those Asiatic practices which are become enormously prevalent ? why can not they be contented with such power as the kings of Rome and the lucumons of Etruria were contented with ? But forsooth they are wiser ! and such customs are obsolete ! Of their wisdom I shall venture to say nothing, for nothing, I believe, is to be said of it ; but the customs are not obsolete in other countries. They have taken deep root in the north, and exhibit the signs of vigour and vitality. Unhappily, the weakest men always think they least want help ; like the mad and the drunk. Princes and geese are fond of standing on one leg, and fancy it (no doubt) a position of gracefulness and security, until the cramp seizes them on a sudden : then they find how helpless they are, and how much better it would have been if they had employed all the support at their disposal.

PETRARCA. When the familiars of absolute princes taunt us, as they are wont to do, with the only apophthegm they ever learnt by heart, namely, that it is better to be ruled by one master than by many, I quite agree with them ; unity of power being the principle of republicanism, while the principle of despotism is division and delegation. In the one system, every man conducts his own affairs, either personally or through the agency of some trustworthy representative, which is essentially the same : in the other system, no man, in quality of citizen, has any affairs of his own to conduct : but a tutor has been as much set over him as over a lunatic, as little with his option or consent, and without any provision, as there is in the case of the lunatic, for returning reason. Meanwhile, the spirit of republics is omnipresent in them, as active in the particles as in the mass, in the circumference as in the centre. Eternal it must be, as truth and justice are, although not stationary. Yet when we look on Venice and Genoa, on the turreted Pisa and our own fair Florence, and many smaller cities self-poised in high serenity; when we see what edifices they have raised, and then glance at the wretched habitations of the slaves around, the Austrians, the French, and other fierce restless barbarians ; difficult is it to believe that the beneficent God, who smiled upon these our labours, will ever in his indignation cast them down, a helpless prey to such invaders.

Morals and happiness will always be nearest to perfection in small communities, where functionaries are appointed by as numerous a body as can be brought together of the industrious and intelligent, who have observed in what manner they super-intend their families, and converse with their equals and dependents. Do we find that farms are better cultivated for being large ? is your neighbour friendlier for being powerful ? is your steward honester and more attentive for having a mortgage on your estate or a claim to a joint property in your mansion ? Yet well-educated men are seen about the streets, so vacant and delirious, as to fancy that a country can only be well governed by somebody who never saw and will never see a twentieth part of it, or know a hundredth part of its necessities ; somebody who has no relationships in it, no con-nexions, no remembrances. A man without soul and sympathy is alone to be the governor of men ! Giovanni ! our Florentines are, beyond all others, a treacherous, tricking, mercenary race. What in the name of heaven will become of them, if ever they listen to these ravings ; if ever they lose, by their cowardice and dissensions, the crust of salt that keeps them from putrescency, their freedom ?

BOCCACCIO. Alas ! I dare hardly look out sometimes, lest I see before me the day when German and Spaniard will split them down the back and throw them upon the coals. Sad thought ! here we will have done with it. We cannot help them : we have made the most of them, like the good tailor who, as Dante says, cuts his coat according to his cloth.

PETRARCA. Do you intend, if they should call upon you again, to give them occasionally some of your strictures on his prose writings ?

BOCCACCIO. It would not be expedient. Enough of his political sentiments is exhibited, in various places of his poem, to render him unacceptable to one party ; and enough of his theological, or rather his ecclesiastical, to frighten both. You and I were never passionately fond of the papacy, to which we trace in great measure the miseries of our Italy, its divisions and its corruptions, the sub-stitution of cunning for fortitude, and of creed for conduct. He burst into indignation at the sight of this, and, because the popes took away our Christianity, he was so angry he would throw her freedom after it. Any thorn in the way is fit enough to toss the tattered rag on. A German king will do ; Austrian or Bavarian, Swabian, or Switzer. And, to humiliate us more and more, and render us the laughing-stock of our household, he would invest the intruder with the title of Roman emperor. What ! it is not enough then that he assumes it ! We must invite him, forsooth, to accept it at our hands !

PETRARCA. Let the other nations of Europe be governed by their hereditary kings and feudal princes : it is more accordant with those ancient habits which have not yet given way to the blandishment of literature and the pacific triumph of the arts : but let the states of Italy be guided by their own citizens. May nations find out by degrees that the next evil to being conquered is to conquer, and that he who assists in making slaves gives over at last by becoming one !

BOCCACCIO. Let us endure a French pope, or any other, as well as we can ; there is no novelty in his being a stranger. The Romans at all times picked up recruits from the thieves, gods, and priests, of all nations. Dante is wrong, I suspect, in imagining the popes to be infidels ; and, no doubt, they would pay for indulgences as honestly as they sell them, if there were anybody at hand to receive the money. But who in the world ever thought of buying the cap he was wearing on his own head ? Popes are no such triflers. After all, an infidel pope (and I do not believe there are three in a dozen) is less noxious than a sanguinary soldier, be his appellation what it may, if his power is only limited by his will. My experience has however taught me, that where there is a great mass of power concentrated, it will always act with great influence on the secondary around it. Whether pope or emperor or native king occupy the most authority within the Alps, the barons will range themselves under his banner, apart from the citizens. Venice, who appears to have received by succession the political wisdom of republican Rome, has less political enterprise : and the jealousies of her rivals will always hold them back, or greatly check them, from any plan suggested by her for the general good.

PETRARCA. It appears to be the will of Providence that power and happiness shall never co-exist. Whenever a state becomes powerful, it becomes unjust ; and injustice leads it first to the ruin of others, and next, and speedily, to its own. We, whose hearts are republican, are dazzled by looking so long and so intently at the eagles, and standards, and golden letters, S. P. Q. R. We are reluctant to admit that the most wretched days of ancient Rome were the days of her most illustrious men ; that they began amid the triumphs of Scipio, when the Gracchi perished, and reached the worst under the dictatorship of Cæsar, when perished Liberty herself. A milder and better race was gradually formed by Grecian instruction. Vespasian, Titus, Nerva, Trajan, the Antonines, the Gordians, Tacitus, Probus, in an almost unbroken series, are such men as never wore the diadem in other countries ; and Rome can show nothing comparable to them in the most renowned and virtuous of her earlier consuls. Humanity would be consoled in some degree by them, if their example had sunk into the breasts of the governed. But ferocity is unsoftened by sensuality ; and the milk of the wolf could always be traced in the veins of the effeminated Romans.

PETRARCA.[1] That is true : and they continue to this day less humane than any other people of Italy. The better part of their character has fallen off from them ; and in courage and perseverance they are far behind the Venetians and Ligurians. These last, a scanty population, were hardly to be conquered by Rome in the plentitude of her power, and with all her confederates : for which reason they were hated by her beyond all other nations. To gratify the pride and malice of Augustus, were written the verses :

Vane Ligus ! frustraque animis elate superbis,
Nequicquam patrias tentasti lubricus artes.[2]

Since that time, the inhabitants of Genoa and Venice have been enriched with the generous blood of the Lombards. This little tribe on the Subalpine territory, and the Norman on the Apulian, demonstrate to us, by the rapidity and extension of their conquests, that Italy is an over-ripe fruit, ready to drop from the stalk under the feet of the first insect that alights on it.

BOCCACCIO. The Germans, although as ignorant as the French,

---

[1] Thus in all eds., including Crump's. By an oversight, Landor has made Petrarca reply to himself.
[2] Æn., xi. 715.

are less cruel, less insolent and rapacious. The French have a separate claw for every object of appetite or passion, and a spring that enables them to seize it. The desires of the German are overlaid with food and extinguished with drink, which to others are stimulants and incentives. The German loves to see everything about him orderly and entire, however coarse and common : the nature of the Frenchman is to derange and destroy everything. Sometimes when he has done so, he will reconstruct and refit it in his own manner, slenderly and fantastically ; oftener leaving it in the middle, and proposing to lay the foundation when he has pointed the pinnacles and gilt the weathercock.

PETRARCA. There is no danger that the French will have a durable footing in this or any other country. Their levity is more intolerable than German pressure, their arrogance than German pride, their falsehood than German rudeness, and their vexations than German exaction.

BOCCACCIO. If I must be devoured, I have little choice between the bear and the panther. May we always see the creatures at a distance and across the grating. The French will fondle us, to show us how vastly it is our interest to fondle them ; watching all the while their opportunity ; looking mild and half-asleep ; making a dash at last ; and laying bare and fleshless the arm we extend to them, from shoulder-blade to wrist.

PETRARCA. No nation, grasping at so much, ever held so little, or lost so soon what it had inveigled. Yet France is surrounded by smaller and by apparently weaker states, which she never ceases to molest and invade. Whatever she has won, and whatever she has lost, has been alike won and lost by her perfidy ; the characteristic of the people from the earliest ages, and recorded by a succession of historians, Greek and Roman.

BOCCACCIO. My father spent many years among them, where also my education was completed ; yet whatever I have seen, I must acknowledge, corresponds with whatever I have read, and corroborates in my mind the testimony of tradition. Their ancient history is only a preface to their later. Deplorable as is the condition of Italy, I am more contented to share in her sufferings than in the frothy festivities of her frisky neighbour.

PETRARCA. So am I : but we must never deny or dissemble the victories of the ancient Gauls, many traces of which are remaining ;

not that a nation's glory is the greener for the ashes it has scattered in the season of its barbarism.

BOCCACCIO. The Cisalpine regions were indeed both invaded and occupied by them ; yet, from inability to retain the acquisition, how inconsiderable a part of the population is Gaulish ! Long before the time of Cæsar, the language was Latin throughout : the soldiers of Marius swept away the last dregs and stains on the ancient hearth. Nor is there in the physiognomy of the people the slightest indication of the Gaul, as we perceive by medals and marbles. These would surely preserve his features ; because they can only be the memorials of the higher orders, which of course would have descended from the conquerors. They merged early and totally in the original mass : and the countenances in Cisalpine busts are as beautiful and dignified as our other Italian races.

PETRARCA. The French imagine theirs are too.

BOCCACCIO. I heartily wish them the full enjoyment of their blessings, real or imaginary : but neither their manners nor their principles coincide with ours, nor can a reasonable hope be entertained of benefit in their alliance. Union at home is all we want, and vigilance to perpetuate the better of our institutions.

PETRARCA. The land, O Giovanni, of your early youth, the land of my only love, fascinates us no longer. Italy is our country ; and not ours only, but every man's, wherever may have been his wanderings, wherever may have been his birth, who watches with anxiety the recovery of the Arts, and acknowledges the supremacy of Genius. Beside, it is in Italy at last that all our few friends are resident. Yours were left behind you at Paris in your adolescence, if indeed any friendship can exist between a Florentine and a Frenchman : mine at Avignon were Italians, and older for the most part than myself. Here we know that we are beloved by some, and esteemed by many. It indeed gave me pleasure the first morning as I lay in bed, to overhear the fondness and earnestness which a worthy priest was expressing in your behalf.

BOCCACCIO. In mine ?

PETRARCA. Yes indeed : what wonder ?

BOCCACCIO. A worthy priest ?

PETRARCA. None else, certainly.

BOCCACCIO. Heard in bed ! dreaming, dreaming ; ay ?

PETRARCA. No indeed : my eyes and ears were wide open

222

THE PENTAMERON

Boccaccio. The little parlour opens into your room. But what priest could that be ? Canonico Casini ? He only comes when we have a roast of thrushes, or some such small matter at table : and this is not the season ; they are pairing. Plover eggs might tempt him hitherward. If he heard a plover he would not be easy, and would fain make her drop her oblation before she had settled her nest.

Petrarca. It is right and proper that you should be informed who the clergyman was, to whom you are under an obligation.

Boccaccio. Tell me something about it, for truly I am at a loss to conjecture.

Petrarca. He must unquestionably have been expressing a kind and ardent solicitude for your eternal welfare. The first words I heard on awakening were these :

" Ser Giovanni, although the best of masters—— "

Boccaccio. Those were Assuntina's.

Petrarca. " —— may hardly be quite so holy (not being priest or friar) as your Reverence."

She was interrupted by the question, " What conversation holdeth he ? "

She answered :

" He never talks of loving our neighbour with all our heart, all our soul, and all our strength, although he often gives away the last loaf in the pantry."

Boccaccio. It was she ! Why did she say that ? the slut !

Petrarca. " He doth well," replied the confessor. " Of the church, of the brotherhood, that is, of me, what discourses holdeth he ? "

I thought the question an indiscreet one ; but confessors vary in their advances to the seat of truth.

She proceeded to answer :

" He never said anything about the power of the church to absolve us, if we should happen to go astray a little in good company, like your Reverence."

Here, it is easy to perceive, is some slight ambiguity. Evidently she meant to say, by the seduction of " bad " company, and to express that his Reverence had asserted his power of absolution ; which is undeniable.

Boccaccio. I have my version.

223

PETRARCA. What may yours be ?

BOCCACCIO. Fra Biagio ; broad as daylight ; the whole frock round !

I would wager a flask of oil against a turnip, that he laid another trap for a penance. Let us see how he went on. I warrant, as he warmed, he left off limping in his paces, and bore hard upon the bridle.

PETRARCA. " Much do I fear," continued the expositor, " he never spoke to thee, child, about another world."

There was a silence of some continuance.

" Speak ! " said the confessor.

" No indeed he never did, poor Padrone ! " was the slow and evidently reluctant avowal of the maiden ; for, in the midst of the acknowledgment her sighs came through the crevices of the door : then, without any farther interrogation, and with little delay, she added,

" But he often makes this look like it."

BOCCACCIO. And now, if he had carried a holy scourge, it would not have been on his shoulders that he would have laid it.

PETRARCA. Zeal carries men often too far afloat ; and confessors in general wish to have the sole steerage of the conscience. When she told him that your benignity made this world another heaven, he warmly and sharply answered,

" It is only we who ought to do that."

" Hush," said the maiden ; and I verily believe she at that moment set her back against the door, to prevent the sounds from coming through the crevices, for the rest of them seemed to be just over my night cap. " Hush," said she, in the whole length of that softest of all articulations, " There is Ser Francesco in the next room : he sleeps long into the morning, but he is so clever a clerk, he may understand you just the same. I doubt whether he thinks Ser Giovanni in the wrong for making so many people quite happy ; and if he should, it would grieve me very much to think he blamed Ser Giovanni."

" Who is Ser Francesco ? " he asked, in a low voice.

" Ser Canonico," she answered.

" Of what Duomo ? " continued he.

" Who knows ? " was the reply ; " but he is Padrone's heart's friend, for certain."

" Cospetto di Bacco ! It can then be no other than Petrarca. He makes rhymes and love like the devil. Don't listen to him, or you are undone. Does he love you too, as well as Padrone ? " he asked, still lowering his voice.

" I can not tell that matter," she answered, somewhat impatiently ; " but I love him."

" To my face ! " cried he, smartly.

" To the Santissima ! " replied she, instantaneously ; " for have not I told your Reverence he is Padrone's true heart's friend ! And are not you my confessor, when you come on purpose ? "

" True, true ! " answered he ; " but there are occasions when we are shocked by the confession, and wish it made less daringly."

" I was bold ; but who can help loving him who loves my good Padrone ? " said she, much more submissively.

BOCCACCIO. Brave girl, for that !

Dog of a Frate ! They are all of a kidney ; all of a kennel. I would dilute their meal well and keep them low. They should not waddle and wallop in every hollow lane, nor loll out their watery tongues at every wash-pool in the parish. We shall hear, I trust, no more about Fra Biagio in the house while you are with us. Ah ! were it then for life.

PETRARCA. The man's prudence may be reasonably doubted, but it were uncharitable to question his sincerity. Could a neighbour, a religious one in particular, be indifferent to the welfare of Boccaccio, or any belonging to him ?

BOCCACCIO. I do not complain of his indifference. Indifferent ! no, not he. He might as well be, though. My Villetta here is my castle : it was my father's ; it was his father's. Cowls did not hang to dry upon the same cord with caps in their *podere ;* they shall not in mine. The girl is an honest girl, Francesco, though I say it. Neither she nor any other shall be befooled and bamboozled under my roof. Methinks Holy Church might contrive some improvement upon confession.

PETRARCA. Hush ! Giovanni ! But, it being a matter of discipline, who knows but she might.

BOCCACCIO. Discipline ! ay, ay, ay ! faith and troth there are some who want it.

PETRARCA. You really terrify me. These are sad surmises.

BOCCACCIO. Sad enough : but I am keeper of my handmaiden's probity.

PETRARCA. It could not be kept safer.

BOCCACCIO. I wonder what the Frate would be putting into her head ?

PETRARCA. Nothing, nothing : be assured.

BOCCACCIO. Why did he ask her all those questions ?

PETRARCA. Confessors do occasionally take circuitous ways to arrive at the secrets of the human heart.

BOCCACCIO. And sometimes they drive at it, methinks, a whit too directly. He had no business to make remarks about me.

PETRARCA. Anxiety.

BOCCACCIO. 'Fore God, Francesco, he shall have more of that ; for I will shut him out the moment I am again up and stirring, though he stand but a nose's length off. I have no fear about the girl ; no suspicion of her. He might whistle to the moon on a frosty night, and expect as reasonably her descending. Never was a man so entirely at his ease as I am about that ; never, never. She is adamant ; a bright sword now first unscabbarded ; no breath can hang about it. A seal of beryl, of chrysolite, of ruby ; to make impressions (all in good time and proper place though) and receive none : incapable, just as they are, of splitting, or cracking, or flawing, or harbouring dirt. Let him mind that. Such, I assure you, is that poor little wench, Assuntina.

PETRARCA. I am convinced that so well-behaved a young creature as Assunta——

BOCCACCIO. Right ! Assunta is her name by baptism ; we usually call her Assuntina, because she is slender, and scarcely yet full grown, perhaps : but who can tell ?

As for those friars, I never was a friend to impudence : I hate loose suggestions. In girls' minds you will find little dust but what is carried there by gusts from without. They seldom want sweeping ; when they do, the broom should be taken from behind the house-door, and the master should be the sacristan.

. . . Scarcely were these words uttered when Assunta was heard running up the stairs ; and the next moment she rapped. Being ordered to come in, she entered with a willow twig in her hand, from the middle of which willow twig (for she held the two ends together) hung a fish, shining with green and gold.

THE PENTAMERON

" What hast there, young maiden ? " said Ser Francesco.

" A fish, Riverenza ! " answered she. " In Tuscany we call it *tinca.*"

PETRARCA. I too am a little of a Tuscan.

ASSUNTA. Indeed ! well, you really speak very like one, but only more sweetly and slowly. I wonder how you can keep up with Signor Padrone—he talks fast when he is in health ; and you have made him so. Why did not you come before ? Your Reverence has surely been at Certaldo in time past.

PETRARCA. Yes, before thou wert born.

ASSUNTA. Ah sir ! it must have been long ago then.

PETRARCA. Thou hast just entered upon life.

ASSUNTA. I am no child.

PETRARCA. What then art thou ?

ASSUNTA. I know not : I have lost both father and mother ; there is a name for such as I am.

PETRARCA. And a place in heaven.

BOCCACCIO. Who brought us that fish, Assunta ? hast paid for it ? there must be seven pounds : I never saw the like.

ASSUNTA. I could hardly lift up my apron to my eyes with it in my hand. Luca, who brought it all the way from the Padule, could scarcely be entreated to eat a morsel of bread or sit down.

BOCCACCIO. Give him a flask or two of our wine ; he will like it better than the sour puddle of the plain.

ASSUNTA. He is gone back.

BOCCACCIO. Gone ! who is he, pray ?

ASSUNTA. Luca, to be sure.

BOCCACCIO. What Luca !

ASSUNTA. Dominedio ! O Riverenza ! how sadly must Ser Giovanni, my poor padrone, have lost his memory in this cruel long illness ! he can not recollect young Luca of the Bientola, who married Maria.

BOCCACCIO. I never heard of either, to the best of my knowledge.

ASSUNTA. Be pleased to mention this in your prayers to-night, Ser Canonico ! May Our Lady soon give him back his memory ! and everything else she has been pleased (only in play, I hope) to take away from him ! Ser Francesco, you must have heard all over the world how Maria Gargarelli, who lived in the service of our paroco, somehow was outwitted by Satanasso. Monsignore thought the paroco had not done all he might have done against his wiles and craftiness, and sent his Reverence over to the monastery in the mountains, Laverna yonder, to make him look sharp ; and there he is yet.

And now does Signor Padrone recollect ?

BOCCACCIO. Rather more distinctly.

ASSUNTA. Ah me ! Rather more distinctly ! have patience, Signor Padrone ! I am too venturous, God help me ! But, Riverenza, when Maria was the scorn or the abhorrence of everybody else, excepting poor Luca Sabbatini, who had always cherished her, and excepting Signor Padrone, who had never seen her in his lifetime . . . for paroco Snello said he desired no visits from any who took liberties with Holy Church . . . as if Padrone did ! Luca one day came to me out of breath, with money in his hand for our duck. Now it so happened that the duck, stuffed with noble chestnuts, was going to table at that instant. I told Signor Padrone.

BOCCACCIO. Assunta, I never heard thee repeat so long and tiresome a story before, nor put thyself out of breath so. Come, we have had enough of it.

PETRARCA. She is mortified : pray let her proceed.

BOCCACCIO. As you will.

ASSUNTA. I told Signor Padrone how Luca was lamenting that Maria was seized with an *imagination*.

PETRARCA. No wonder then she fell into misfortune, and her neighbours and friends avoided her.

ASSUNTA. Riverenza ! how can you smile ? Signor Padrone ! and you too ? You shook your head and sighed at it when it happened. The Demonio, who had caused all the first mischief, was not contented until he had given her the *imagination*.

PETRARCA. He could not have finished his work more effectually.

ASSUNTA. He was balked, however. Luca said,

" She shall not die under her wrongs, please God ! "

I repeated the words to Signor Padrone . . . He seems to listen, Riverenza ! and will remember presently . . . and Signor Padrone cut away one leg for himself, clean forgetting all the chestnuts inside, and said sharply, " Give the bird to Luca ; and, hark ye, bring back the minestra."

Maria loved Luca with all her heart, and Luca loved Maria with all his : but they both hated paroco Snello for such neglect

228

about the evil one. And even Monsignore, who sent for Luca on purpose, had some difficulty in persuading him to forbear from choler and discourse. For Luca, who never swears, swore bitterly that the devil should play no such tricks again, nor alight on girls napping in the parsonage. Monsignore thought he intended to take violent possession, and to keep watch there himself without consent of the incumbent. " I will have no scandal," said Monsignore ; so there was none. Maria, though she did indeed, as I told your Reverence, love her Luca dearly, yet she long refused to marry him, and cried very much at last on the wedding-day, and said, as she entered the porch,

" Luca ! it is not yet too late to leave me."

He would have kissed her, but her face was upon his shoulder.

Pievano Locatelli married them, and gave them his blessing : and going down from the altar, he said before the people, as he stood on the last step, " Be comforted, child ! be comforted ! God above knows that thy husband is honest, and that thou art innocent." Pievano's voice trembled, for he was an aged and holy man, and had walked two miles on the occasion. Pulcheria, his governante, eighty years old, carried an apronful of lilies to bestrew the altar ; and partly from the lilies, and partly from the blessed angels who (although invisible) were present, the church was filled with fragrance. Many who heretofore had been frightened at hearing the mention of Maria's name, ventured now to walk up toward her ; and some gave her needles, and some offered skeins of thread, and some ran home again for pots of honey.

BOCCACCIO. And why didst not thou take her some trifle ?

ASSUNTA. I had none.

BOCCACCIO. Surely there are always such about the premises.

ASSUNTA. Not mine to give away.

BOCCACCIO. So then at thy hands, Assunta, she went off not overladen. Ne'er a bone-bodkin out of thy bravery, ay ?

ASSUNTA. I ran out knitting, with the woodbine and syringa in the basket for the parlour. I made the basket, . . . I and . . . but myself chiefly, for boys are loiterers.

BOCCACCIO. Well, well : why not bestow the basket, together with its rich contents ?

ASSUNTA. I am ashamed to say it—I covered my half-stocking with them as quickly as I could, and ran after her, and presented it. Not knowing what was under the flowers, and never minding the liberty I had taken, being a stranger to her, she accepted it as graciously as possible, and bade me be happy.

PETRARCA. I hope you have always kept her command.

ASSUNTA. Nobody is ever unhappy here, except Fra Biagio, who frets sometimes : but that may be the walk ; or he may fancy Ser Giovanni to be worse than he really is.

. . . Having now performed her mission and concluded her narrative, she bowed, and said,

" Excuse me, Riverenza ! excuse me, Signor Padrone ! my arm aches with this great fish."

Then, bowing again, and moving her eyes modestly toward each, she added, " with permission ! " and left the chamber.

" About the Sposina," after a pause began Ser Francesco : " about the Sposina, I do not see the matter clearly."

" You have studied too much for seeing all things clearly," answered Ser Giovanni ; " you see only the greatest. In fine, the devil, on this count, is acquitted by acclamation ; and the paroco Snello eats lettuce and chicory up yonder at Laverna. He has mendicant friars for his society every day ; and snails, as pure as water can wash and boil them, for his repast on festivals. Under this discipline, if they keep it up, surely one devil out of legion will depart from him."

FOURTH DAY'S INTERVIEW

PETRARCA. Do not throw aside your *Paradiso* for me. Have you been reading it again so early ?

BOCCACCIO. Looking into it here and there. I had spare time before me.

PETRARCA. You have coasted the whole poem, and your boat's bottom now touches ground. But tell me what you think of Beatrice.

BOCCACCIO. I think her in general more of the seraphic doctor than of the seraph. It is well she retained her beauty where she was, or she would scarcely be tolerable now and then. And yet, in other parts, we forget the captiousness in which Theology takes delight, and feel our bosoms refreshed by the perfect presence of the youthful and innocent Bice.

There is something so sweetly sanctifying in pure love.

PETRARCA.

> Pure love ? there is no other ; nor shall be,
> Till the worst angels hurl the better down
> And heaven lie under hell : if God is one
> And pure, so surely love is pure and one.

BOCCACCIO. You understand it better than I do : you must have your own way.

Above all, I have been admiring the melody of the cadence in this portion of the *Divina Commedia*. Some of the stanzas leave us nothing to desire in facility and elegance.

Alighieri grows harmonious as he grows humane, and does not, like Orpheus, play the better with the beasts about him.

PETRARCA. It is in Paradise that we might expect his tones to be tried and modulated.[1]

BOCCACCIO. None of the imitative arts should repose on writhings and distortions. Tragedy herself, unless she lead from Terror to Pity, has lost her way.

[1] 1st ed. reads : " moderated.

THE PENTAMERON

PETRARCA. What then must be thought of a long and crowded work, whence Pity is violently excluded, and where Hatred is the first personage we meet, and almost the last we part from ?

BOCCACCIO. Happily the poet has given us here a few breezes of the morning, a few glimpses of the stars, a few similes of objects to which we have been accustomed among the amusements or occupations of the country. Some of them would be less admired in a meaner author, and are welcome here chiefly as a variety and relief to the mind, after a long continuance in a painful posture. Have you not frequently been pleased with a short quotation of verses in themselves but indifferent, from finding them in some tedious dissertation ? and especially if they carry you forth a little into the open air.

PETRARCA. I am not quite certain whether, if the verses were indifferent, I should willingly exchange the prose for them ; bad prose being less wearisome than bad poetry : so much less indeed, that the advantage of the exchange might fail to balance the account.

BOCCACCIO. Let me try whether I can not give you an example of such effect, having already given you the tedious dissertation.

PETRARCA. Do your worst.

BOCCACCIO. Not that neither, but bad enough.

THE PILGRIM'S SHELL

Under a tuft of eglantine, at noon,
I saw a pilgrim loosen his broad shell
To catch the water off a stony tongue ;
Medusa's it might be, or Pan's, erewhile,
For the huge head was shapeless, eaten out
By time and tempest here, and here embost
With clasping tangles of dark maidenhair.
" How happy is thy thirst ! how soon assuaged !
How sweet that coldest water this hot day ! "
Whispered my thoughts ; not having yet observ'd
His shell so shallow and so chipt around.
Tall though he was, he held it higher, to meet
The sparkler at its outset : with fresh leap,
Vigorous as one just free upon the world,
Impetuous too as one first checkt, with stamp
Heavy as ten such sparklers might be deemed,
Rusht it amain, from cavity and rim

And rim's divergent channels, and dropt thick
(Issuing at wrist and elbow) on the grass.
The pilgrim shook his head, and fixing up
His scallop,
          " There is something yet," said he,
" Too scanty in this world for my desires ! "

PETRARCA. O Giovanni ! these are better thoughts and oppor-
tuner than such lonely places formerly supplied us with. The
whispers of rose-bushes were not always so innocent : under the
budding and under the full-blown we sometimes found other images :
sometimes the pure fountain failed in bringing purity to the heart.

Unholy fire sprang up in fields and woods ;
The air that fann'd it came from solitudes.

If our desires are worthy ones and accomplished, we rejoice in
after-time ; if unworthy and unsuccessful, we rejoice no less at
their discomfiture and miscarriage. We can not have all we wish
for. Nothing is said oftener, nothing earlier, nothing later. It
begins in the arms with the chidings of the nurse ; it will terminate
with the milder voice of the physician at the death-bed. But
although everybody has heard and most have said it, yet nobody
seems to have said or considered, that it is much, very much, to be
able to form and project our wishes ; that, in the voyage we take
to compass and turn them to account, we breathe freely and hope-
fully ; and that it is chiefly in the stagnation of port we are in
danger of disappointment and disease.

BOCCACCIO. The young man who resolves to conquer his love,
is only half in earnest or has already half conquered it. But fields
and woods have no dangers now for us. I may be alone until dooms-
day, and loose thoughts will be at fault if they try to scent me.

PETRARCA. When the rest of our smiles have left us, we may
smile at our immunities. There are indeed, for nearly all,

Rocks on the shore wherefrom we launch on life,
Before our final harbour rocks again,
And (narrow sun-paced plains sailed swiftly by)
Eddies and breakers all the space between.

Yet Nature preserves her sedater charms for us both, and I
doubt whether we do not enjoy them the more, by exemption from

233

solicitations and distractions. We are not old while we can hear and enjoy, as much as ever,

> The lonely bird, the bird of even-song,
> When, catching one far call, he leaps elate,
> In his full fondness drowns it, and again
> The shrill shrill glee through Serravalle rings.

BOCCACCIO. The nightingale is a lively bird to the young and joyous, a melancholy one to the declining and pensive. He has notes for every ear ; he has feelings for every bosom ; and he exercises over gentle souls a wider and more welcome dominion than any other creature. If I must not offer you my thanks, for bringing to me such associations as the bed-side of sickness is rarely in readiness to supply ; if I must not declare to you how pleasant and well placed are your reflections on our condition ; I may venture to remark on the nightingale, that our Italy is the only country where this bird is killed for the market. In no other is the race of Avarice and Gluttony so hard run. What a triumph for a Florentine, to hold under his fork the most delightful being in all animated nature ! the being to which every poet, or nearly every one, dedicates the first fruits of his labours. A cannibal who devours his enemy, through intolerable hunger, or, what he holds as the measure of justice and of righteousness, revenge, may be viewed with less abhorrence than the heartless gormandiser, who casts upon his loaded stomach the little breast that has poured delight on thousands.

PETRARCA. The English, I remember Ser Geoffreddo * telling us, never kill singing-birds nor swallows.

BOCCACCIO. Music and hospitality are sweet and sacred things with them, and well may they value their few warm days, out of which, if the produce is not wine and oil, they gather song and garner sensibility.

PETRARCA. Ser Geoffreddo felt more pleasure in the generosity and humanity of his countrymen, than in the victories they had recently won, with incredibly smaller numbers, over their boastful enemy.

BOCCACCIO. I know not of what nation I could name so amusing a companion as Ser Geoffreddo. The Englishman is rather an island than an islander ; bluff, stormy, rude, abrupt, repulsive,

* Chaucer.—W. S. L.

inaccessible. We must not however hold back or dissemble the learning, and wisdom, and courtesy, of the better. While France was without one single man above a dwarf in literature, and we in Italy had only a small sprinkling of it, Richard de Bury was sent ambassador to Rome by King Edward. So great was his learning, that he composed two grammars, one Greek, one Hebrew ; neither of which labours had been attempted by the most industrious and erudite of those who spoke the languages : he likewise formed so complete a library as belongs only to the Byzantine emperors. This prelate came into Italy attended by Ser Geoffreddo, in whose company we spent, as you remember, two charming evenings at Arezzo.

PETRARCA. What wonderful things his countrymen have been achieving in this century !

BOCCACCIO. And how curious it is to trace them up into their Norwegian coves and creeks three or four centuries back !

PETRARCA. Do you think it possible that Norway, which never could maintain sixty thousand * male adults, was capable of sending, from her native population, a sufficient force of warriors to conquer the best province of France, and the whole of England ? And you must deduct from these sixty thousand, the aged, the artisans, the cultivators, and the clergy, together with all the dependents of the church : which numbers, united, we may believe amounted to above one-half.

BOCCACCIO. That she could embody such an army from her own very scanty and scattered population ; no, indeed : but if you recollect that a vast quantity of British had been ejected by incursions of Picts, and that also there had been on the borders a general insurrection against the Romans, and against those of half-blood (which is always the case in a rebellion of the Aboriginals), and if you believe, as I do, that the ejected Romans of the coast at least, became pirates, and were useful to the Scandinavians, by introducing what was needful of their arts and saleable of their plunder, taking in exchange their iron and timber, you may readily admit as a probability, that by the display of spoils and the spirit of enterprise, they encouraged, headed, and carried into effect the

---

* With the advantage of her fisheries, which did not exist in the age of Petrarca, and of her agriculture, which probably is quintupled since, Norway does not contain at present the double of the number.—W. S. L.

invasion of France, and subsequently of England. The English gentlemen of Norman descent have neither blue eyes, in general, nor fair complexions, differing in physiognomy altogether both from the Belgic race and the Norwegian. Beside, they are remarkable for a sedate and somewhat repulsive pride, very different from the effervescent froth of the one, and the sturdy simplicity of the other. Ser Geoffreddo is not only the greatest genius, but likewise the most amiable of his nation. He gave his thoughts and took yours with equal freedom. His countrymen, if they give you any, throw them at your head ; and, if they receive any, cast them under their feet before you. Courtesy is neither a quality of native growth, nor communicable to them. Their rivals, the French, are the best imitators in the world ; the English the worst ; particularly under the instruction of the Graces. They have many virtues, no doubt ; but they reserve them for the benefit of their families, or of their enemies ; and they seldom take the trouble to unpack them in their short intercourse abroad.

PETRARCA. Ser Geoffreddo, I well remember, was no less remarkable for courtesy than for cordiality.

BOCCACCIO. He was really as attentive and polite toward us as if he had made us prisoners. It is on that occasion the English are most unlike their antagonists and themselves. What an evil must they think it to be vanquished ! when, struggling with their bashfulness and taciturnity, they become so solicitous and inventive in raising the spirits of the fallen. The Frenchman is ready to truss you on his rapier, unless you acknowledge the perfection of his humanity, and to spit in your face, if you doubt for a moment the delicacy of his politeness. The Englishman is almost angry if you mention either of these as belonging to him, and turns away from you that he may not hear it.

PETRARCA. Let us felicitate ourselves that we rarely are forced to witness his self-affliction.

BOCCACCIO. In palaces, and especially the pontifical, it is likely you saw the very worst of them : indeed there are few in any country of such easy, graceful, unaffected manners as our Italians. We are warmer at the extremities than at the heart : sunless nations have central fires. The Englishman is more gratified when you enable him to show you a fresh kindness, than when you remind him of a past one ; and he forgets what he has conferred as readily as we

236

forget what we have received. In our civility, in our good-nature, in our temperance, in our frugality, none excel us ; and greatly are we in advance of other men, in the arts, in the sciences, in the culture, in the application, and in the power of intellect. Our faculties are perfect, with the sole exception of memory ; and our memory is only deficient in its retentiveness of obligation.

PETRARCA. Better had it failed in almost all its other functions. Yet, if our countrymen presented any flagrant instances of ingratitude, Alighieri would have set apart a *bolga* for their reception.

BOCCACCIO. When I correct and republish my *Commentary*, I must be careful to gratify, as my author was to affront them. I know, from the nature of the Florentines and of the Italians in general, that in calling on me to produce one, they would rather I should praise indiscriminately than parsimoniously. And respect is due to them for repairing, by all the means in their power, the injustice their fathers committed ; for enduring in humility his resentment ; and for investing him with public honours, as they would some deity who had smitten them. Respect is due to them, and I will offer it, for placing their greatness on so firm a plinth, for deriving their pride from so wholesome a source, and for declaring to the world that the founder of a city is less than her poet and instructor.

PETRARCA. In the precincts of those lofty monuments, those towers and temples, which have sprung up amid her factions, the name of Dante is heard at last, and heard with such reverence as only the angels or the saints inspire.

BOCCACCIO. There are towns so barbarous, that they must be informed by strangers of their own great man, when they happen to have produced one ; and would then detract from its merits, that they might not exhibit their awkwardness in doing him honour, or their shame in withholding it. There are such ; but not in Italy. I have seen youths standing and looking with seriousness, and indeed with somewhat of veneration, on the broad and low stone bench, to the south of the Cathedral, where Dante sat to enjoy the fresh air in summer evenings ; and where Giotto, in conversation with him, watched the scaffolding rise higher and higher up his gracefullest of towers. It was truly a bold action, when a youngster pushed another down on the poet's seat. The surprised one blushed and struggled, as those do who unwittingly have been drawn into a penalty (not lightened by laughter) for having sitten in the imperial or the papal chair.

PETRARCA. These are good signs, and never fallacious. In the presence of such young persons we ought to be very cautious how we censure a man of genius. One expression of irreverence may eradicate what demands the most attentive culture, may wither the first love for the fair and noble, and may shake the confidence of those who are about to give the hand to a guidance less liable to error. We have ever been grateful to the Deity, for saving us from among the millions swept away by the pestilence, which depopulated the cities of Italy, and ravaged the whole of Europe : let us be equally grateful for an exemption as providential and as rare in the world of letters ; an exemption from that *Plica Polonica* of invidiousness, which infests the squalider of poetical heads, and has not always spared those which [1] ought to have been cleanlier.

BOCCACCIO. Critics are indignant if we are silent, and petulant if we complain. You and I are so kindly and considerate in regard to them, that we rather pat their petulance than prick up their indignation. Marsyas,[2] while Apollo was flaying him leisurely and dexterously, with all the calmness of a God, shortened his upper lip prodigiously, and showed how royal teeth are fastened in their gums : his eyes grew bloodshot, and expanded to the size of rock-melons, though naturally, in length and breadth, as well as colour, they more resembled a well-ripened bean-pod. And there issued from his smoking breast, and shook the leaves above it, a rapid irregular rush of yells and howlings. Remarking so material a change in his countenance and manners, a satyr, who was much his friend and deeply interested in his punishment, said calmly, " Marsyas ! Marsyas ! is it thou who cries out so unworthily ? If thou couldst only look down from that pleasant, smooth, shady beech-tree, thou wouldst have the satisfaction of seeing that thy skin is more than half drawn off thee : it is hardly worth while to make a bustle about it now."

PETRARCA. Every Marsyas hath his consoling satyr. Probably when yours was flayed, he was found out to be a good musician, by those who recommended the flaying and celebrated the flayer. Among authors, none hath so many friends as he who is just now

---

[1] 1st ed. reads : " who."
[2] 1st ed. absurdly reads : " Midas."

dead, and had the most enemies last week. Those who were then his adversaries are now sincerely his admirers, for moving out of the way, and leaving one name less in the lottery. And yet, poor souls ! the prize will never fall to them. There is something sweet and generous in the tone of praise, which captivates an ingenuous mind, whatever may be the subject of it ; while propensity to censure not only excites suspicion of malevolence, but reminds the hearer of what he can not disentangle from his earliest ideas of vulgarity. There being no pleasure in thinking ill, it is wonderful there should be any in speaking ill. You, my friend, can find none of it : but every step you are about to take in the revisal of your Lectures will require much caution. Aware you must be that there are many more defects in our author than we have touched or glanced at : principally the loose and shallow foundation of so vast a structure ; its unconnectedness ; its want of manners, of passion, of action, consistently and uninterruptedly at work toward a distinct and worthy purpose ; and lastly (although less importantly as regards the poetical character) that splenetic temper, which seems to grudge brightness to the flames of hell, to delight in deepening its gloom, in multiplying its miseries, in accumulating weight upon depression, and building labyrinths about perplexity.

BOCCACCIO. Yet, O Francesco ! when I remember what Dante had suffered and was suffering from the malice and obduracy of his enemies ; when I feel (and how I do feel it !) that you also have been following up his glory through the same paths of exile ; I can rest only on what is great in him, and the exposure of a fault appears to me almost an inhumanity.

The first time I ever walked to his villa on the Mugnone, I felt a vehement desire to enter it ; and yet a certain awe came upon me, as about to take an unceremonious and an unlawful advantage of his absence. While I was hesitating, its inhabitant opened the gate, saluted, and invited me. My desire vanished at once ; and although the civility far exceeded what a stranger as I was, and so young a stranger too, could expect, or what probably the more illustrious owner would have vouchsafed, the place itself and the disparity of its occupier made me shrink from it in sadness, and stand before him almost silent. I believe I should do the same at the present day.

PETRARCA. With such feelings, which are ours in common, there is little danger that we should be unjust toward him ; and, if ever our opinions come before the public, we may disregard the petulance and aspersions of those whom Nature never constituted our judges, as she did us of Dante. It is our duty to speak with freedom ; it is theirs to listen with respect.

BOCCACCIO. History would come much into the criticism, and would perform the most interesting part in it. But I clearly see how unsafe it is to meddle with the affairs of families : and every family in Florence is a portion of the government, or has been lately. Everyone preserves the annals of the republic ; the facts being nearly the same, the inferences widely diverging, the motives utterly dissimilar. A strict examination of Dante would involve the bravest and most intelligent ; and the court of Rome, with its royal agents, would persecute them as conspirators against religion, against morals, against the peace, the order, the existence of society. When studious and quiet men get into power, they fancy they can not show too much activity, and very soon prove, by exerting it, that they can show too little discretion. The military, the knightly, the baronial, are spurred on to join in the chase ; but the fleshers have other names and other instincts.

PETRARCA. Posterity will regret that many of those allusions to persons and events, which we now possess in the pages of Dante, have not reached her. Among the ancients there are few poets who more abound in them than Horace does, and yet we feel certain that there are many which are lost to us.

BOCCACCIO. I wonder you did not mention him before. Perhaps he is no favourite with you.

PETRARCA. Why can not we be delighted with an author, and even feel a predilection for him, without a dislike to others ? An admiration of Catullus or Virgil, of Tibullus or Ovid, is never to be heightened by a discharge of bile on Horace.

BOCCACCIO. The eyes of critics, whether in commending or carping, are both on one side, like a turbot's.

PETRARCA. There are some men who delight in heating themselves with wine, and others with headstrong frowardness. These are resolved to agitate the puddle of their blood by running into parties, literary or political, and espouse a champion's cause with such ardour that they run against everything in their way. Perhaps they never knew or saw the person, or understood his merits : what

THE PENTAMERON

matter ? No sooner was I about to be crowned, than it was predicted by these astrologers, that Protonotary Nerucci and Cavallerizzo Vuotasacchetti (two lampooners, whose hands had latterly been kept from their occupation by drawing gold-embroidered gloves on them) would be rife in the mouths of men after my name had fallen into oblivion.

Boccaccio. I never heard of them before.

Petrarca. So much the better for them, and none the worse for you. Vuotasacchetti had been convicted of filching in his youth ; and Nerucci was so expert a logician, and so rigidly economical a moralist, that he never had occasion for veracity.

Boccaccio. The upholders of such gentry are like little girls with their dolls : they must clothe them, although they strip every other doll in the nursery. It is reported that our Giotto, a great mechanician as well as architect and painter, invented a certain instrument by which he could contract the dimensions of any head laid before him. But these gentlemen, it appears, have improved upon it, and not only can contract one, but enlarge another.

Petrarca. He could perform his undertaking with admirable correctness and precision ; can they theirs ?

Boccaccio. I never heard they could : but well enough for their customers and their consciences.

Petrarca. I see then no great accuracy is required.

Boccaccio. If they heard you they would think you very dull.

Petrarca. They have always thought me so : and, if they change their opinion, I shall begin to think so myself.

Boccaccio. They have placed themselves just where, if we were mischievous, we might desire to see them. We have no power to make them false and malicious, yet they become so the moment they see or hear of us, and thus sink lower than our force could ever thrust them. Pigs, it is said, driven into a pool beyond their depth, cut their throats by awkward attempts at swimming. We could hardly wish them worse luck, although each had a devil in him. Come, let us away ; we shall find a purer stream and pleasanter company on the Sabine farm.

Petrarca. We may indeed think the first ode of little value, the second of none, until we come to the sixth stanza.

Boccaccio. Bad as are the first and second, they are better than that wretched one, sounded so lugubriously in our ears at school.

as the masterpiece of the pathetic ; I mean the ode addressed to
Virgil on the death of Quinctilius Varus.

> Præcipe lugubres
> Cantus, Melpomene, cui liquidam pater
> Vocem cum citharâ dedit.[1]

Did he want anyone to help him to cry ?   What man immersed
in grief cares a quattrino about Melpomene, or her father's fairing
of an artificial cuckoo and a gilt guitar ?   What man, on such an
occasion, is at leisure to amuse himself with the little plaster images
of Pudor and Fides, of Justitia and Veritas, or disposed to make a
comparison of Virgil and Orpheus ?   But if Horace had written a
thousand-fold as much trash, we are never to forget that he also
wrote

> Cœlo tonantem, etc.,[2]

in competition with which ode, the finest in the Greek language
itself has, to my ear, too many low notes, and somewhat of a wooden
sound.   And give me *Vixi puellis*, and give me *Quis multa gracilis*,
and as many more as you please ; for there are charms in nearly all
of them.   It now occurs to me that what is written, or interpolated,

> Acer et *Mauri* peditis cruentum
> Vultus in hostem,[3]

should be *manci ;* a foot soldier *mutilated*, but looking with indignant
courage at the trooper who inflicted the wound.   The Mauritanians
were celebrated only for their cavalry.   In return for my suggestion,
pray tell me what is the meaning of

> *Obliquo laborat*
> *Lympha fugax trepidare rivo.*[4]

PETRARCA. The moment I learn it you shall have it.   *Laborat
trepidare ! lympha rivo ! fugax* too !   *Fugacity* is not the action
for hard work, or *labour*.

BOCCACCIO. Since you can not help me out, I must give up the
conjecture, it seems, while it has cost me only half a century.
Perhaps it may be *curiosa felicitas*.

PETRARCA. There again !   Was there ever such an unhappy

---

[1] Horace, *Carm.*, I. xxiv. 2.   [2] *Carm.*, I. iii. 5.
[3] *Carm.*, I. ii. 39.   [4] *Carm.*, II. iii. 11.

(not to say absurd) expression ! And this from the man who wrote the most beautiful sentence in all latinity.

BOCCACCIO. What is that ?

PETRARCA. I am ashamed of repeating it, although in itself it is innocent. The words are :

> Gratias ago languori tuo, quo diutius sub
> umbrâ voluptatis lusimus.

BOCCACCIO. Tear out this from the volume ; the rest, both prose and poetry, may be thrown away. In the *Dinner of Nasidienus*, I remember the expression *nosse laboro ; I am anxious to know :* this expedites the solution but little. In the same piece there is another odd expression :

> Tum in lecto quôque *videres*
> *Stridere* secretâ divisos aure *susurros*.[1]

PETRARCA. I doubt Horace's felicity in the choice of words, being quite unable to discover it, and finding more evidences of the contrary than in any contemporary or preceding poet ; but I do not doubt his infelicity in his *transpositions* of them, in which certainly he is more remarkable than whatsoever writer of antiquity. How simple, in comparison are Catullus * and Lucretius in the structure of their sentences ! but the most simple and natural of all are Ovid and Tibullus. Your main difficulty lies in another road : it consists not in making explanations, but in avoiding them. Some scholars will assert that everything I have written in my sonnets is allegory or allusion ; others will deny that anything is ; and similarly of Dante. It was known throughout Italy that he was the lover of *Beatrice* Portinari. He has celebrated her in many compositions ; in prose and poetry, in Latin and Italian. Hence it became the safer for him afterward to introduce her as an allegorical personage, in opposition to the *Meretrice ;* under which appellation he (and I subsequently) signified the Papacy. Our great poet wandered among the marvels of the Apocalypse, and fixed his eyes the most attentively on the words.

> Veni, et ostendam tibi sponsam, uxorem Agni.

---

[1] *Sat.*, II. viii. 19, 77.

* Except "Non, ita me divi, vera gemunt, juêrint."—W. S. L. [Note added in 2nd ed.] But the line construes easily : "No, so may the gods help me, not truly they lament."

He, as you know, wrote a commentary on his *Commedia* at the close of his Treatise *de Monarchiâ*. But he chiefly aims at showing the duties of pope and emperor, and explaining such parts of the poem as manifestly relate to them. The Patarini accused the pope of despoiling and defiling the church ; the Ghibellines accused him of defrauding and rebelling against the emperor ; Dante enlists both under his flaming banner, and exhibits the *Meretrice* stealing from *Beatrice* both the *divine* and the *august* chariot ; the church and empire. Grave critics will protest their inability to follow you through such darkness, saying you are not worth the trouble, and they must give you up. If Laura and Fiametta were allegorical, they could inspire no tenderness in our readers, and little interest. But, alas ! these are no longer the days to dwell on them.

> Let human art exert her utmost force,
> Pleasure can rise no higher than its source ;
> And there it ever stagnates where the ground
> Beneath it, O Giovanni ! is unsound.

Boccaccio. You have given me a noble quaternion [1] ; for which I can only offer you such a string of beads as I am used to carry about with me. Memory, they say, is the mother of the Muses : this is her gift, not theirs.

DEPARTURE FROM FIAMETTA

> When go I must, as well she knew,
> And neither yet could say adieu,
> Sudden was my Fiametta's fear
> To let me see or feel a tear.
> It could but melt my heart away,
> Nor add one moment to my stay.
> But it was ripe and would be shed . . .
> So from her cheek upon my head
> It, falling on the neck behind,
> Hung on the hair she oft had twined.
> Thus thought she, and her arm's soft strain
> Claspt it, and down it fell again.

Come, come, bear your disappointment, and forgive my cheating you in the exchange ! Ah Francesco ! Francesco ! well may you sigh ; and I too ; seeing we can do little now but make verses and

[1] 1st ed. reads : " quotation."

doze, and want little but medicine and masses, while Fra Biagio is merry as a lark, and half master of the house. Do not look so grave upon me for remembering so well another state of existence. He who forgets his love may still more easily forget his friendships. I am weak, I confess it, in yielding my thoughts to what returns no more ; but you alone know my weakness.

PETRARCA. We have loved * ; and so fondly as we believe none other ever did ; and yet, although it was in youth, Giovanni, it was not in the earliest white dawn, when we almost shrink from its freshness, when everything is pure and quiet, when little of earth is seen, and much of heaven. It was not so with us ; it was with Dante. The little virgin Beatrice Portinari breathed all her purity into his boyish heart, and inhaled it back again ; and if war and disaster, anger and disdain, seized upon it in her absence, they never could divert its course nor impede its destination. Happy the man who carries love with him in his opening day ! he never loses its freshness in the meridian of life, nor its happier influence in the later hour. If Dante enthroned his Beatrice in the highest heaven, it was Beatrice who conducted him hither. Love, preceding passion, ensures, sanctifies, and I would say survives it, were it not rather an absorption and transfiguration into its own most perfect purity and holiness.

BOCCACCIO. Up ! up ! look into that chest of letters, out of which I took several of yours to run over yesterday morning. All those of a friend whom we have lost, to say nothing of a tenderer affection, touch us sensibly, be the subject what it may. When, in taking them out to read again, we happen to come upon him in some pleasant mood, it is then the dead man's hand is at the heart. Opening the same paper long afterward, can we wonder if a tear has raised its little island in it ? Leave me the memory of all my friends, even of the ungrateful ! They must remind me of some kind feeling ; and perhaps of theirs ; and for that very reason they deserve another. It was not my fault if they turned out less worthy than I hoped and

---

* The tender and virtuous Shenstone, in writing the most beautiful of epitaphs, was unaware how near he stood to Petrarca. Heu quanto minus est cum aliis versari quàm tui meminisse,

> Pur mi consola che morir per lei
> Meglio è che gioir d'altra.—W. S. L.

[Note added in 2nd ed. The reference is to Shenstone's lines for Miss Dolman.]

fancied them. Yet half the world complains of ingratitude, and the remaining half of envy. Of the one I have already told you my opinion, and heard yours ; and the other we may surely bear with quite as much equanimity. For rarely are we envied, until we are so prosperous that envy is rather a familiar in our train than an enemy who waylays us. If we saw nothing of such followers and outriders, and no scabbard with our initials upon it, we might begin to doubt our station.

PETRARCA. Giovanni, you are unsuspicious, and would scarcely see a monster in a minotaur. It is well, however, to draw good out of evil, and it is the peculiar gift of an elevated mind. Nevertheless, you must have observed, although with greater curiosity than concern, the slipperiness and tortuousness of your detractors.

BOCCACCIO. Whatever they detract from me, they leave more than they can carry away. Beside, they always are detected.

PETRARCA. When they are detected, they raise themselves up fiercely, as if their nature were erect and they could reach your height.

BOCCACCIO. Envy would conceal herself under the shadow and shelter of contemptuousness, but she swells too huge for the den she creeps into. Let her lie there and crack, and think no more about her. The people you have been talking of can find no greater and no other faults in my writings than I myself am willing to show them, and still more willing to correct. There are many things, as you have just now told me, very unworthy of their company.

PETRARCA. He who has much gold is none the poorer for having much silver too. When a king of old displayed his wealth and magnificence before a philosopher, the philosopher's exclamation was :

" How many things are here which I do not want ! "

Does not the same reflection come upon us, when we have laid aside our compositions for a time, and look into them again more leisurely ? Do we not wonder at our own profusion, and say like the philosopher,

" How many things are here which I do not want ! "

It may happen that we pull up flowers with weeds ; but better this than rankness. We must bear to see our first-born despatched before our eyes, and give them up quietly.

BOCCACCIO. The younger will be the most reluctant. There are poets among us who mistake in themselves the freckles of the hay-fever for beauty-spots. In another half century their volumes will be enquired after ; but only for the sake of cutting out an illuminated letter from the title-page, or of transplanting the willow at the end, that hangs so prettily over the tomb of Amaryllis. If they wish to be healthy and vigorous, let them open their bosoms to the breezes of Sunium ; for the air of Latium is heavy and overcharged. Above all, they must remember two admonitions ; first, that sweet things hurt digestion ; secondly, that great sails are ill adapted to small vessels. What is there lovely in poetry unless there be moderation and composure ? Are they not better than the hot, uncontrollable harlotry of a flaunting, dishevelled enthusiasm ? Whoever has the power of creating, has likewise the inferior power of keeping his creation in order. The best poets are the most impressive, because their steps are regular; for without regularity there is neither strength nor state. Look at Sophocles, look at Æschylus, look at Homer.

PETRARCA. I agree with you entirely to the whole extent of your observations ; and, if you will continue, I am ready to lay aside my Dante for the present.

BOCCACCIO. No, no ; we must have him again between us : there is no danger that he will sour our tempers.

PETRARCA. In comparing his and yours, since you forbid me to declare all I think of your genius, you will at least allow me to congratulate you as being the happier of the two.

BOCCACCIO. Frequently, where there is great power in poetry, the imagination makes encroachments on the heart, and uses it as her own. I have shed tears on writings which never cost the writer a sigh, but which occasioned him to rub the palms of his hands together, until they were ready to strike fire, with satisfaction at having overcome the difficulty of being tender.

PETRARCA. Giovanni ! are you not grown satirical ?

BOCCACCIO. Not in this. It is a truth as broad and glaring as the eye of the Cyclops. To make you amends for your shuddering, I will express my doubt, on the other hand, whether Dante felt all the indignation he threw into his poetry. We are immoderately fond of warming ourselves ; and we do not think, or care, what the fire is composed of. Be sure it is not always of cedar, like Circe's.*

* Dives inaccessis ubi Solis filia lucis
  Urit odoratam nocturna in lumina cedrum.
  Æn.—W. S. L.

THE PENTAMERON

Our Alighieri had slipt into the habit of vituperation ; and he thought it fitted him ; so he never left it off.

PETRARCA. Serener colours are pleasanter to our eyes and more becoming to our character. The chief desire in every man of genius is to be thought one ; and no fear or apprehension lessens it. Alighieri, who had certainly studied the gospel, must have been conscious that he not only was inhumane, but that he betrayed a more vindictive spirit than any pope or prelate [1] who is enshrined within the fretwork of his golden grating.

BOCCACCIO. Unhappily, his strong talon had grown into him, and it would have pained him to suffer amputation. This eagle, unlike Jupiter's, never loosened the thunderbolt from it under the influence of harmony.

PETRARCA. The only good thing we can expect in such minds and tempers, is good poetry : let us at least get that ; and, having it, let us keep and value it. If you had never written some wanton stories, you would never have been able to show the world how much wiser and better you grew afterward.

BOCCACCIO. Alas ! if I live, I hope to show it. You have raised my spirits : and now, dear Francesco ! do say a couple of prayers for me, while I lay together the materials of a tale ; a right merry one, I promise you. Faith ! it shall amuse you, and pay decently for the prayers ; a good honest litany-worth. I hardly know whether I ought to have a nun in it : do you think I may ?

PETRARCA. Can not you do without one ?

BOCCACCIO. No ; a nun I must have : say nothing against her ; I can more easily let the abbess alone. Yet Frate Biagio *—

---

[1] 1st ed. reads : " prelate enshrined."

* Our San Vivaldo is enriched by his deposit. In the church, on the fifth flagstone from before the high altar, is this inscription :

HIC SITUS EST,

BEATAM IMMORTALITATEM EXPECTANS,

D. BLASIUS DE BLASIIS,

HUJUS CŒNOBII ABBAS,

SINGULARI VIR CHARITATE,

MORIBUS INTEGERRIMIS,

REI THEOLOGICÆ NEC NON PHYSICÆ

PERITISSIMUS.

ORATE PRO ANIMA EJUS.

To the word *orate* have been prefixed the letters PL, the aspiration, no doubt, of some friendly monk ; although Monsignore thinks it susceptible of two interpretations ; the other he reserves *in petto*. *Domenico Grigi.*—W. S. L.

that Frate Biagio, who never came to visit me but when he thought I was at extremities or asleep—Assuntia ! are you there ?

PETRARCA. No ; do you want her ?

BOCCACCIO. Not a bit. That Frate Biagio has heightened my pulse when I could not lower it again. The very devil is that Frate for heightening pulses. And with him I shall now make merry—God willing—in God's good time—should it be his divine will to restore me ! which I think he has begun to do miraculously. I seem to be within a frog's leap of well again ; and we will presently have some rare fun in my *Tale of the Frate.*

PETRARCA. Do not openly name him.

BOCCACCIO. He shall recognise himself by one single expression. He said to me, when I was at the worst,

" Ser Giovanni ! it would not be much amiss (with permission !) if you begin to think (at any spare time) just a morsel, of eternity."

" Ah ! Fra Biagio ! " answered I, contritely, " I never heard a sermon of yours but I thought of it seriously and uneasily, long before the discourse was over."

' ' So must all," replied he, " and yet few have the grace to own it."

Now mind, Francesco ! if it should please the Lord to call me unto him, I say, *The Nun and Fra Biagio* will be found, after my decease, in the closet cut out of the wall, behind yon Saint Zacharias in blue and yellow.

Well done ! well done ! Francesco. I never heard any man repeat his prayers so fast and fluently. Why ! how many (at a guess) have you repeated ? Such is the power of friendship, and such the habit of religion ! They have done me good : I feel myself stronger already. To-morrow I think I shall be able, by leaning on that stout maple stick in the corner, to walk half over my podere.

Have you done ? have you done ?

PETRARCA. Be quiet : you may talk too much.

BOCCACCIO. I can not be quiet for another hour ; so, if you have any more prayers to get over, stick the spur into the other side of them : they must verily speed, if they beat the last.

PETRARCA. Be more serious, dear Giovanni.

BOCCACCIO. Never bid a convalescent be more serious : no, nor a sick man neither. To health it may give that composure which it takes away from sickness. Every man will have his hours of seriousness ; but, like the hours of rest, they often are ill chosen and unwholesome. Be assured, our heavenly Father is as well pleased to see his children in the playground as in the schoolroom. He has provided both for us, and has given us intimations when each should occupy us.

PETRARCA. You are right, Giovanni ! but we know which bell is heard the most distinctly. We fold our arms at the one, try the cooler part of the pillow, and turn again to slumber ; at the first stroke of the other, we are beyond our monitors. As for you, hardly Dante himself could make you grave.

BOCCACCIO. I do not remember how it happened that we slipped away from his side. One of us must have found him tedious.

PETRARCA. If you were really and substantially at his side, he would have no mercy on you.

BOCCACCIO. In sooth, our good Alighieri seems to have had the appetite of a dogfish or shark, and to have bitten the harder the warmer he was. I would not voluntarily be under his manifold rows of dentals. He has an incisor to every saint in the calendar. I should fare, methinks, like Brutus and the Archbishop. He is forced to stretch himself, out of sheer listlessness, in so idle a place as Purgatory : he loses half his strength in Paradise : Hell alone makes him alert and lively : there he moves about and threatens as tremendously as the serpent that opposed the legions on their march in Africa. He would not have been contented in Tuscany itself, even had his enemies left him unmolested. Were I to write on his model a tripartite poem, I think it should be entitled, *Earth, Italy, and Heaven.*

PETRARCA. You will never give yourself the trouble.

BOCCACCIO. I should not succeed.

PETRARCA. Perhaps not : but you have done very much, and may be able to do very much more.

BOCCACCIO. Wonderful is it to me, when I consider that an infirm and helpless creature, as I am, should be capable of laying thoughts up in their cabinets of words, which Time, as he rushes by, with the revolutions of stormy and destructive years, can never move from their places. On this coarse mattress, one among the homeliest in the fair at Impruneta, is stretched an old burgess of Certaldo, of whom perhaps more will be known hereafter than we know of the Ptolemies and the Pharaohs ; while popes and princes are lying as unregarded as the fleas that are shaken out of the

250

window. Upon my life, Francesco! to think of this is enough to make a man presumptuous.

PETRARCA. No, Giovanni! not when the man thinks justly of it, as such a man ought to do, and must. For, so mighty a power over Time, who casts all other mortals under his, comes down to us from a greater; and it is only if we abuse the victory that it were better we had encountered a defeat. Unremitting care must be taken that nothing soil the monuments we are raising : sure enough we are that nothing can subvert, and nothing but our negligence, or worse than negligence, efface them. Under the glorious lamp entrusted to your vigilance, one among the lights of the world, which the ministering angels of our God have suspended for his service, let there stand, with unclosing eyes, Integrity, Compassion, Self-denial.

BOCCACCIO. These are holier and cheerfuller images than Dante has been setting up before us. I hope every thesis in dispute among his theologians will be settled ere I set foot among them. I like Tuscany well enough : it answers all my purposes for the present : and I am without the benefit of those preliminary studies which might render me a worthy auditor of incomprehensible wisdom.

PETRARCA. I do not wonder you are attached to Tuscany. Many as have been your visits and adventures in other parts, you have rendered it pleasanter and more interesting than any : and indeed we can scarcely walk in any quarter from the gates of Florence, without the recollection of some witty or affecting story related by you. Every street, every farm, is peopled by your genius : and this population can not change with seasons or with ages, with factions or with incursions. Ghibellines and Guelphs will have been contested for only by the worms, long before the *Decameron* has ceased to be recited on our banks of blue lilies and under our arching vines. Another plague may come amidst us : and something of a solace in so terrible a visitation would be found in your pages, by those to whom letters are a refuge and relief.

BOCCACCIO. I do indeed think my little bevy from Santa Maria Novella would be better company on such an occasion, than a devil with three heads, who diverts the pain his claws inflicted, by sticking his fangs in another place.

PETRARCA. This is atrocious, not terrific nor grand. Alighieri is grand by his lights, not by his shadows ; by his human affections, not by his infernal. As the minutest sands are the labours of some profound sea, or the spoils of some vast mountain, in like manner his horrid wastes and wearying minutenesses are the chafings of a turbulent spirit, grasping the loftiest things and penetrating the deepest, and moving and moaning on the earth in loneliness and sadness.

BOCCACCIO. Among men he is what among waters is

The strange, mysterious, solitary Nile.

PETRARCA. Is that his verse ? I do not remember it.

BOCCACCIO. No, it is mine for the present : how long it may continue mine I can not tell. I never run after those who steal my apples : it would only tire me : and they are hardly worth recovering when they are bruised and bitten, as they are usually. I would not stand upon my verses : it is a perilous boy's trick, which we ought to leave off when we put on square shoes. Let our prose show what we are, and our poetry what we have been.

PETRARCA. You would never have given this advice to Alighieri.

BOCCACCIO. I would never plough porphyry ; there is ground fitter for grain. Alighieri is the parent of his system, like the sun, about whom all the worlds are but particles thrown forth from him. We may write little things well, and accumulate one upon another ; but never will any be justly called a great poet unless he has treated a great subject worthily. He may be the poet of the lover and of the idler, he may be the poet of green fields or gay society ; but whoever is this can be no more. A throne is not built of birds'-nests, nor do a thousand reeds make a trumpet.

PETRARCA. I wish Alighieri had blown his on nobler occasions.

BOCCACCIO. We may rightly wish it : but, in regretting what he wanted, let us acknowledge what he had : and never forget (which we omitted to mention) that he borrowed less from his predecessors than any of the Roman poets from theirs. Reasonably may it be expected that almost all who follow will be greatly more indebted to antiquity, to whose stores we, every year, are making some addition.

PETRARCA. It can be held no flaw in the title-deeds of genius, if the same thoughts re-appear as have been exhibited long ago. The indisputable sign of defect should be looked for in the proportion they bear to the unquestionably original. There are ideas which necessarily must occur to minds of the like magnitude and materials, aspect and temperature. When two ages are in the same phasis, they will excite the same humours, and produce the same coincidences and combinations. In addition to which a great poet may really borrow : he may even condescend to an obligation at the hand of an equal or inferior : but he forfeits his title if he borrows more than the amount of his own possessions. The nightingale himself takes somewhat of his song from birds less glorified : and the lark, having beaten with her wing the very gates of heaven, cools her breast among the grass. The lowlier of intellect may lay out a table in their field, at which table the highest one shall sometimes be disposed to partake : want does not compel him. Imitation, as we call it, is often weakness, but it likewise is often sympathy.

BOCCACCIO. Our poet was seldom accessible in this quarter. Invective picks up the first stone on the wayside, and wants leisure to consult a forerunner.

PETRARCA. Dante (original enough everywhere) is coarse and clumsy in this career. Vengeance has nothing to do with comedy, nor properly with satire. The satirist who told us that Indignation made his verses * for him, might have been told in return that she excluded him thereby from the first class, and thrust him among the rhetoricians and declaimers. Lucretius, in his vituperation, is graver and more dignified than Alighieri. Painful ; to see how tolerant is the atheist, how intolerant the catholic : how anxiously the one removes from among the sufferings of Mortality, her last and heaviest, the fear of a vindictive Fury pursuing her shadow across rivers of fire and tears : how laboriously the other brings down Anguish and Despair, even when Death has done his work. How grateful the one is to that beneficent philosopher who made him at peace with himself, and tolerant and kindly toward his fellow creatures ! how importunate the other that God should forego his divine mercy, and hurl everlasting torments both upon the dead and the living !

BOCCACCIO. I have always heard that Ser Dante was a very good man and sound catholic : but Christ forgive me if my heart is oftener on the side of Lucretius ! † Observe, I say, my heart ; nothing more. I devoutly hold to the sacraments and the mysteries : yet

---

* Facit indignatio versum. *Juv.*—W. S. L.

† Qy. How much of Lucretius (or Petronius or Catullus, before cited) was then known ? *Remark by Monsignore.*—W. S. L.

somehow I would rather see men tranquillised than frightened out of their senses, and rather fast asleep than burning. Sometimes I have been ready to believe, as far as our holy faith will allow me, that it were better our Lord were nowhere, than torturing in his inscrutable wisdom, to all eternity, so many myriads of us poor devils, the creatures of his hands. Do not cross thyself so thickly, Francesco! nor hang down thy nether lip so loosely, languidly, and helplessly; for I would be a good catholic, alive or dead. But, upon my conscience, it goes hard with me to think it of him, when I hear that woodlark yonder, gushing with joyousness, or when I see the beautiful clouds, resting so softly one upon another, dissolving—and not damned for it. Above all, I am slow to apprehend it, when I remember his great goodness vouchsafed to me, and reflect on my sinful life heretofore, chiefly in summer time, and in cities, or their vicinity. But I was tempted beyond my strength; and I fell as any man might do. However, this last illness, by God's grace, has well nigh brought me to my right mind again in all such matters : and if I get stout in the present month, and can hold out the next without sliding, I do verily think I am safe, or nearly so, until the season of beccaficoes.

PETRARCA. Be not too confident!

BOCCACCIO. Well, I will not be.

PETRARCA. But be firm.

BOCCACCIO. Assuntina! what! are you come in again?

ASSUNTA. Did you or my master call me, Riverenza?

PETRARCA. No, child!

BOCCACCIO. O! get you gone! get you gone! you little rogue you!

Francesco, I feel quite well. Your kindness to my playful creatures in the *Decameron* has revived me, and has put me into good-humour with the greater part of them. Are you quite certain the Madonna will not expect me to keep my promise? You said you were : I need not ask you again. I will accept the whole of your assurances, and half your praises.

PETRARCA. To represent so vast a variety of personages so characteristically as you have done, to give the wise all their wisdom, the witty all their wit, and (what is harder to do advantageously) the simple all their simplicity, requires a genius such as you alone possess. Those who doubt it are the least dangerous of your rivals.

FIFTH DAY'S INTERVIEW

It being now the last morning that Petrarca could remain with his friend, he resolved to pass early into his bed-chamber. Boccaccio had risen, and was standing at the open window, with his arms against it. Renovated health sparkled in the eyes of the one; surprise and delight and thankfulness to heaven, filled the other's with sudden tears. He clasped Giovanni, kissed his flaccid and sallow cheek, and falling on his knees, adored the Giver of life, the source of health to body and soul. Giovanni was not unmoved: he bent one knee as he leaned on the shoulder of Francesco, looking down into his face, repeating his words, and adding,

" Blessed be thou, O Lord ! who sendest me health again ! and blessings on thy messenger who brought it."

He had slept soundly; for ere he closed his eyes he had unburdened his mind of its freight, not only by employing the prayers appointed by Holy Church, but likewise by ejaculating; as sundry of the fathers did of old. He acknowledged his contrition for many transgressions, and chiefly for uncharitable thoughts of Fra Biagio : on which occasion he turned fairly round on his couch, and leaning his brow against the wall, and his body being in a becomingly curved position, and proper for the purpose, he thus ejaculated :

" Thou knowest, O most Holy Virgin ! that never have I spoken to handmaiden at this villetta, or within my mansion at Certaldo, wantonly or indiscreetly, but have always been, inasmuch as may be, the guardian of innocence ; deeming it better, when irregular thoughts assailed me, to ventilate them abroad than to poison the house with them. And if, sinner as I am, I have thought uncharitably of others, and more especially of Fra Biagio, pardon me, out of thy exceeding great mercies ! And let it not be imputed to me, if I have kept, and may keep hereafter, an eye over him, in wariness and watchfulness ; not otherwise. For thou knowest, O Madonna ! that many who have a perfect and unwavering faith in thee, yet do cover up their cheese from the nibblings of vermin."

Whereupon, he turned round again, threw himself on his back

at full length, and feeling the sheets cool, smooth, and refreshing, folded his arms, and slept instantaneously. The consequence of his wholesome slumber was a calm alacrity : and the idea that his visitor would be happy at seeing him on his feet again, made him attempt to get up : at which he succeeded, to his own wonder. And it was increased by the manifestation of his strength in opening the casement, stiff from being closed, and swelled by the continuance of the rains. The morning was warm and sunny : and it is known that on this occasion he composed the verses below :

> My old familiar cottage-green !
> I see once more thy pleasant sheen ;
> The gossamer suspended over
> Smart celandine by lusty clover ;
> And the last blossom of the plum
> Inviting her first leaves to come ;
> Which hang a little back, but show
> 'Tis not their nature to say no.
> I scarcely am in voice to sing
> How graceful are the steps of Spring ;
> And ah ! it makes me sigh to look
> How leaps along my merry brook,
> The very same to-day as when
> He chirrupt first to maids and men.

PETRARCA. I can rejoice at the freshness of your feelings : but the sight of the green turf reminds me rather of its ultimate use and destination.

> For many serves the parish pall,
> The turf in common serves for all.

BOCCACCIO. Very true ; and, such being the case, let us carefully fold it up, and lay it by until we call for it.

Francesco, you made me quite light-headed yesterday. I am rather too old to dance either with Spring, as I have been saying, or with Vanity : and yet I accepted her at your hand as a partner. In future, no more of comparisons for me ! You not only can do me no good, but you can leave me no pleasure : for here I shall remain the few days I have to live, and shall see nobody who will be disposed to remind me of your praises. Beside, you yourself will get hated for them. We neither can deserve praise nor receive it with impunity.

THE PENTAMERON

PETRARCA. Have you never remarked that it is into quiet water that children throw pebbles to disturb it ? and that it is into deep caverns that the idle drop sticks and dirt ? We must expect such treatment.

BOCCACCIO. Your admonition shall have its wholesome influence over me, when the fever your praises have excited has grown moderate.

—After the conversation on this topic and various others had continued some time, it was interrupted by a visitor. The clergy and monkery at Certaldo had never been cordial with Messer Giovanni, it being suspected that certain of his *Novelle* were modelled on originals in their orders. Hence, although they indeed both professed and felt esteem for Canonico Petrarca, they abstained from expressing it at the villetta. But Frate Biagio of San Vivaldo was (by his own appointment) the friend of the house ; and, being considered as very expert in pharmacy, had, day after day, brought over no indifferent store of simples, in ptisans, and other refections, during the continuance of Ser Giovanni's ailment. Something now moved him to cast about in his mind whether it might not appear dutiful to make another visit. Perhaps he thought it possible that, among those who peradventure had seen him lately on the road, one or other might expect from him a solution of the questions, What sort of person was the *crowned martyr ?* whether he carried a palm in his hand ? whether a seam was visible across the throat ? whether he wore a ring over his glove, with a chrysolite in it, like the bishops, but representing the city of Jerusalem and the judgment seat of Pontius Pilate ? Such were the reports ; but the inhabitants of San Vivaldo could not believe the Certaldese, who, inhabiting the next township to them, were naturally their enemies. Yet they might believe Frate Biagio, and certainly would interrogate him accordingly. He formed his determination, put his frock and hood on, and gave a curvature to his shoe, to evince his knowledge of the world, by pushing the extremity of it with his breast-bone against the corner of his cell. Studious of his figure and of his attire, he walked as much as possible on his heels, to keep up the reformation he had wrought in the workmanship of the cordwainer. On former occasions he had borrowed a horse, as being wanted to hear confession or to carry medicines, which might otherwise be too late. But, having put on an entirely new habiliment, and it being the season when horses are beginning to do the same, he deemed it prudent to travel on foot. Approaching the villetta, his first intention was to walk directly into his patient's room : but he found it impossible to resist the impulses of pride, in showing Assunta his rigid and stately frock, and shoes rather of the equestrian order than the monastic. So he went into the kitchen where the girl was at work, having just taken away the remains of the breakfast.

" Frate Biagio ! " cried she, " is this you ? Have you been sleeping at Comte Jeronimo's ? "

" Not I," replied he.

" Why ! " said she, " those are surely his shoes ! Santa Maria ! you must have put them on in the dusk of the morning, to say your prayers in ! Here ! here ! take these old ones of Signor Padrone, for the love of God ! I hope your Reverence met nobody."

FRATE. What dost smile at ?

ASSUNTA. Smile at ! I could find in my heart to laugh outright, if I only were certain that nobody had seen your Reverence in such a funny trim. Riverenza ! put on these.

FRATE. Not I indeed.

ASSUNTA. Allow me then ?

FRATE. No, nor you.

ASSUNTA. Then let me stand upon yours, to push down the points.

—Frate Biagio now began to relent a little, when Assunta, who had made one step toward the project, bethought herself suddenly, and said,

" No ; I might miss my footing. But, mercy upon us ! what made you cramp your Reverence with those ox-yoke shoes ? and strangle your Reverence with that hang-dog collar ? "

" If you must know," answered the Frate, reddening, " it was because I am making a visit to the Canonico of Parma. I should like to know something about him : perhaps you could tell me ? "

ASSUNTA. Ever so much.

FRATE. I thought no less : indeed I knew it. Which goes to bed first ?

ASSUNTA. Both together.

FRATE. Demonio ! what dost mean ?

ASSUNTA. He tells me never to sit up waiting, but to say my prayers and dream of the Virgin.

FRATE. As if it was any business of his ! Does he put out his lamp himself ?

ASSUNTA. To be sure he does : why should not he ? what should he be afraid of ? It is not winter : and beside, there is a mat upon the floor, all round the bed, excepting the top and bottom.

FRATE. I am quite convinced he never said anything to make you blush. Why are you silent ?

ASSUNTA. I have a right.

FRATE. He did then ? ay ? Do not nod your head : that will never do. Discreet girls speak plainly.

ASSUNTA. What would you have ?

FRATE. The truth ; the truth ; again, I say, the truth.

ASSUNTA. He *did* then.

FRATE. I knew it ! The most dangerous man living !

ASSUNTA. Ah ! indeed he is ! Signor Padrone said so.

FRATE. He knows him of old : he warned you, it seems.

ASSUNTA. Me ! He never said it was I who was in danger.

FRATE. He might : it was his duty.

ASSUNTA. Am I so fat ? Lord ! you may feel every rib. Girls who run about as I do, slip away from apoplexy.

FRATE. Ho ! ho ! that is all, is it ?

ASSUNTA. And bad enough too ! that such good-natured men should ever grow so bulky ; and stand in danger, as Padrone said they both do, of such a seizure ?

FRATE. What ? and art ready to cry about it ? Old folks can not die easier : and there are always plenty of younger to run quick enough for a confessor. But I must not trifle in this manner. It is my duty to set your feet in the right way : it is my bounden duty to report to Ser Giovanni all irregularities I know of, committed in his domicile. I could indeed, and would, remit a trifle, on hearing the worst. Tell me now, Assunta ! tell me, you little angel ! did you—we all may, the very best of us may, and do—sin, my sweet ?

ASSUNTA. You may be sure I do not : for whenever I sin I run into church directly, although it snows or thunders ; else I never could see again Padrone's face, or any one's.

FRATE. You do not come to me.

ASSUNTA. You live at San Vivaldo.

FRATE. But when there is sin so pressing I am always ready to be found. You perplex, you puzzle me. Tell me at once how he made you blush.

ASSUNTA. Well then !

FRATE. Well then ! you did not hang back so before him. I lose all patience.

ASSUNTA. So famous a man !—

FRATE. No excuse in that.

ASSUNTA. So dear to Padrone—

FRATE. The more shame for him !

ASSUNTA. Called me—

FRATE. And *called* you, did he ! the traitorous swine !

ASSUNTA. Called me—*good girl.*

FRATE. Psha ! the wenches, I think, are all mad : but few of them in this manner.

—Without saying another word, Fra Biagio went forward and opened the bedchamber-door, saying, briskly,

" Servant ! Ser Giovanni ! Ser Canonico ! most devoted ! most obsequious ! I venture to incommode you. Thanks to God, Ser Canonico, you are looking well for your years. They tell me you were formerly (who would believe it ?) the handsomest man in Christendom, and worked your way glibly, yonder at Avignon.

" Capperi ! Ser Giovanni ! I never observed that you were sitting bolt-upright in that long-backed arm-chair, instead of lying abed. Quite in the right. I am rejoiced at such a change for the better. Who advised it ? "

BOCCACCIO. So many thanks to Fra Biagio ! I not only am sitting up, but have taken a draught of fresh air at the window, and every leaf had a little present of sunshine for me.

There is one pleasure, Fra Biagio, which I fancy you never have experienced, and I hardly know whether I ought to wish it you ; the first sensation of health after a long confinement.

FRATE. Thanks ! infinite ! I would take any man's word for that, without a wish to try it. Everybody tells me I am exactly what I was a dozen years ago ; while, for my part, I see everybody changed : those who ought to be much about my age, even those— Per Bacco ! I told them my thoughts when they had told me theirs; and they were not so agreeable as they used to be in former days.

THE PENTAMERON

BOCCACCIO. How people hate sincerity.

Cospetto! why, Frate! what hast got upon thy toes? Hast killed some Tartar and tucked his bow into one, and torn the crescent from the vizier's tent to make the other match it? Hadst thou fallen in thy mettlesome expedition (and it is a mercy and a miracle thou didst not) those sacrilegious shoes would have impaled thee.

FRATE. It was a mistake in the shoemaker. But no pain or incommodity whatsoever could detain me from paying my duty to Ser Canonico, the first moment I heard of his auspicious arrival, or from offering my congratulations to Ser Giovanni, on the annuncia tion that he was recovered and looking out of the window. All Tuscany was standing on the watch for it, and the news flew like lightning. By this time it is upon the Danube.

And pray, Ser Canonico, how does Madonna Laura do?

PETRARCA. Peace to her gentle spirit! she is departed.

FRATE. Ay, true. I had quite forgotten : that is to say, I recollect it. You told us as much, I think, in a poem on her death. Well, and do you know! our friend Giovanni here is a bit of an author in his way.

BOCCACCIO. Frate! you confuse my modesty.

FRATE. Murder will out. It is a fact, on my conscience. Have you never heard anything about it, Canonico? Ha! we poets are sly fellows : we can keep a secret.

BOCCACCIO. Are you quite sure you can?

FRATE. Try, and trust me with any. I am a confessional on legs : there is no more a whisper in me than in a woolsack.

I [1] am in feather again, as you see ; and in tune, as you shall hear. April is not the month for moping. Sing it lustily.

BOCCACCIO. Let it be your business to sing it, being a Frate ; I can only recite it.

FRATE. Pray do then.

BOCCACCIO.

> Frate Biagio! sempre quando
> Quà tu vieni cavalcando,
> Pensi che le buone strade
> Per il mondo sien ben rade ;

---

[1] 1st ed. reads : " woolsack. BOCCACCIO. I am . . . as you shall hear. FRATE. April," etc.

THE PENTAMERON

E, di quante sono brutte,
La più brutta è tua di tutte.
Badi, non cascare sulle
Graziosissime fanciulle,
Che con capo dritto, alzato,
Uova portano al mercato.
Pessima mi pare l'opra
Rovesciarle sottosopra.
Deh ! scansando le erte e sassi,
Sempre con premura passi.
Caro amico ! Frate Biagio !
Passi pur, ma passi adagio.*

FRATE. Well now really, Canonico, for one not exactly one of us, that canzone of Ser Giovanni has merit : has not it ? I did not ride, however, to-day ; as you may see by the lining of my frock. But *plus non vitiat ;* ay, Canonico ! About the roads he is right enough ; they are the devil's own roads ; that must be said for them.

Ser Giovanni ! with permission ; your mention of eggs in the canzone, has induced me to fancy I could eat a pair of them. The hens lay well now : that white one of yours is worth more than the goose that laid the golden : and you have a store of others, her equals or betters : we have none like them at poor St Vivaldo. *A rivederci, Ser Giovanni ! Schiavo ! Ser Canonico ! mi comandino.*

—Fra Biagio went back into the kitchen, helped himself to a quarter of a loaf, ordered a flask of wine, and, trying several eggs against his lips, selected seven, which he himself fried in oil, although the maid offered her services. He never had been so little disposed to enter into conversation with her ; and, on her asking him how

* Avendo io fatto comparire nel nostro idioma toscano, e senza traduzione, i leggiadri versi sopra stampati, chiedo perdono da chi legge. Non potei, badando con dovuta premura ai miei interessi ed a quelli del proposito mio, non potei, dico, far di meno ; stanteche una riunione de' critici, i più vistosi de Regno unito d'Inghilterra ed Irlanda, avrà con unanimità dichiarato, che nessuno, di quanti esistono i mortali, saprà mai indovinare la versione. Stimo assai il tradduttore ; lavore per poco, e agevolmente ; mi pare piutosto galantuomo ; non c' è male ; ma poeta poco felice poi. Parlano que' Signori critici riveritissimi di certi poemetti e frammenti già da noi ammessi in questo volume, ed anche di altri del medesimo autore forse originali, e restano di avviso commune, che non vi sia neppure una sola parola veramente da intendersi ; che il senso (chi sa ?) sarà di *ateismo,* ovvero di *alto tradimento.* Che *questo* non lo sia, nè palesamente nè occultamente, fermo col proprio pugno.   *Domenico Grigi.*—W. S. L.

he found her master, he replied, that in bodily health Ser Giovanni, by his prayers and ptisans, had much improved, but that his faculties were wearing out apace. " He may now run in the same couples with the Canonico : they can not catch the mange one of the other : the one could say nothing to the purpose, and the other nothing at all. The whole conversation was entirely at my charge," added he. " And now, Assunta, since you press it, I will accept the service of your master's shoes. How I shall ever get home I don't know." He took the shoes off the handles of the bellows, where Assunta had placed them out of her way, and tucking one of his own under each arm, limped toward St Vivaldo.

The unwonted attention to smartness of apparel, in the only article wherein it could be displayed, was suggested to Frate Biagio by hearing that Ser Francesco, accustomed to courtly habits and elegant society, and having not only small hands, but small feet, usually wore red slippers in the morning. Fra Biagio had scarcely left the outer door, than he cordially cursed Ser Francesco for making such a fool of him, and wearing slippers of black list. " These canonicos," said he, " not only lie themselves, but teach everybody else to do the same. He has lamed me for life : I burn as if I had been shod at the blacksmith's forge."

The two friends said nothing about him, but continued the discourse which his visit had interrupted.

PETRARCA. Turn again, I entreat you, to the serious ; and do not imagine that because by nature you are inclined to playfulness, you must therefore write ludicrous things better. Many of your stories would make the gravest men laugh, and yet there is little wit in them.

BOCCACCIO. I think so myself ; though authors, little disposed as they are to doubt their possession of any quality they would bring into play, are least of all suspicious on the side of wit. You have convinced me. I am glad to have been tender, and to have written tenderly : for I am certain it is this alone that has made you love me with such affection.

PETRARCA. Not this alone, Giovanni ! but this principally. I have always found you kind and compassionate, liberal and sincere, and when Fortune does not stand very close to such a man, she leaves only the more room for Friendship.

BOCCACCIO. Let her stand off then, now and for ever ! To my

heart, to my heart, Francesco ! preserver of my health, my peace of mind, and (since you tell me I may claim it) my glory.

PETRARCA. Recovering your strength you must pursue your studies to complete it. What can you have been doing with your books ? I have searched in vain this morning for the [1] treasury. Where are they kept ? Formerly they were always open. I found only a short manuscript, which I suspect is poetry, but I ventured not on looking into it, until I had brought it with me and laid it before you.

BOCCACCIO. Well guessed ! They are verses written by a gentleman who resided long in this country, and who much regretted the necessity of leaving it. He took great delight in composing both Latin and Italian, but never kept a copy of them latterly, so that these are the only ones I could obtain from him. Read : for your voice will improve them.

TO MY CHILD CARLINO

Carlino ! what art thou about, my boy ?
Often I ask that question, though in vain,
For we are far apart : ah ! therefore 'tis
I often ask it ; not in such a tone
As wiser fathers do, who know too well.
Were we not children, you and I together ?
Stole we not glances from each other's eyes ?
Swore we not secrecy in such misdeeds ?
Well could we trust each other. Tell me then
What thou art doing. Carving out thy name,
Or haply mine, upon my favourite seat,
With the new knife I sent thee over sea ?
Or hast thou broken it, and hid the hilt
Among the myrtles, starr'd with flowers, behind ?
Or under that high throne whence fifty lilies
(With sworded tuberoses dense around)
Lift up their heads at once, not without fear
That they were looking at thee all the while.

Does Cincirillo follow thee about ?
Inverting one swart foot suspensively
And wagging his dread jaw at every chirp
Of bird above him on the olive-branch ?

---

[1] 1st ed. reads : " that."

THE PENTAMERON

Frighten him then away ! 'twas he who slew
Our pigeons, our white pigeons peacock-tailed,
That fear'd not you and me . . . alas, nor him !
I flattened his striped sides along my knee,
And reasoned with him on his bloody mind,
Till he looked blandly, and half-closed his eyes
To ponder on my lecture in the shade.
I doubt his memory much, his heart a little,
And in some minor matters (may I say it ?)
Could wish him rather sager. But from thee
God hold back wisdom yet for many years !
Whether in early season or in late
It always comes high-priced. For thy pure breast
I have no lesson ; it for me has many.
Come throw it open then ! what sports, what cares
(Since there are none too young for these) engage
Thy busy thoughts ? Are you again at work,
Walter and you, with those sly labourers,
Geppo, Giovanni, Cecco, and Poeta,
To build more solidly your broken dam
Among the poplars, whence the nightingale
Inquisitively watch'd you all day long ?
I was not of your council in the scheme,
Or might have saved you silver without end,
And sighs too without number. Art thou gone
Below the mulberry, where that cold pool
Urged to devise a warmer, and more fit
For mighty swimmers, swimming three abreast ?
Or art thou panting in this summer noon
Upon the lowest step before the hall,
Drawing a slice of watermelon, long
As Cupid's bow, athwart thy wetted lips
(Like one who plays Pan's pipe) and letting drop
The sable seeds from all their separate cells,
And leaving bays profound and rocks abrupt,
Redder than coral round Calypso's cave.

PETRARCA. There have been those anciently who would have
been pleased with such poetry, and perhaps there may be again.
I am not sorry to see the Muses by the side of childhood, and forming
a part of the family.[1] But now tell me about the books.

---

[1] 1st ed. reads : " family. What is this at the end ? BOCCACCIO. I am not
quite certain that the author would have allowed you to read those. Indeed, I
had forgotten they were in the same paper. Although he was under no obligation
to the house of Este, nor wished nor needed it, he felt at a distance the general

THE PENTAMERON

BOCCACCIO. Resolving to lay aside the more valuable of those I had collected or transcribed, and to place them under the guardian-ship of richer men, I locked them up together in the higher story of my tower at Certaldo. You remember the old tower ?

PETRARCA. Well do I remember the hearty laugh we had together (which stopped us upon the staircase) at the calculation we made, how much longer you and I, if we continued to thrive as we had thriven latterly, should be able to pass within its narrow circle. Although I like this little villa much better, I would gladly see the place again, and enjoy with you, as we did before, the vast expanse of woodlands and mountains and maremma ; frowning fortresses inexpugnable ; and others more prodigious for their ruins ; then below them, lordly abbeys, overcanopied with stately trees and girded with rich luxuriance ; and towns that seem approaching them to do them honour, and villages nestling close at their sides for sustenance and protection.

BOCCACCIO. My disorder, if it should keep its promise of leaving me at last, will have been preparing me for the accomplishment of such a project. Should I get thinner and thinner at this rate, I shall soon be able to mount not only a turret or a belfry, but a tube of macarone,* while a Neapolitan is suspending it for deglutition.

What I am about to mention, will show you how little you can

joy which announced the destinies of the lady Victoria. This little poem is curious as being the only one upon the occasion, which never left its native place for court or crowd, contented with one solitary aspiration. I think there are only two stanzas. My neighbour was able without a wrench or a pother, to put into four or five verses, what another (yet handy enough) brought cramps and pot-hooks to protract into a baker's dozen. Come give me your voice again.

PETRARCA. I will not look into the sky
            To augur aught of future years :
            Enough the heavens have shown us, why
            Our hopes are sure and vain our fears.
            Victoria ! thou art risen to save
            The land thy earliest smiles have blest.
            A brave man's child will cheer the brave,
            A tender mother's the distrest.

But now," etc.

* This is valuable, since it shows that *macarone* (here called *pasta*) was invented in the time of Boccaccio ; so are the letters of Petrarca, which inform us equally in regard to *spectacles*. Ad *ocularium* (occhiali) [1] mihi confugiendum esset auxilium.   *Domenico Grigi.*—W. S. L.

---

[1] Savigno degli Armati, a Florentine (*ob.* 1317), is said to have invented *occhiali*.

rely on me ! I have preserved the books, as you desired, but quite contrary to my resolution : and, no less contrary to it, by your desire I shall now preserve the *Decameron*. In vain had I determined not only to mend in future, but to correct the past ; in vain had I prayed most fervently for grace to accomplish it, with a final aspiration to Fiammetta that she would unite with your beloved Laura, and that, gentle and beatified spirits as they are, they would breathe together their purer prayers on mine. See what follows.

PETRARCA. Sigh not at it. Before we can see all that follows from their intercession, we must join them again. But let me hear anything in which they are concerned.

BOCCACCIO. I prayed ; and my breast, after some few tears, grew calmer. Yet sleep did not ensue until the break of morning, when the dropping of soft rain on the leaves of the fig-tree at the window, and the chirping of a little bird, to tell another there was shelter under them, brought me repose and slumber. Scarcely had I closed my eyes, if indeed time can be reckoned any more in sleep than in heaven, when my Fiammetta seemed to have led me into the meadow. You will see it below you : turn away that branch : gently ! gently ! do not break it ; for the little bird sat there.

PETRARCA. I think, Giovanni, I can divine the place. Although this fig-tree, growing out of the wall between the cellar and us, is fantastic enough in its branches, yet that other which I see yonder, bent down and forced to crawl along the grass by the prepotency [1] of the young shapely walnut-tree, is much more so. It forms a seat, about a cubit above the ground, level and long enough for several.

BOCCACCIO. Ha ! you fancy it must be a favourite spot with me, because of the two strong forked stakes wherewith it is propped and supported !

PETRARCA. Poets know the haunts of poets at first sight ; and he who loved Laura—O Laura ! did I say he who *loved* thee ?—hath whisperings where those feet would wander which have been restless after Fiammetta.

BOCCACCIO. It is true, my imagination has often conducted her thither ; but there in this chamber she appeared to me more visibly in a dream.

---

[1] 1st ed. reads : " prepotence."

THE PENTAMERON

" Thy prayers have been heard, O Giovanni," said she.

I sprang to embrace her.

" Do not spill the water ! Ah ! you have spilt a part of it."

I then observed in her hand a crystal vase. A few drops were sparkling on the sides and running down the rim : a few were trickling from the base and from the hand that held it.

" I must go down to the brook," said she, " and fill it again as it was filled before."

What a moment of agony was this to me ! Could I be certain how long might be her absence ? She went : I was following : she made a sign for me to turn back : I disobeyed her only an instant : yet my sense of disobedience, increasing my feebleness and confusion, made me lose sight of her. In the next moment she was again at my side, with the cup quite full. I stood motionless : I feared my breath might shake the water over. I looked her in the face for her commands—and to see it—to see it so calm, so beneficent, so beautiful. I was forgetting what I had prayed for, when she lowered her head, tasted of the cup, and gave it me. I drank ; and suddenly sprang forth before me, many groves and palaces and gardens, and their statues and their avenues, and their labyrinths of alaternus and bay, and alcoves of citron, and watchful loopholes in the retirements of impenetrable pomegranate. Farther off, just below where the fountain slipt away from its marble hall and guardian gods, arose, from their beds of moss and drosera and darkest grass, the sisterhood of oleanders, fond of tantalising with their bosomed flowers and their moist and pouting blossoms the little shy rivulet, and of covering its face with all the colours of the dawn. My dream expanded and moved forward. I trod again the dust of Posilipo, soft as the feathers in the wings of Sleep. I emerged on Baia ; I crossed her innumerable arches ; I loitered in the breezy sunshine of her mole ; I trusted the faithful seclusion of her caverns, the keepers of so many secrets ; and I reposed on the buoyancy of her tepid sea. Then Naples, and her theatres and her churches, and grottoes and dells and forts and promontories, rushed forward in confusion, now among soft whispers, now among sweetest sounds, and subsided, and sank, and disappeared. Yet a memory seemed to come fresh from every one : each had time enough for its tale, for its pleasure, for its reflection, for its pang. As I mounted with silent steps the narrow staircase of the old palace, how distinctly did I feel against the palm of my hand the coldness of that smooth stonework, and the greater of the cramps of iron in it !

" Ah me ! is this forgetting ? " cried I anxiously to Fiammetta.

" We must recall these scenes before us," she replied : " such is the punishment of them. Let us hope and believe that the apparition, and the compunction which must follow it, will be accepted as the full penalty, and that both will pass away almost together."

I feared to lose anything attendant on her presence : I feared to approach her forehead with my lips : I feared to touch the lily on its long wavy leaf in her hair, which filled my whole heart with fragrance. Venerating, adoring, I bowed my head at last to kiss her snow-white robe, and trembled at my presumption. And yet the effulgence of her countenance vivified while it chastened me. I loved her—I must not say *more* than ever—*better* than ever ; it was Fiammetta who had inhabited the skies. As my hand opened toward her,

" Beware ! " said she, faintly smiling ; " beware, Giovanni ! Take only the crystal ; take it, and drink again."

" Must all be then forgotten ? " said I sorrowfully.

" Remember your prayer and mine, Giovanni. Shall both have been granted—O how much worse than in vain ? "

I drank instantly ; I drank largely. How cool my bosom grew ; how could it grow so cool before her ! But it was not to remain in its quiescency ; its trials were not yet over. I will not, Francesco ! no, I may not commemorate the incidents she related to me, nor which of us said, " I blush for having loved *first* " ; nor which of us replied, " Say *least*, say *least*, and blush again."

The charm of the words (for I felt not the encumbrance of the body nor the acuteness of the spirit) seemed to possess me wholly. Although the water gave me strength and comfort, and somewhat of celestial pleasure, many tears fell around the border of the vase as she held it up before me, exhorting me to take courage, and inviting me with more than exhortation to accomplish my deliverance. She came nearer, more tenderly, more earnestly ; she held the dewy globe with both hands, leaning forward, and sighed and shook her head, drooping at my pusillanimity. It was only when a ringlet had touched the rim, and perhaps the water (for a sunbeam on the surface could never have given it such a golden hue) that I took courage, clasped it, and exhausted it.   Sweet as was the water, sweet as was the serenity it gave me—alas ! that also which it moved away from me was sweet !

" This time you can trust me alone," said she, and parted my hair, and kissed my brow.   Again she went toward the brook : again my agitation, my weakness, my doubt, came over me : nor could I see her while she raised the water, nor knew I whence she drew it.   When she returned, she was close to me at once : she smiled : her smile pierced me to the bones : it seemed an angel's. She sprinkled the pure water on me ; she looked most fondly ; she took my hand ; she suffered me to press hers to my bosom ; but, whether by design I cannot tell, she let fall a few drops of the chilly element between.

" And now, O my beloved ! " said she, " we have consigned to the bosom of God our earthly joys and sorrows.   The joys can not return, let not the sorrows.   These alone would trouble my repose among the blessed."

" Trouble thy repose !   Fiammetta !   Give me the chalice ! " cried I—" not a drop will I leave in it, not a drop."

" Take it ! " said that soft voice.   " O now most dear Giovanni ! I know thou hast strength enough ; and there is but little—at the bottom lies our first kiss."

" Mine ! didst thou say, beloved one ? and is that left thee still ? "

" *Mine*," said she, pensively ; and as she abased her head, the broad leaf of the lily hid her brow and her eyes ; the light of heaven shone through the flower.

" O Fiammetta !   Fiammetta ! " cried I in agony, " God is the God of mercy, God is the God of love—can I, can I ever ? "   I struck the chalice against my head, unmindful that I held it ; the water covered my face and my feet.   I started up, not yet awake, and I heard the name of Fiammetta in the curtains.

PETRARCA. Love, O Giovanni, and life itself, are but dreams at best.   I do think

> Never so gloriously was Sleep attended
> As with the pageant of that heavenly maid.

But to dwell on such subjects is sinful.   The recollection of them, with all their vanities, brings tears into my eyes.

Boccaccio. And into mine too—they were so very charming.

Petrarca. Alas, alas! the time always comes when we must regret the enjoyments of our youth.

Boccaccio. If we have let them pass us.

Petrarca. I mean our indulgence in them.

Boccaccio. Francesco! I think you must remember Raffaellino degli Alfani.

Petrarca. Was it Raffaellino who lived near San Michele in Orto?

Boccaccio. The same. He was an innocent soul, and fond of fish. But whenever his friend Sabbatelli sent him a trout from Pratolino, he always kept it until next day or the day after, just long enough to render it unpalatable. He then turned it over in the platter, smelt at it closer, although the news of its condition came undeniably from a distance, touched it with his forefinger, solicited a testimony from the gills which the eyes had contradicted, sighed over it, and sent it for a present to somebody else. Were I a lover of trout as Raffaellino was, I think I should have taken an opportunity of enjoying it while the pink and crimson were glittering on it.

Petrarca. Trout, yes.

Boccaccio. And all other fish I could encompass.

Petrarca. O thou grave mocker! I did not suspect such slyness in thee: proof enough I had almost forgotten thee.

Boccaccio. Listen! listen! I fancied I caught a footstep in the passage. Come nearer; bend your head lower, that I may whisper a word in your ear. Never let Assunta hear you sigh. She is mischievous: she may have been standing at the door: not that I believe she would be guilty of any such impropriety: but who knows what girls are capable of! She has no malice, only in laughing; and a sigh sets her windmill at work, van over van, incessantly.

Petrarca. I should soon check her. I have no notion——

Boccaccio. After all, she is a good girl—a trifle of the wilful. She must have it that many things are hurtful to me—reading in particular—it makes people so odd. Tina is a small matter of the madcap—in her own particular way—but exceedingly discreet, I do assure you, if they will only leave her alone.

I find I was mistaken, there was nobody.

Petrarca. A cat perhaps.

THE PENTAMERON

Boccaccio. No such thing. I order him over to Certaldo while the birds are laying and sitting : and he knows by experience, favourite as he is, that it is of no use to come back before he is sent for. Since the first impetuosities of youth, he has rarely been refractory or disobliging. We have lived together now these five years, unless I miscalculate ; and he seems to have learnt something of my manners, wherein violence and enterprise by no means predominate. I have watched him looking at a large green lizard ; and, their eyes being opposite and near, he has doubted whether it might be pleasing to me if he began the attack ; and their tails on a sudden have touched one another at the decision.

Petrarca. Seldom have adverse parties felt the same desire of peace at the same moment, and none ever carried it more simultaneously and promptly into execution.

Boccaccio. He enjoys his *otium cum dignitate* at Certaldo : there he is my castellan, and his chase is unlimited in those domains. After the doom of relegation is expired, he comes hither at midsummer. And then if you could see his joy ! His eyes are as deep as a well, and as clear as a fountain : he jerks his tail into the air like a royal sceptre, and waves it like the wand of a magician. You would fancy that, as Horace with his head, he was about to smite the stars with it. There is ne'er such another cat in the parish ; and he knows it, a rogue ! We have rare repasts together in the bean-and-bacon time, although in regard to the bean he sides with the philosopher of Samos ; but after due examination. In cleanliness he is a very nun ; albeit in that quality which lies between cleanliness and godliness, there is a smack of Fra Biagio about him. What is that book in your hand ?

Petrarca. My breviary.

Boccaccio. Well, give me mine too—there, on the little table in the corner, under the glass of primroses. We can do nothing better.

Petrarca. What prayer were you looking for ? let me find it.

Boccaccio. I don't know how it is : I am scarcely at present in a frame of mind for it. We are of one faith : the prayers of the one will do for the other : and I am sure, if you omitted my name, you would say them all over afresh. I wish you could recollect in any book as dreamy a thing to entertain me as I have been just repeating. We have had enough of Dante : I believe few of his beauties have escaped us : and small faults, which we readily pass by, are fitter for small folks, as grubs are the proper bait for gudgeons.

PETRARCA. I have had as many dreams as most men. We are all made up of them, as the webs of the spider are particles of her own vitality. But how infinitely less do we profit by them ! I will relate to you, before we separate, one among the multitude of mine, as coming the nearest to the poetry of yours, and as having been not totally useless to me. Often have I reflected on it ; sometimes with pensiveness, with sadness never.

BOCCACCIO. Then, Francesco, if you had with you as copious a choice of dreams as clustered on the elm-trees where the Sibyl led Æneas, this, in preference to the whole swarm of them, is the queen dream for me.

PETRARCA. When I was younger I was fond of wandering in solitary places, and never was afraid of slumbering in woods and grottoes. Among the chief pleasures of my life, and among the commonest of my occupations, was the bringing before me such heroes and heroines of antiquity, such poets and sages, such of the prosperous and the unfortunate, as most interested me by their courage, their wisdom, their eloquence, or their adventures. Engaging them in the conversation best suited to their characters, I knew perfectly their manners, their steps, their voices : and often did I moisten with my tears the models I had been forming of the less happy.

BOCCACCIO. Great is the privilege of entering into the studies of the intellectual ; great is that of conversing with the guides of nations, the movers of the mass, the regulators of the unruly will, stiff, in its impurity and rust, against the finger of the Almighty Power that formed it : but give me, Francesco, give me rather the creature to sympathise with ; apportion me the sufferings to assuage. Ah, gentle soul ! thou wilt never send them over to another ; they have better hopes from thee.

PETRARCA. We both alike feel the sorrows of those around us. He who suppresses or allays them in another, breaks many thorns off his own ; and future years will never harden fresh ones.

My occupation was not always in making the politician talk politics, the orator toss his torch among the populace, the philosopher run down from philosophy to cover the retreat or the advances of his sect ; but sometimes in devising how such characters must act and discourse, on subjects far remote from the beaten track of their career. In like manner the philologist, and again the dialectician, were not indulged in the review and parade of their trained bands, but, at times, brought forward to show in what manner and in what degree external habits had influenced the conformation of the internal man. It was far from unprofitable to set passing events before past actors, and to record the decisions of those whose interests and passions are unconcerned in them.

BOCCACCIO. This is surely no easy matter. The thoughts are in fact your own, however you distribute them.

PETRARCA. All can not be my own; if you mean by *thoughts* the opinions and principles I should be the most desirous to inculcate. Some favourite ones perhaps may obtrude too prominently, but otherwise no misbehaviour is permitted them : reprehension and rebuke are always ready, and the offence is punished on the spot.

BOCCACCIO. Certainly you thus throw open, to its full extent, the range of poetry and invention ; which can not but be very limited and sterile, unless where we find displayed much diversity of character as disseminated by nature, much peculiarity of sentiment as arising from position, marked with unerring skill through every shade and gradation ; and finally and chiefly, much intertexture and intensity of passion. You thus convey to us more largely and expeditiously the stores of your understanding and imagination, than you ever could by sonnets or canzonets, or sinewless and sapless allegories.

But weightier works are less captivating. If you had published any such as you mention, you must have waited for their acceptance. Not only the fame of Marcellus, but every other,

Crescit occulto velut arbor ævo ;

and that which makes the greatest vernal shoot is apt to make the least autumnal. Authors in general who have met celebrity at starting, have already had their reward ; always their utmost due, and often much beyond it. We can not hope for both celebrity and fame : supremely fortunate are the few who are allowed the liberty of choice between them. We two prefer the strength that springs from exercise and toil, acquiring it gradually and slowly : we leave to others the earlier blessing of that sleep which follows enjoyment. How many at first sight are enthusiastic in their favour ! Of these

274

how large a portion come away empty-handed and discontented! like idlers who visit the seacoast, fill their pockets with pebbles bright from the passing wave, and carry them off with rapture. After a short examination at home, every streak seems faint and dull, and the whole contexture coarse, uneven, and gritty : first one is thrown away, then another ; and before the week's end the store is gone, of things so shining and wonderful.

PETRARCA. Allegory, which you named with sonnets and canzonets, had few attractions for me, believing it to be the delight in general of idle, frivolous, inexcursive minds, in whose mansions there is neither hall nor portal to receive the loftier of the Passions. A stranger to the Affections, she holds a low station among the handmaidens of Poetry, being fit for little but an apparition in a mask. I had reflected for some time on this subject, when, wearied with the length of my walk over the mountains, and finding a soft old molehill, covered with grey grass, by the way-side, I laid my head upon it, and slept. I can not tell how long it was before a species of dream or vision came over me.

Two beautiful youths appeared beside me ; each was winged ; but the wings were hanging down, and seemed ill adapted to flight. One of them, whose voice was the softest I ever heard, looking at me frequently, said to the other,

" He is under my guardianship for the present : do not awaken him with that feather."

Methought, hearing the whisper, I saw something like the feather on an arrow ; and then the arrow itself ; the whole of it, even to the point ; although he carried it in such a manner that it was difficult at first to discover more than a palm's length of it ; the rest of the shaft, and the whole of the barb, was behind his ankles.

" This feather never awakens any one," replied he, rather petulantly ; " but it brings more of confident security, and more of cherished dreams, than you without me are capable of imparting."

" Be it so ! " answered the gentler . . . " none is less inclined to quarrel or dispute than I am. Many whom you have wounded grievously, call upon me for succour. But so little am I disposed to thwart you, it is seldom I venture to do more for them than to whisper a few words of comfort in passing. How many reproaches on these occasions have been cast upon me for indifference and infidelity! Nearly as many, and nearly in the same terms, as upon you!"

"Odd enough that we, O Sleep! should be thought so alike!" said Love, contemptuously. "Yonder is he who bears a nearer resemblance to you: the dullest have observed it." I fancied I turned my eyes to where he was pointing, and saw at a distance the figure he designated. Meanwhile the contention went on uninterruptedly. Sleep was slow in asserting his power or his benefits. Love recapitulated them; but only that he might assert his own above them. Suddenly he called on me to decide, and to choose my patron. Under the influence, first of the one, then of the other, I sprang from repose to rapture, I alighted from rapture on repose—and knew not which was sweetest. Love was very angry with me, and declared he would cross me throughout the whole of my existence. Whatever I might on other occasions have thought of his veracity, I now felt too surely the conviction that he would keep his word. At last, before the close of the altercation, the third Genius had advanced, and stood near us. I can not tell how I knew him, but I knew him to be the Genius of Death. Breathless as I was at beholding him, I soon became familiar with his features. First they seemed only calm; presently they grew contemplative; and lastly beautiful: those of the Graces themselves are less regular, less harmonious, less composed. Love glanced at him unsteadily, with a countenance in which there was somewhat of anxiety, somewhat of disdain; and cried, "Go away! go away! nothing that thou touchest, lives."

"Say rather, child!" replied the advancing form, and advancing grew loftier and statelier. "Say rather that nothing of beautiful or of glorious lives its own true life until my wing hath passed over it."

Love pouted, and rumpled and bent down with his forefinger the stiff short feathers on his arrow-head; but replied not. Although he frowned worse than ever, and at me, I dreaded him less and less, and scarcely looked toward him. The milder and calmer Genius, the third, in proportion as I took courage to contemplate him, regarded me with more and more complacency. He held neither flower nor arrow, as the others did; but, throwing back the clusters of dark curls that overshadowed his countenance, he presented to me his hand, openly and benignly. I shrank on looking at him so near, and yet I sighed to love him. He smiled, not without an expression of pity, at perceiving my diffidence, my timidity ; for I remembered how soft was the hand of Sleep, how warm and entrancing was Love's. By degrees, I became ashamed of my ingratitude ; and turning my face away, I held out my arms, and felt my neck within his. Composure strewed and allayed all the throbbings of my bosom ; the coolness of freshest morning breathed around ; the heavens seemed to open above me ; while the beautiful cheek of my deliverer rested on my head. I would now have looked for those others ; but knowing my intention by my gesture, he said, consolatorily,

" Sleep is on his way to the Earth, where many are calling him ; but it is not to these he hastens ; for every call only makes him fly farther off. Sedately and gravely as he looks, he is nearly as capricious and volatile as the more arrogant and ferocious one."

" And Love ! " said I, " whither is he departed ? If not too late, I would propitiate and appease him."

" He who can not follow me, he who can not overtake and pass me," said the Genius, " is unworthy of the name, the most glorious in earth or heaven. Look up ! Love is yonder, and ready to receive thee."

I looked : the earth was under me : I saw only the clear blue sky, and something brighter above it.

PIEVANO GRIGI TO THE READER

BEFORE I proceeded on my mission, I had a final audience of Monsignore, in which I asked his counsel, whether a paper sewed and pasted to the *Interviews*, being the substance of an intended *Confession*, might, according to the *Decretals*, be made public. Monsignore took the subject into his consideration, and assented. Previously to the solution of this question, he was graciously pleased to discourse on Boccaccio, and to say, " I am happy to think he died a good catholic, and contentedly."

" No doubt, Monsignore ! " answered I, " for when he was on his death-bed, or a little sooner, the most holy man in Italy admonished him terribly of his past transgressions, and frightened him fairly into Paradise."

" Pievano ! " said Monsignore, " it is customary in the fashionable literature of our times to finish a story in two manners. The most approved is, to knock on the head every soul that has been interesting you : the second is, to put the two youngest into bed together, promising the same treatment to another couple, or more. Our forefathers were equally zealous about those they dealt with. Every pagan turned Christian : every loose woman had bark to grow about her, as thick and astringent as the ladies had in Ovid's Metamorphoses ; and the gallants, who had played false with them, were driven mad by the monks at their death-bed. I neither hope nor believe that poor Boccaccio gave way to their importunities, but am happy in thinking that his decease was as tranquil as his life was inoffensive. He was not exempt from the indiscretions of youth : he allowed his imagination too long a dalliance with his passions ; but malice was never found among them. Let us then, in charity to him and to ourselves, be persuaded that such a pest as this mad zealot had no influence over him—

> Nè turbò il tuono di nebbiosa mente
> Acqua si limpida e ridente.*

---

* Nor did the thunderings of a cloudy mind
Trouble so limpid and serene a water.—W. S. L.

THE PENTAMERON

I can not but break into verse, although no poet, while I am thinking of him. Such men as he would bring over more to our good-natured, honest old faith again than fifty monks with scourges at their shoulders."

" Ah, Monsignore ! " answered I, " could I but hope to be humbly instrumental in leading back the apostate church to our true catholic, I should be the happiest man alive."

" God forbid you should be without the hope ! " said Mon signore. " The two chief differences now are ; with ours, that we must not eat butcher's meat on a Friday ; with the Anglican, that they must not eat baked meat on a Sunday. Secondly, that *we* say, *Come, and be saved ;* the Anglican says, *Go, and be damned.*"

Since the exposition of Monsignore, the Parliament has issued an Act of Grace in regard to eating. One article says :

" Nobody shall eat on a Sunday roast, or baked, or other hot victuals whatsoever, unless he goes to church in his own carriage ; if he goes thither in any other than his own, be he halt or blind, he shall be subject to the penalty of twenty pounds. Nobody shall dance on a Sunday, or play music, unless he also be able to furnish three *écarté* tables at the least, and sixteen wax-lights."

I write from memory ; but if the wording is inexact, the sense is accurate. Nothing can be more gratifying to a true Catholic than to see the amicable game played by his bishops with the Anglican. The Catholic never makes a false move. His fish often slips into the red square, marked *Sunday*, but the shoulder of mutton can never get into its place, marked *Friday* : it lies upon the table, and nobody dares touch it. Alas ! I am forgetting that this is purely an English game, and utterly unknown among us, or indeed in any other country under heaven.

To promote still farther the objects of religion, as understood in the Universities and the Parliament, it was proposed that public prayers should be offered up for rain on every Sabbath-day, the more effectually to encompass the provisions of the Bill. But this clause was cancelled in the Committee, on the examination of a groom, who deposed that a coach-horse of his master's, the Bishop of London, was touched in the wind, and might be seriously a sufferer : " *for the bishop*," said he, " *is no better walker than a goose.*"

THE PENTAMERON

There [1] is, moreover, great and general discontent in the lower orders of the clergy, that some should be obliged to serve a couple of churches, and perhaps a jail or hospital to boot, for a stipend of a hundred pounds, and even less, while others are incumbents of pluralities, doing no duty at all, and receiving three or four thousands. It is reported that several of the more fortunate are so utterly shameless as to liken the Church to a Lottery-office, and to declare that, unless there were great prizes, no man in his senses would enter into the service of our Lord. I myself have read with my own eyes this declaration, but I hope the signature is a forgery. What is certain is, that the emoluments of the bishopric of London are greater than the united revenue of *twelve* cardinals ; that they are amply sufficient for the board, lodging, and education of *three hundred* young men destined to the ministry ; and that they might relieve from famine, rescue from sin, and save, perhaps, from eternal punishment, *three thousand fellow-creatures yearly*. On a narrow inspection of one manufacturing town in England, I deliver it as my firm opinion that it contains more crime and wretchedness than all the four continents of our globe. If these enormous masses of wealth had been fairly sub-divided and carefully expended, if a more numerous and a more efficient clergy had been appointed, how very much of sin and sorrow had been obviated and allayed ! Ultimately the poor will be driven to desperation, there being no check upon them, no guardian over them ; and the eyes of the sleeper, it is to be feared, will be opened by pincers. In the midst of such woes, originating in her iniquities and aggravated by her supineness, the Church of England, the least reformed church in Christendom, and the most opposite to the institutions of the State, boasts of being the purest member of the Reformation. Shocked at such audacity and impudence, the conscientious and pious, not only of her laity but also of her clergy, fall daily off from her, and resigning all hope of parks and palaces, embrace the cross.

Never since the Reformation (so called) have our prospects been so bright as at the present day. Our own prelates, and those of the English church, are equally at work to the same effect ; and the Catholic clergy will come into possession of their churches with as little change in the temporals as in the spirituals. It is the law of

[1] From " There " to " cross " added in 2nd ed.

the land that the church can not lose her rights and possessions by lapse of time ; impossible then that she should lose it by fraud and fallacy. Although the bishops of England, regardless of their vocations and vows, have, by deceit and falsehood, obtained Acts of Parliament, under sanction of which they have severed from their sees, and made over to their families, the possessions of the episcopacy, it can not be questioned that what has been wrongfully alienated will be rightfully restored. No time, no trickery, no subterfuge can conceal it. The exposure of such thievery in such eminent stations, worse and more shameful than any on the Thames or in the lowest haunts of villany and prostitution, and of attempts to seize from their poorer brethren a few decimals to fill up a deficiency in many thousands, has opened wide the eyes of England. Consequently, there are religious men who resort from all quarters to the persecuted mother they had so long abandoned. God at last has made his enemies perform his work ; and the English prelates, not indeed on the stool of repentance, as would befit them, but thrust by the scorner into his uneasy chair, are mending with scarlet silk, and seaming with threads of gold, the copes and dalmatics of their worthy predecessors. I am overjoyed in declaring to my townsmen that the recent demeanour of these prelates, refractory and mutinous as it has been (in other matters) to the government of their patron the king, has ultimately (by joining the malcontents in abolishing the favourite farce of religious freedom, and in forbidding roast meat and country air on the Sabbath) filled up my subscription for the bell of San Vivaldo.

Salve Regina Cœli !

Prete Domenico Grigi.

London, *June 17th,* 1837.

HEADS OF CONFESSION; A MONTHFUL

Printed and published Superiorum Licentia

March 14. Being ill at ease, I cried, " Diavolo ! I wish that creaking shutter was at thy bedroom instead of mine, old fellow ! " Assuntina would have composed me, showing me how wrong it was. Perverse ; and would not acknowledge my sinfulness to her. I said she had nothing to do with it ; which vexed her.

March 23. Reproved Assuntina, and called her *ragazzaccia !* for asking of Messer Piero Pimperna half the evening's milk of his goat. Very wrong in me ; it being impossible she should have known that Messer Piero owed me four *lire* since—I forget when.

March 31. It blowing tramontana, I was ruffled : suspected a feather in the minestra : said the rice was as black as a coal. Sad falsehood ! made Assuntina cry—Saracenic doings.

Recapitulation. Shameful all this month ; I did not believe such bad humour was in me.

Reflection. The devil, if he can not have his walk one way, will take it another ; never at a fault. Manifold proof ; poor sinner !

April 2. Thought uncharitably of Fra Biagio. The Frate took my hand, asking me to confess, reminding me that I had not confessed since the 3rd of March, although I was so sick and tribulated I could hardly stir. Peevish ; said, " Confess yourself ; I won't ; I am not minded ; you will find those not far off who——" and then I dipped my head under the coverlet, and saw my error.

April 6. Whispers of Satanasso ; pretty clear ! A sprinkling of vernal thoughts, much too advanced for the season. About three hours before sunset Francesco came. Forgot my prayers ; woke at midnight ; recollected, and did not say them. Might have told him ; never occurred that, being a Canonico, he could absolve me ; now gone again these three days, this being the fourteenth. Must unload ere heavier-laden. Gratiæ plena ! have mercy upon me !

THE TRANSLATOR'S REMARKS

On the Alleged Jealousy of Boccaccio and Petrarca

AMONG the most heinous crimes that can be committed against society is the

temerati crimen amici,[1]

and no other so loosens the bonds by which it is held together. Once, and only once in my life, I heard it defended by a person of intellect and integrity. It was the argument of a friendly man, who would have invalidated the fact; it was the solicitude of a prompt and dexterous man, holding up his hat to cover the shame of genius. I have indeed had evidence of some who saw nothing extraordinary or amiss in these filchings and twitchings; but there are persons whose thermometer stands higher by many degrees at other points than honour. There are insects on the shoals and sands of literature, shrimps which must be half-boiled before they redden; and there are blushes (no doubt) in certain men, of which the precious vein lies so deep that it could hardly be brought to light by cordage and windlass. Meanwhile their wrathfulness [2] shows itself at once by a plashy and puffy superficies, with an exuberance of coarse rough stuff upon it, and is ready to soak our shoes with its puddle at the first pressure.

" Thou shalt not bear false witness against thy neighbour " is a commandment which the literary cast down from over their communion-table to nail against the doors of the commonalty, with a fist and forefinger pointing at it. Although the depreciation of any work is dishonest, the attempt is more infamous when committed against a friend. The calumniator on such occasions may in some measure err from ignorance, or from inadequate information, but nothing can excuse him if he speaks contemptuously. It is impossible to believe that such writers as Boccaccio and Petrarca could

---

[1] Ovid, *Amor.*, III. ix. 63.
[2] 1st ed. reads : " watchfulness."

be widely erroneous in each other's merits ; no less incredible is it that, if they did err at all, they would openly avow a disparaging opinion.   This baseness was reserved for days when the study opens into the market-place, when letters are commodities, and authors chapmen.   Yet even upon their stalls, where an antique vase would stand little chance with a noticeable piece of blue-and-white crockery, and shepherds and sailors and sunflowers in its circumference, it might be heartily and honestly derided ; but less probably by the fellow-villager of the vendor, with whom he had been playing at quoits every day of his life.   When an ill-natured story is once launched upon the world, there are many who are careful that it shall not soon founder.   Thus the idle and inconsiderate rumour, which has floated through ages, about the mutual jealousy of Boccaccio and Petrarca, finds at this day a mooring in all quarters. Never were two men so perfectly formed for friendship ; never were two who fulfilled so completely that happy destination.   True it is, the studious and exact Petrarca had not elaborated so entirely to his own satisfaction his poem, *Africa*, as to submit it yet to the inspection of Boccaccio, to whom unquestionably he would have been delighted to show it the moment he had finished it.   He died, and left it incomplete.   We have, it must be acknowledged, the authority of Petrarca himself, that he never had read the *Decameron* through, even to the last year of his life, when he had been intimate with Boccaccio four-and-twenty.   How easy would it have been for him to dissemble this fact !   how certainly would any man have dissembled it who doubted of his own heart or of his friend's !   I must request the liberty of adducing his whole letter, as already translated.

   " I have only run over your *Decameron*, and therefore I am not capable of forming a true judgment of its merit : but upon the whole it has given me a great deal of pleasure.   *The freedoms in it are excusable ; from having been written in youth, from the subjects it treats of, and from the persons for whom it was designed.*   Among a great number of gay and witty jokes, there are however many grave and serious sentiments.   I did as most people do : I paid most attention to the beginning and the end.   Your description of the people in the Plague is very true and pathetic : and the touching story of Griseldis has *been ever since laid up in my memory, that I may relate it in my conversations with my friends*.   A friend of mine at

THE PENTAMERON

Padua, a man of wit and knowledge, undertook to read it aloud ; but he had scarcely got through half of it, when his tears prevented him going on. He attempted it a second time ; but his sobs and sighs obliged him to desist. Another of my friends determined on the same venture ; and, having read it from beginning to end, without the least alteration of voice or gesture, he said, on returning the book,

" ' It must be owned this is an affecting history, and I should have wept could I have believed it true ; but there never was and never will be a woman like Griseldis.' "

Here was the termination of Petrarca's literary life : he closed it with the last words of this letter ; which are, " Adieu, my friends ! adieu, my correspondence." Soon afterward he was found dead in his library, with his arm leaning on a book. In the whole of his composition, what a carefulness and solicitude to say everything that could gratify his friend ; with what ingenuity are those faults not palliated but *excused* (his own expression) which must nevertheless have appeared very grievous ones to the purity of Petrarca.

But why did not Boccaccio send him his *Decameron* long before ? Because there never was a more perfect gentleman, a man more fearful of giving offence, a man more sensitive to the delicacy of friendship, or more deferential to sanctity of character. He knew that the lover of Laura could not amuse his hours with mischievous or idle passions ; he knew that he rose at midnight to repeat his matins, and never intermitted them. On what succeeding hour could he venture to seize ? with what countenance could he charge it with the levities of the world ? Perhaps the Recluse of Arqua, the visitor of old Certaldo, read at last the *Decameron*, only that he might be able the better to defend it. And how admirably has the final stroke of his indefatigable pen effected the purpose ! Is this the jealous rival ? Boccaccio received the last testimony of unaltered friendship in the month of October 1373, a few days after the writer's death.[1] December was not over when they met in heaven : and never were two gentler spirits united there.

The character of Petrarca shows itself in almost every one of his various works. Unsuspicious, generous, ardent in study, in

[1] Petrarca died July 18, 1374 : Boccaccio Dec. 11, 1375.

liberty, in love, with a self-complacence which in less men would be vanity, but arising in him from the general admiration of a noble presence, from his place in the interior of a heart which no other could approach or merit, and from the homage of all who held the principalities of Learning in every part of Europe.

Boccaccio is only reflected in full from a larger mass of compositions : yet one letter is quite sufficient to display the beauty and purity of his mind. It was written from Venice, when finding there not Petrarca whom he expected to find, but Petrarca's daughter, he describes to the father her modesty, grace, and cordiality in his reception. The imagination can form to itself nothing more lovely than this picture of the gentle Ermissenda : and Boccaccio's delicacy and gratitude are equally affecting. No wonder that Petrarca, in his will, bequeathed to his friend a sum the quintuple in amount of that which he bequeathed to his only brother, whom however he loved tenderly. Such had been, long before their acquaintance, the celebrity of Petrarca, such the honours conferred on him wherever he resided or appeared, that he never thought of equality or rivalry. And such was Boccaccio's reverential modesty, that, to the very close of his life, he called Petrarca his master. Immeasurable as was his own superiority, he no more thought himself the equal of Petrarca than Dante (in whom the superiority was almost as great) thought himself Virgil's. These, I believe, are the only instances on record where poets have been very tenaciously erroneous in the estimate of their own inferiority. The same observation can not be made so confidently on the decisions of contemporary critics. Indeed, the balance in which works of the highest merit are weighed, vibrates long before it is finally adjusted. Even the most judicious men have formed injudicious opinions on the living and the recently deceased. Bacon and Hooker could not estimate Shakespeare, nor could Taylor and Barrow give Milton his just reward. Cowley and Dryden were preferred to both, by a great majority of the learned. Many, although they believe they discover in a contemporary the qualities which elevate him above the rest, yet hesitate to acknowledge it ; part, because they are fearful of censure for singularity ; part, because they differ from him in politics or religion ; and part, because they delight in hiding, like dogs and foxes, what they can at any time surreptitiously draw out for their sullen solitary repast. Such persons have little delight in the glory of our country, and would hear with disapprobation and moroseness it has produced four persons so pre-eminently great, that no name, modern or ancient, excepting Homer, can stand very near the lowest : these are, Shakespeare, Bacon, Milton, and Newton. Beneath the least of these (if any one can tell which is least) are Dante and Aristoteles, who are unquestionably the next.* Out of Greece and England, Dante is the only man of the first order ; such he is, with all his imperfections. Less ardent and energetic, but having no less at command the depths of thought and treasures of fancy, beyond him in variety, animation, and interest, beyond him in touches of nature and truth of character, is Boccaccio. Yet he believed his genius was immeasurably inferior to Alighieri's ; and it would have surprised and pained him to find himself preferred to his friend Petrarca ; which indeed did not happen in his lifetime. So difficult is it to shake the tenure of long possession, or to believe that a living man is as valuable as an old statue, that for five hundred years together the critics held Virgil far above his obsequious but high-souled scholar, who now has at least the honour of standing alone, if not first. Milton and Homer may be placed together : on the continent Homer will be seen at the right hand ; in England, Milton. Supreme, above all, immeasurably supreme, stands Shakespeare. I do not think Dante is any more the equal of Homer than Hercules is the equal of Apollo. Though Hercules may display more muscles, yet Apollo is the powerfuller without any display of them at all. Both together are just equivalent to Milton, shorn of his *Sonnets*, and of his *Allegro* and *Penseroso ;* the most delightful of what (wanting a better name) we call *lyrical* poems. But in the contemplation of these prodigies we must not lose the company we entered with. Two contemporaries so powerful in interesting our best affections, as Giovanni and Francesco, never existed before or since. Petrarca was honoured and beloved by all conditions. He collated with the student and investigator, he planted with the husbandman, he was the counsellor of kings, the reprover of pontiffs, and the pacificator of nations. Boccaccio, who never had occasion to sigh for solitude, never sighed *in* it : there was his station, there his studies, there his happiness. In the vivacity and versatility of

* We can speak only of those whose works are extant. Democritus and Anaxagoras were perhaps the greatest in discovery and invention.—W. S. L. (Note added in 2nd ed.)

imagination, in the narrative, in the descriptive, in the playful, in the pathetic, the world never saw his equal, until the sunrise of our Shakespeare. Ariosto and Spenser may stand at no great distance from him in the shadowy and unsubstantial ; but multiform Man was utterly unknown to them. The human heart, through all its foldings, vibrates to Boccaccio.